Across The River

Murder at Accomac

Michael Maloney

Cover Design, Michael Maloney

Cover illustration: "*View of Glatz's Ferry, Hellam Tp.*"
Pennsylvania Historical and Museum Commission
(available at www.phmc.state.pa.us)
Pennsylvania State Archives, Manuscript Group 11, Map #44
Shearer's Map of York County, 1860

Cover Text: "Horrible Murder," *Lancaster Daily Intel*, May 30, 1881
"This morning ...," *York Dispatch*, May 30, 1881

THIRD PRINTING

ISBN: 978-0-9850466-0-6

Printed in the United States of America

Susquehanna Design & Printing
Millersburg, Pa.

To the Reader

My recent journey *Across the River* began in a riverfront bar three years ago, when I overheard the locals discussing a grave located behind the nearby Accomac Inn. It piqued my natural curiosity and I rushed home to Google the subject to see what I could find. The brief description of the murder of Emily Myers at the Accomac Inn led me to her murderer, John Coyle, Jr., and to his lonely grave along the Susquehanna River.

It inspired me to dig even deeper, and I discovered that even before there was a United States, there was a ferry crossing at Accomac. The more I read, the more I realized how much the area was ingrained in American history. So I began to research, visiting historical and government archives in York, Lancaster, Gettysburg, and Harrisburg, Pennsylvania. The wealth of newspaper articles, maps, county land records, and historical journals available on the local history of the area, and the crime, was staggering. Each subject led to the next, and the number of tangents I followed resulted in my writing over 700 pages. I realized there was just too much information, and knew some things had to go. So, I began the process of eliminating some of my tangents. It was hard to do, deleting paragraphs in a second that had taken me weeks to research and write.

The journey actually began when I was much younger. As a boy, I spent many summers at my grandparents' house. I explored the river shore (as my father had done before me), listened to the whistle of the train, and absorbed the stories of Marietta, where so many of my relatives lived and died. This book is dedicated to Benjamin and Rebecca Maloney (Pap and Mam), and to everyone who so patiently endured my endless enthusiasm and listened to the daily details of what I had researched the previous night. I would also like to thank all those who assisted in the research and editing over the course of the last three years.

Across the River is a blend of historical-fiction and non-fiction. In Part I, *Beginnings*, the history of the Accomac area is traced from the early 1700s in a series of non-fiction chapters. These are interspersed with historical-fiction chapters on a timeline beginning May 15, 1881. Both threads end on Memorial Day weekend, 1881. Part II, *Endings*, begins with the murder of Emily Myers, documents the legal proceedings against John Coyle, Jr., and finishes with the contemporary history of Accomac. For those who must know, the non-fiction chapters begin with a quote pertaining to the subject, and the historical-fiction chapters do not. The incidents and conversations in the historical-fiction chapters are based on newspaper accounts of the period and transcripts of the Coyle trial.

However personally satisfying it was for me to research and write *Across the River*, I do have one regret. Despite the countless hours I spent walking through numerous cemeteries searching for the final resting place of Emily Myers, her grave could not be found, and I am convinced it is lost forever. So, ultimately, this book is for her, in the hopes that she won't be forgotten. Remember Emily next Decoration Day.

G. Michael Maloney
York, Pa.
December, 2011

Part I

Beginnings

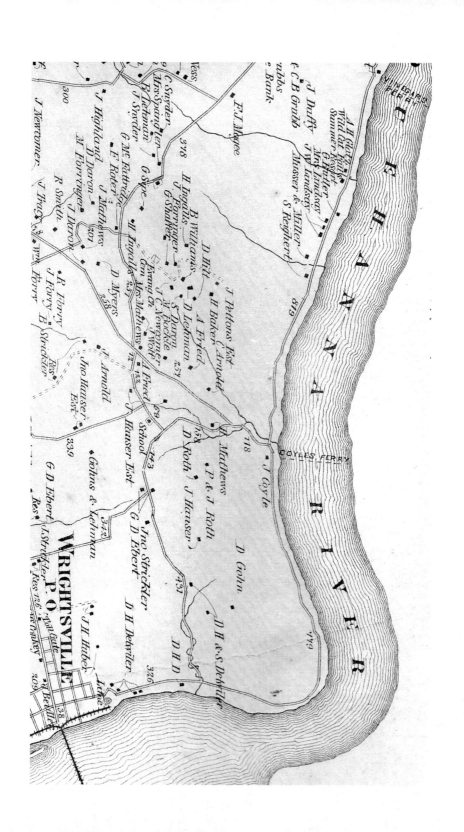

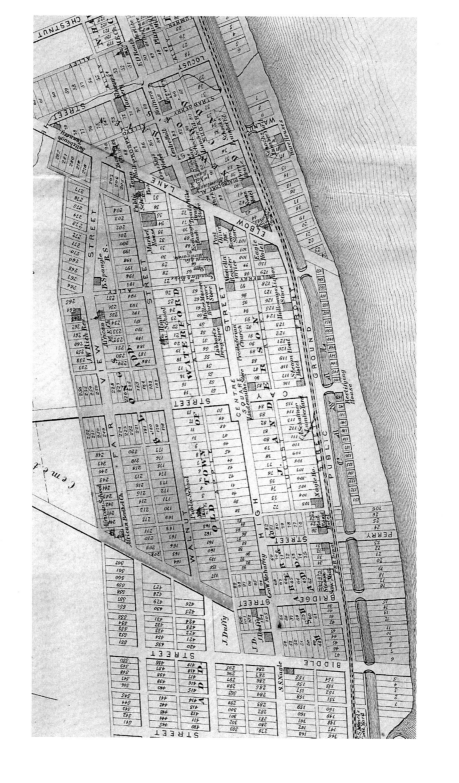

Chapter 1

Coyle's Ferry
York County, Pa.
Sunday, May 15, 1881

All them rings. Too many for her fine lookin fingers. What's anybody want with all that gold anyway? You can bet she's never seen a day of work. Never got up at five in the morning to do the milking or roll bread. Not like my Emma's hands. Not by a long shot. Emma's hands need some of them rings. Not to make 'em pretty, but to make 'em prettier.

The morning sun was already bright, flashing in sharp spokes of light as it glanced off the ripples in the wide Susquehanna River and the rings on her fingers, stinging his eyes as he watched her. The young girl seated on the bench beside him was painfully aware of his deliberate staring, and nervously smoothed the non-existent wrinkles in her heavy skirts. Like the imperceptible colors that lure bees to an enticing flower, his eyes were irresistibly drawn to the gold bands that circled three fingers on each of her pale thin hands, and he intently followed their movement as she anxiously fidgeted.

He was thoroughly enjoying making her tense and uneasy. Sensing his menacing intentions, the girl slowly slipped her ring fingers into one of the many folds of her newly pressed skirt, and their eyes met briefly. Despite her growing apprehension, she found it difficult to look away, but eventually lowered her glance so he wouldn't get the wrong idea.

Only a few passengers were on board the boat so far that morning, and as they waited for the rest to arrive for the first trip of the day, John's thoughts darted from one thing to another, the way the bees in his mother's garden behind the ferry house moved nervously from one flower to the next. Never lingering long on any one in particular, but spending as little time as needed to take what they wanted before moving on.

As he averted his dark eyes and not-so-friendly thoughts from the girl with the gold rings to the man sitting next to her on the rough wooden seat, he reached around and threw another shovel full of coal into the boiler at the back of the boat. If they didn't leave soon, he would have to go back up to the barn and get another pail for the trip across the river. Something he really didn't want to have to do. At least, something he didn't want to let his father see him doing. Leaving on time and not wasting coal were two of the many rules of the house, and John would surely hear about it if he were seen.

Don't they know how hot it's gonna get today wearing all those heavy clothes? Just to climb up on the rocks above the river, laughing as they try to impress each other with their so-called feats of bravery. At least they don't have to work all damn day in the sun. But I do.

Although it was only 10 o'clock, the heat was already oppressive, seeming to roll off the river in waves in time with the water lapping against the side of the docked boat. Almost all of the heavy fog that blanketed the river in the early morning had burned off and the remaining little streamers of mist swirling on the surface of the water did little to provide any protection from the sun. The sweat was heavy on his forehead from the heat coming off the steaming boiler, and he was anxious to get moving. At least then the breeze, whatever little it was, would keep the heat from having a chance to get a grip on him.

The old, faded canvas canopy which ran the length of the dilapidated ferry barely provided any protection from the sun for the row of benches lining each side. Most of the time it only shaded the strip of deck in the middle of the boat where there were no seats. On sunny days, the passengers usually suffered from the heat as much as John did, sitting in the back next to the infernal boiler that was constantly hissing steam and belching heat.

Damn it's hot. Vennor was sure right this time. Better be right about it getting cooler and raining soon. Gotta get the tobacco set, or I'll hear about it, that's for sure. As long as it gets cooler, leastwise by Decoration Day. I got big plans for Emma across the river that day, and she better not say no to me then.

Many of the locals relied on Vennor's Almanac, and the Coyles kept a well-read dog-eared copy behind the bar in the tavern. Although published in Montreal, the occasionally accurate predictions of Professor Henry Vennor, the "Canadian Weather Prophet,"[1] were widely printed in the local newspapers, and the majority of farmers who lived in the vicinity of Coyle's Ferry religiously based their planting calendars on its prognostications.

It was unseasonably hot for the middle of May, reaching ninety-six degrees the day before. Even though the winter of 1880-81 was severe in south-central Pennsylvania, the heavy rains and mild temperatures in early April caused the river hills around Coyle's Ferry to green rapidly. However, with the unexpected hot spell during the beginning of May, the ground had quickly dried up.

The immediate concern was when to set the tobacco in the ground. The weather needed to be cooler and wetter to allow the young plants to push rapidly and develop the quality tobacco that York County was known for. Everyone anxiously waited to see if the almanac's prophecies would come true, as the Professor predicted "between the 20th and the 25th the weather will probably be cold. The month will end hot and sultry."[2]

Had John been able to see a few weeks into the future, he would have known that by Decoration Day there would be a sudden reversal from the oppressive heat. With temperatures reaching the low forties and plenty of fine rains for the tobacco, the first week of June 1881 would be the coolest on record for many years, with the old-timers hardly being able to remember a week like it for early summer.

They always have their pretty little umbrellas to shade them when they start to roast. That blue one would look good twirling in Emma's hand, the hand with those shiny gold rings she'll have one day. I'm gonna get her one, to keep her cool as we stroll down the street in Marietta. Why do their men carry those canes anyway? Not much shade from a cane, you dandy.

He smirked and laughed under his breath at the thought, and the girl's companion gave him a sharp, disapproving look. John's eyes moved lazily away from her blue umbrella, deliberately lingering while travelling up the full curves of her body, past her pouting lips, into her deep brown eyes, across her curly black hair and out over the side of the boat. He purposely took his time and let his eyes loiter, knowing her escort was seething at his boldness. But, they needed him to get up the river, so they had no choice except to endure his leering.

If there was one thing John enjoyed, it was watching people. He noticed the clothes they wore, the way they talked, and how the girls hung on every word the men said. Giggling and laughing and doing whatever they wanted to do, whenever they wanted to. John guessed he was the butt of some of their jokes and they were probably laughing at him, but he didn't care.

John had lost one of his fingers on his left hand in a hunting accident and was constantly ridiculed about his disfigurement. It didn't help matters that most young folks found him simple-minded and took every opportunity to poke fun at his ignorance. However, the thing that bothered him the most was that nearly everyone ignored him and disregarded the fact that he even existed.

Instead of making friends with boys and girls his own age, John spent most of his free time with the younger boys across the river in Marietta. Even though he was much older, he played marbles, shot rats at the trash dump in the woods, and went swimming in the river with them whenever he could. The most important thing to John was that they paid attention to him, listened to what *he* had to say, and even looked up to him.

'Course if it was my Emma going to Wild Cat today, she would light up the place like a glowing lantern. All these boys would know she was mine and they wouldn't look at me like I was a nobody. What kind of name is Wild Cat anyway? There hasn't been a cat spotted there in fifty years, and then only once. Heck, it was probably never even there in the first place. Me, I would have shot it dead and made me a nice hat to wear. A sight better than the black fancy hats these boys wear.

The falls at Wild Cat Glen was a popular place for the younger crowd to climb the rickety steps beside the falls, picnic on the rocks and wade in the creek which ran through a sharp break in the hillside on its way to join the river. On weekends, most of his passengers were people his own age from York and Marietta who were going to Wild Cat. They paid their half dollar to take his ferry up the river to spend the day idly at Wild Cat Falls, something John never seemed to have the time to do.

The water was low, as it had been for the past week, and it was going to be challenging for John just to get the boat moving. If he managed to steer clear of the rocks and the grasses starting to show in the shallows along the bank and move out into the main current, the trip up to Wild Cat would be much easier, as the water was deeper in the middle and free of obstructions.

With the ferry landing situated as it was, on an outside corner of a bend in the Susquehanna River, not only were there rocks, but debris from the swollen water just a few months earlier had piled up along the shore where the dock was located. A month previous, high water had caused fear that the Williamsport log boom would break and runaway timber would make its way down the river. Only a portion had broken loose, and John spent the better part of late April and early May clearing logs from the ferry landing and the banks around it.

Now that it was so hot, with no rain for some time, the river conditions were just beginning to hint at the tough summer the ferry was going to face. With the covered bridge a few miles downstream providing an easy way for people and their horses and wagons to cross between Lancaster County and York County, the ferry business wasn't what it used to be.

The bridge over the Susquehanna River between Columbia and Wrightsville was originally completed in 1814, and rebuilt twenty years later following its destruction by high water and massive ice floes in early February 1832. The new bridge used the surviving stone piers and most of the oak timbers salvaged from the first bridge, and included a carriageway, a pedestrian walkway, a shingled roof and a whitewashed interior. Like the bridge it replaced, it was considered to be the longest covered bridge in the world at just over a mile long.

By 1840, when the low-head Wrightsville Dam was completed, two stacked towpaths were added to the downriver side of the bridge, providing a link from the Pennsylvania Canal on the east side of the river to the Susquehanna and Tidewater Canal on the Wrightsville side. Canal boats were towed across the river in both directions at the same time in the slack water pool formed behind the dam.

"Columbia Bridge" by W.H. Barlett ca. 1850
Library of Congress

Since the entire bridge was constructed of wood, fear of fire was always a major concern. In the late 1840's, when a double track railroad line was added to the bridge to connect the Philadelphia and Columbia Railroad on the east side with the Baltimore and Susquehanna Railroad on the west side, locomotives running under steam power were prohibited. Rail cars were pulled across the span by horse or mule teams due to the risk of fire that the steam boilers on the engines presented.

By 1863, the bridge was an important regional crossing, providing a way for both trains and wagons to move commercial goods across the river. During the Civil War, it allowed troops, cavalry, and artillery to cross the river in large numbers. Union troops regularly used the bridge when moving from New York and Philadelphia to points west and south.

After the bridge was burned by the Union Army in June of 1863 to keep the Rebels from getting any further east, there was no other way to cross the river without using one of the local ferries. The Coyles bought their ferry and tavern in early July, 1864, almost exactly a year after the Rebel occupation of Wrightsville. Business was good for a time following the Great Rebellion, but with more ferry operators working the area, and less people using their services, competition had been intense.

Wright's Ferry was about two miles downstream, Vinegar Ferry the same distance upriver, and all were doing what they could to attract more passengers. The year before, Wrights had added a larger propelling side-wheel to one of their steam-driven boats, the *Columbia*, giving them a speed of twelve miles an hour to ply the trade between Wrightsville, Columbia and Wild Cat Glen. Vinegar Ferry was situated in Lancaster County, next to the Pennsylvania Railroad's Wild Cat Station, and catered to people travelling on the train from Harrisburg or Columbia and going to the popular picnic and gathering spot.

Coyle's Ferry in York County was directly opposite the center of Marietta and had a steady stream of passengers wanting to avoid the crowds at Wrights. In addition to carrying passengers and wagons whenever they happened to show up and blow the horn, the ferry kept to a strict timetable on weekends. The previous spring, in order to draw more business, John's father added scheduled weekend runs upriver just to accommodate people going to Wild Cat for the day. On Saturday and Sunday there were morning and afternoon departures and Mr. Coyle insisted they leave on time.

Used to be so much easier, just making the couple of daily runs, when people needed it. Straight shot across the river to Marietta, with good water all the way.

Realizing that the passengers demanded better and faster service, the Coyles had purchased one of the small, broken down rear-paddle steamers left over from Wright's Ferry after they had upgraded to their newer, larger boats. Over the winter, when the severe weather prevented any outside labor, John was kept busy repairing the boat, and he frequently had words with his father over the constant work.

John had the boat ready by the spring of 1881 and today was only the second time he was using it on the river. He already despised the noise, the heat, and the smoke it produced and preferred the Coyle's old flatboats. John liked doing the rowing and poling, and he could occasionally make the passengers steer, follow his directions, and let them know *he* was in charge.

John liked to think he had the reputation as a fine ferryman, taking people across when the weather was bad and the water rough, and even when the water was low like it was now. His father was also a strong rower, and at eighty was the oldest river pilot still on the water. Most of the younger men on the river had trouble keeping up with John Sr., including John Jr.

Going to Marietta was a constant diversion for John, and he frequently stayed there for hours after dropping off passengers, sometimes not going home at all. John often met the stern gaze, and regularly the stern hand, of his father when he was late getting back. Over there, he would see people and things he never got to see on his side of the river. He would get caught up playing in the street with the boys from town, visiting with his Aunt Kate, or getting drunk at the public houses along the canal on Front Street.

When he was late bringing the boat home, his father always seemed to be waiting for him on the wide front porch, watching as John tied off the boat, pulled the oars and made his way up the road from the dock to the house. The accusations would start and they would have harsh words, which occasionally escalated into threats. Many of their heated arguments were intense and could be heard across the river in Marietta, and everyone knew that the Coyles were an explosive, dysfunctional family. More than once John left the house after these fights and disappeared into the woods for days at a time, waiting for things to cool off.

Getting more work on the weekends just so the boys from York and Marietta could take their girls for a relaxing do-nothing day while he worked in the sun made John even more irritable. The Coyles plan hadn't worked very well the summer before, as it seemed like more people were taking their horses and wagons up the dirt path along the river to Wild Cat Glen instead of using one of their boats. Of course, that was poor for the ferry business, but in a way it was fine with John, for it meant less hot work outside.

The roads leading from Hellam and Wrightsville to Wild Cat passed directly in front of Coyle's Ferry and people travelling to the falls frequently stopped at their tavern for a hot meal or a drink. In addition, the Coyles rented some of their upstairs rooms to travelers and a few semi-permanent boarders, so there was never a lack of inside work for John when there nothing to do outside.

Any income the Coyles lost taking people back and forth across the river had been replaced with people eating, drinking, and staying at the inn. Whenever John wasn't running the ferry, or working in the fields on the hillside behind the house, his father had him inside getting hot water for the guests, sweeping the floors, and cleaning out the stalls which held the horses belonging to foot passengers crossing the river to Marietta.

Working more at the house wasn't all bad as far as John was concerned, except when his father was around. The more time he spent working inside the house, the more he got to sneak the liquor they kept stored in the cellar and the more he got to see Emma. The hired girl was Emily to everyone else, but John insisted on calling her Emma, or Em. Not that she wanted him to call her by those names, or even given him permission to be that familiar, but John took it upon himself, knowing in his mind that she must feel the same way about him as he did about her.

Since both his parents were very old, he knew it wouldn't be long until the inn and ferry would be his and he could do as he pleased. John had his own big plans to make the ferry house and grounds a summer resort for picnicking and parties, and spent all his idle time thinking and scheming, with Emily a big part of those dreams.

Emily Myers started working for the Coyles the previous winter after their other hired help, another domestic named Emma, left unexpectedly in September of 1880, leaving half of her things behind. John always made the former Emma nervous, with all his drunken talk of marriage, and she took up with one of the Wrightsville quarrymen and moved out the first chance she had without so much as a goodbye.

John's mother had been livid about her leaving and insisted they find a replacement as soon as possible, with John picking up the slack in the meantime. John had cursed her back for all the extra chores he had to do and swore to himself that the next girl he loved would never turn down his proposals or leave him to do all the work.

Emily, a distant relative of Mrs. Coyles, was born on December 29, 1863, in Chambersburg, about forty-five miles west of Coyle's Ferry in Franklin County. Emily lived with her parents in Harrisburg until they both passed away when she was five years old. Her father, George Myers, died of complications from the wounds he received in the Civil War. Following his death, Emily moved back to Franklin County to be raised by her grandparents, Samuel and Mary Myers, in Guilford Township.

Living with elderly relatives whom she hardly knew held no excitement and no adventure for the young, pretty orphaned girl. She was anxious to be out on her own, making her own money, and buying the stylish clothes and things she always envied the other girls her age for having. She was just sixteen and desperately looking for a way out of her grandparents' house, and was temporarily living with her sister Annie in Harrisburg.

While Emily was visiting her Uncle Simon in Marietta, Mrs. Coyle mentioned they were short of help and looking for someone, the sooner the better. The pay wasn't all that good, but there were plenty of ways to meet new friends and maybe even a husband, especially with everyone travelling the river and going to Wild Cat. Her older sister Annie tried to convince her not to get involved with the Coyles, as she knew the family's reputation for hard living, even harder drinking, and constant quarreling. However, Emily had a mind of her own, and by early October she had moved to the imposing stone ferry house and into an upstairs bedroom with Mrs. Coyle.

In addition to cleaning the inn, working in the tavern, milking the cows and working in the garden, Emily was to provide help to Mrs. Coyle, who suffered from rheumatism and was frequently bedridden. Emily was tidy and industrious, always cheerful, and neat in her dress. She was regarded as very pretty, short but well-proportioned, with black hair and large grey eyes. She had good habits and a good moral character, and was completely opposite from John in almost every way.

As soon as John laid eyes on her, he forgot all about the other girls he was currently in love with, and told himself he was going to make Emily his wife, one way or another. She was friendly with all the customers, boarders and passengers, and was always flirting and laughing with them. Towards John she was frequently standoffish, but he felt that she liked him even though she didn't let on that way.

Just the day before, when he rowed John Thompson, a canal pilot from Liverpool, over to Marietta, John confided that he was having trouble at home with Emily. He had the tendency to have personal conversations with people he hardly knew, perhaps because he felt that those who knew him well had already written him off as crazy. Sometimes he would take people like Thompson by surprise, hoping they would believe he was sincere and give him advice.

John explained there was a hired girl living at his house he wanted to marry, and although she was willing, his parents were opposed to it. After Thompson offered no advice, John said he loved her and thought she loved him. They sat in silence for a few moments, and seeing that he was going to get no sympathy, John ended the conversation as they neared the shore with "I am determined if I can't have her no one else shall get her!"[3]

Emily tried to avoid John, but now that he was working more in the house and not on the river, it was hard to keep from running in to him. It seemed like everywhere she turned, John was there. He could be a handsome man if he chose to take care of himself, but she felt he thought too much of himself. He was always acting like Emily should stop what she was doing and spend time with him, and all he wanted to do was talk about getting married. She knew if she took the time to have a conversation with him, his mother would get angry and demand that she get back to work and stop wasting her time.

John drank heavily and was moody most of the time, and Emily knew she could do much better. She tried not to encourage his immature persistence, but he refused to let it drop. John figured that if he kept at it long enough, maybe Emily would notice him and not act like he was one of the dogs that always hung around the place, tossing him a glance now and then like the occasional scraps she gave them from the kitchen.

He had proposed to Emily twice in the last few weeks, and even though she told him in no uncertain terms that she wasn't interested in marrying him, he continued to pester her about being his wife. When he worked around the tavern, it gave him even more opportunity to leer at her, and she was perpetually on edge.

Many nights, John lay in his room above the tavern room, listening to the men downstairs drinking, playing cards, and talking loosely about women. It was usually the same type of rough men, riding up from the lime furnaces lining Front Street in Wrightsville, working the canal boats in Marietta, or coming off the lumber rafts which ran the river in the spring after the ice broke.

With the railroad making its way from Wrightsville up the river towards the Ferry, there were even more transient workers staying at the inn. They eventually made it to a point a mile below the ferry, but after the rocky hillside had been blasted, there was not enough money to continue the construction any further north.

The workers came in to get drunk on the Jersey Lightning his father brought in to avoid the taxes, and more often than not John drank with them. They stared at Emily, made rude jokes behind her back, and tugged at her skirts whenever she passed by. Their comments were crude and dirty, and it angered John to hear them talk that way to her. She was *his* girl, whether she wanted to be or not, and whether she knew it or not.

Yep, it's goin to be a long trip this morning. What are you looking at, Fancy Boy? You gonna start something with that cane? At least your girl has enough sense to bring an umbrella for the sun.

The young man began insistently tapping the brass-tipped end of his cane on the deck, trying to divert John's attention away from his girl. John knew what he was doing, so he ignored him and continued his furtive glances. What he really wanted was to slip the rope and get moving, but all he could do was to keep watching, and thinking.

As John and his passengers waited, a dirty haze began to lift off the road and drift towards the boat. The slight breeze provided just enough incentive to animate the dust into brushes of filth which painted everything in its path, including the clothes the passengers were trying to be so careful with.

The winter snowmelt was long gone, but the resulting floods earlier in the spring left the river banks saturated after it had receded. The never-ending rains turned the road and ferry landing into rutted paths of mud, which had since dried into a deep layer of dry, loose dirt. The desiccated ground was constantly stirred up by the horses and heavy wagons travelling the road in front of the ferry, and the dust needed little excuse to coat everything in sight with a fine layer of brown powder.

Wonder how many of these fancy dresses and skirts and suits and hats will come back wet and dirty tonight?

Sitting here in the hot morning sun, John was becoming impatient to leave, but the girls pleaded and begged with him to wait a little while longer for their friends. He had gone across the river to Marietta that morning on schedule and picked up his current group of passengers, but instead of taking them directly upriver to Wild Cat, they had asked him to return to the York County side to pick some additional friends who were joining them on their picnic.

As the late arrivals finally came down the winding road along the creek and pulled up to the barn, his father came out of the house and took charge of the horses, unhitching them from the carriages and tying them to the rail. His sideways glance told John he would hear about the delay in leaving when he got home, so maybe today would be a good one to be slow in getting back from Marietta at the end of the day. He could hear his father now, asking him why he was just sitting there in the heat making people wait.

He would try to explain that he was just doing what the passengers asked him to do, but he knew his argument would fall on deaf ears. The Coyles could use the extra money this time of year, before the summer season when more people came to their side of the river to picnic, and John was hoping he would catch a break from his father's anger just this once. Maybe he would already be gone when John got back, working the rocky fields on the hills behind the ferry or running errands in town, and not be back until after dark.

The new passengers paid their fares, boarded the ferry, and took their places on the rows of benches with their friends. John threw one last shovel of coal in the boiler, untied the ropes from the dock, started the paddle wheel behind him, and pulled away. With one last glimpse at the dark-haired girl, the day began.

All them rings.

<u>Chapter 2</u>

Accomac
April 1722

"What's in a Name"

... William Shakespeare

No one knows exactly why the area around Coyle's Ferry became known as Accomac.

All along the Susquehanna's 448 mile length, from its humble origins in Lake Otsego in Cooperstown, New York, to the Chesapeake Bay in Havre De Grace, Maryland, most river ferries inherited their names from the families that owned the landings or from the proprietors that leased and operated them. As the ownership of the land changed hands over the years, so did the names of the ferries, making an accurate count of unique operations over time difficult. In fact, by the time John Coyle, Sr. took ownership of his ferry during the Civil War in 1864, it had already been known as Andersons, Keeseys, Stricklers, and Glatz.

From the Coyles southward to the mouth of the river in Maryland, there were at least twelve ferries operating during the eighteenth and nineteenth centuries. Coyles, Wrights, Blue Rock, Cresaps, Sauers, Shenks, Stoners (a.k.a. Reeds and Fultons), McCalls (a.k.a. Ashmores, Nelsons, Stevensons, Whites) and others provided a critical, and sometimes the only, means of crossing the mile-wide river.

The Susquehanna, the largest non-navigable river in North America, drains half the state of Pennsylvania, some 27,500 square miles, and supplies more fresh water to the Atlantic Ocean than any other eastern U.S. river.[1] Cutting the state of Pennsylvania roughly in half from north to south, the wide expanse of the Susquehanna presented a major obstacle to the westward migration of the expanding population of the United States beginning in the early 1700s.

Since large-scale commercial river traffic was impractical due to the frequently rocky and shallow conditions, those who were granted ferry charters provided an essential link to the West. For the next two centuries, until bridge construction doomed the ferries to obsolescence, the operators prospered, carrying people, livestock and goods back and forth across the river.

Although almost all of the ferry crossing along the Susquehanna River are long gone, many of their names have survived, having been adopted by the small towns that grew up alongside them or the roads leading to them. The last operating ferry on the river in Pennsylvania is the Millersburg ferry, named by Daniel Miller in the early 1800s. Located twenty-five miles north of Harrisburg, it still provides seasonal service between Millersburg on the east bank and Liverpool on the west side, using the last two remaining stern-wheel ferry boats in the country.

The Pennsylvania river towns of Fisher's Ferry, Homet's Ferry, and Shenk's Ferry still persist as historical namesakes of those who built and operated ferries. However, sometime in the late 1880s, Amos Grove, who purchased the ferry from John Coyle, decided the crossing would no longer be known as Coyle's Ferry. From that point forward, the area along the west bank of the Susquehanna opposite Marietta has been called Accomac.

The name Accomac (or Accomak) is of Native American origin, meaning "on the other side of water place" or "across the river." Like most names of Native American derivation, spelling depended on local interpretation. The tribe has also been referred to as the Aquamackes, Acomaks, Acawmacks, and Captain John Smith spelled it "Accowmacke" in his *History of Virginia* in 1629.[2] By 1608 their numbers had dwindled to only eighty warriors, and they gradually were absorbed into other area tribes.

Although the word Accomac has a rich historical pedigree, Grove's motivation for adopting it was most likely not to honor the long gone tribe, to pay homage to their culture, or due to any Native American ethnicity of his own. It was probably a necessary decision of economic survival, as the bad publicity from the infamous events which were to unfold in late May of 1881 gained Coyle's Ferry local and national notoriety. Chances are Amos Grove wanted to distance his livelihood from being associated with the Coyle family name. By marketing it under a new, romantic sounding Native American name, he hoped to attract paying passengers and boarders, instead of only curiosity-seekers from York and Lancaster counties.

The land west of the Susquehanna River in Pennsylvania was originally the territory of the Susquehannock tribe until their defeat to the Five Nations of the Iroquois in 1675. The Native Americans used the unbroken wilderness for their hunting grounds, growing crops, and establishing settlements. Beginning as early as 1719, an increasing number of people were starting to cross the river and illegally settle on homesteads on the west side of the Susquehanna.

Due to an ongoing border dispute between the provincial governments of Pennsylvania and Maryland, ownership of the land in what would eventually become York County, Pennsylvania, was questionable until it was finally settled by the establishment of the Mason-Dixon Line, surveyed in 1763-1767. Prior to that time, both provinces claimed territorial control and issued survey Warrants and land Patents in the same areas.

Maryland laid claim to just north of the 40th parallel, approximately six miles above Wrightsville, Pennsylvania, where the Codorus Creek enters the Susquehanna River, and far above where their jurisdiction was generally accepted to lie. The Pennsylvania proprietors claimed land as far south as the 39th parallel, which would have included the city of Baltimore.

William Penn's fundamental motive for wanting the boundaries of his province to extend below the 40th parallel was a desire to have a direct navigable water route to the Chesapeake Bay. "Whatever may be the prevailing opinion as to the character of William Penn, it is clear that in dealing with the Catholic lord proprietor of Maryland, his Quaker principles did not cause the spirit of brotherly love to control his actions. On the contrary, after his strong desire to acquire for his province the command of a suitable water communication with the ocean had made him extremely covetous of the northwestern part of Maryland ..."[3]

Although both colonies asserted rights to the Accomac area, the rules and policies for establishing legal claim to unsettled land differed greatly between the two provinces. Pennsylvania had self-imposed regulations which prohibited issuing permanent land grants, known as Patents, unless appropriate treaties were negotiated with the local tribes currently occupying the land. Once clear title was obtained and a deed conveyed by the natives, granting Patents for property in Pennsylvania could legally occur.

For the Accomac area, Pennsylvania's legal right to the land did not occur until October of 1736, when the Proprietors obtained from the Five Nations of the Iroquois the deeds for the lands south of the Blue Mountains and west of the Susquehanna. Pennsylvania then began to issue Warrants for new surveys and grant Patents for surveys completed prior to the treaty.

Maryland, on the other hand, had no such restrictions in settling occupied Native American lands, and freely surveyed and issued grants to settlers prior to any treaties being established with the local tribes. Their intention was to encourage settlements as far north as possible, and after taking possession of the land, to hold it by any means possible, including force. Lord Baltimore was not hindered by the same religious or moral ethics as William Penn, and encouraged encroachment of the disputed land whenever practical.

This naturally caused tension between the two colonies, as well as among the settlers vying for the same ground which lay along their common border. Further complicating the legal process of obtaining Patents was the fact that multiple factions within Pennsylvania itself often competed for the same land. The Provincial Proprietors were looking after the interests of the Penn family, and the governors were interested in preserving the rights of ordinary citizens, both settlers and Native Americans, and occasionally themselves.

The procedure to legally establish title to a tract of land in Pennsylvania was a complicated procedure. Once a Warrant was issued by the land office in Philadelphia, a survey was conducted by a Deputy Surveyor General of the county, who drew an official plat.[*] Following the filing of the Warrant, an application for a Patent was created and reviewed. If accepted, a Patent was issued, which constituted the official granting of title to the land by the Proprietors Land Office.

Patents generally required a small down payment and stipulated the amount of ground rent, or quit rent, which needed to be paid each year. Quit rents were basically taxes levied on an annual basis, intended to provide a steady income for the Penn family and their heirs. The process of applying for the Patent and the granting of official ownership sometimes happened decades after the original Warrant and survey, and was frequently initiated well after the land had already been settled.

Pennsylvania's interest in the Accomac area on the west bank of the Susquehanna began as early as 1703, when it was first explored by Lewis Michelle (Mitchel), a Swiss Mennonite employed by religious elements in Bern, Switzerland, to search for suitable vacant land in America. A miner by trade, he eventually made his way to western Lancaster County, Pennsylvania, directly across the river from Accomac, searching for both land and potential mineral deposits.

In 1707, after the local Conestoga tribe lodged a formal complaint against Michelle for the exploration of their land and his insistence that they serve as his guides, he turned his sights westward. Michelle had the cooperation of the Pennsylvania Proprietors in his explorations, as the financially strapped colony was always looking for ways to meet their obligations to the Penn family, including the exploitation of the hoped for, yet untapped, mineral wealth of the area.

---

[*] *A plat is a sketch outlining the shape and size of a surveyed property.*

John Evans, the twenty-six year old deputy governor appointed by William Penn in 1704, took a personal interest in Michelle's explorations and hoped the discovery of mineral wealth would lead to his own gain. This led to suspicion of Evans, and of subsequent governors, by the Proprietors. They realized the governors were not interested in claiming potentially rich lands solely for the province, but for personal profit as well. This lack of confidence was evidenced by a letter written in 1708 by William Penn from England, to his secretary and trusted friend James Logan in America, saying "Remember the mines which the Governor yet makes a secret, even to thee and all the world but himself and Michelle."[4]

Mistrust of Governor Evans grew after he staged a mock attack on the city of Philadelphia in 1706. Following several unsuccessful efforts to solicit military defense funds from the Provincial Assembly, Evans decided to pursue more aggressive means of convincing Queen Anne of the need for a militia. On May 16, he enlisted allies from Delaware to pose as express messengers and ride madly into the city on the day of the annual fair, proclaiming the advance of the French fleet up the coast. Instead of shocking the defenseless city into realizing the value of a standing militia, he caused mass panic. Evans was regarded with scorn, and Logan soon after wrote to Penn "In short, the whole is looked upon to be a most mischievous, boyish trick."[5]

Evans managed to survive for another three years as governor, and was replaced by Charles Gookin in 1709. In 1717, Gookin was removed due to conflicts with the Pennsylvania Council and his perceived mental imbalance. Hannah Penn, the second wife of William Penn, who assumed administrative control of the Province after a series of strokes debilitated her husband in 1712, appointed William Keith to succeed Gookin as Governor of Pennsylvania. It was under Keith's leadership that the Accomac area was officially surveyed and settled.

The locale called Accomac is situated along the west bank of the Susquehanna River in Hellam Township, York County, Pennsylvania. Long before the Coyles took ownership, the area had already enjoyed a rich and often controversial history, beginning when the first white men crossed the river and surveyed the land on the west side. The almost simultaneous surveys of the area by the governor of Pennsylvania and the Provincial councils of Pennsylvania and Maryland changed the undeveloped wilderness into the contested front line of civilization in a matter of months. April 1722 proved to be a turning point in the history of the area.

It was under Governor Keith's tenure that the first Pennsylvania survey west of the Susquehanna was completed on April 5, 1722. Like Evans before him, Keith was aware of the possibility that copper existed in the area. His record of developing natural resources was one of the reasons he was appointed governor, and he took personal advantage whenever possible. Information alluding to the presence of copper had come to the Land Office in Philadelphia and subsequently to Governor Keith, prompting him to action.

Although authorized Patents to the land could not be given as the land was not officially in possession of the Province, Keith was not hindered by legal technicalities. He was counting on the fact that once a treaty was reached with the Native Americans, which he himself would broker, the Patent would go to the person who could prove they held the first warranted survey.

Keith acted quickly, staking a claim to the suspected copper wealth lying across the river on April 4, 1722. While travelling with Deputy Surveyor Jacob Taylor, the governor had a chance meeting with Philip Syng from Philadelphia. During the conversation, Keith discovered that Syng and his partners had obtained a Warrant from Maryland to survey the very same area west of the river that he was planning to investigate for himself. Governor Keith was quick to inform Syng that the land was not within the limits of the Maryland province, and if he should continue with his plans, he would have him arrested.

Syng and Keith parted ways, and the governor rushed across the river with Jacob Taylor in order to be the first to arrive. In a survey completed the next day, he instructed Taylor to lay off an area of 500 acres, making "Keith's Tract" the first, albeit unapproved and unsanctioned, survey on the west side of the river. As it was done without any authority of the Land Office, but rather under the direct order of the governor, the survey was not filed upon completion. Furthermore, there are no surviving copies of the Warrant or survey, and it is unclear how far north Keith's Tract actually extended.

Unfortunately for Keith, the Provincial Council had access to the same information concerning the possible existence of valuable ore in the area. Learning of the unusual trip made by the governor, and knowing that he had taken a surveyor along with him, the Commissioners of Property were suspicious of his motives. Suspecting Keith's real reason to be a personal interest to acquire any untapped mineral rights, they took immediate action to counter his survey.

On April 5, 1722, the very same day that Jacob Taylor completed his survey work for Governor Keith, the Commissioners issued a hasty Warrant for their own survey to supersede it. They sent the Warrant with another Deputy Surveyor, James Steel, with instructions to intercept Jacob Taylor, turn him around, and accompany him to resurvey the area for the Proprietors.

Steel headed west, met up with Taylor, and explained the conflicting situation. Together they crossed back over to the west side of the Susquehanna on April 10. They were met by John McNeal, one of the governor's deputies, whom Keith had posted on the tract to prevent anyone, including the Commissioners of Property, from conducting another survey. McNeal made clear the governor's express orders forbidding them from trespassing, but the surveyors persisted and continued with their work, completing it the following day. Keith's bold defense of his survey and defiance of the official representatives of the Provincial Council reveals the lack of clear lines of authority regarding land matters at the time.

The Commissioners of Property had a vested interest in surveying the land so supposedly rich in copper ore. The deed to Pennsylvania granted to the Trustees by William Penn in 1708 stipulated a payment of £6000 plus six percent interest to be raised by rents, the sale of lands, or any other means. The modest land taxes charged for patented land were an attempt to insure a lasting income for Penn and his heirs. As of 1722, this amount had not been fully remitted to Penn's heirs and the Trustees viewed the potential value of the property west of the Susquehanna River as a way to satisfy this debt, as evidenced by the wording of the Warrant for their survey:

"And whereas, It is reported that there is a valuable Copper Mine or Mines discovered in this Province beyond the river Sasquehannnah, not far from that part which is inhabited by Christians on or near the banks on this side of the said River the Profits whereof may probably in a little time be sufficient to raise the whole remainder of the said sum yet unpaid with the interest due thereon. We doe therefore hereby authorize and direct you James Steel and Jacob Taylor or either of you forthwith to survey and lay out to the use of the said Henry Goudney and others the surviving said Trustees the full quantity of Two thousand Acres of Land where the said Copper Mine or Mines have been discovered in one or more tracts inclosing the said Mines ..."[6]

A mere six days after Governor Keith's covert survey, the first Pennsylvania survey officially approved by the Council was completed on April 11, 1722 and was subsequently referred to as the "Newberry Tract." On the plat, the significance of the potential copper deposits is noted by the description of the tract as "Mine Land." It encompassed the 500 acres previously surveyed by Keith and included the Accomac area, whose location on the draft would have been approximately half way between the end points along the river.

The resulting return of the Warrant by Jacob Taylor and James Steel outlined the physical boundaries of the Newberry Tract: "... situate on ye southwest side of Susquehanna river, beginning at ye mouth of a branch opposite to ye Sawanna Indian town and a little below the settlement made by John Grist and running up ye same on the several courses thereof one thousand and fifty perches to a marked white oak standing on the bank of a small meadow near ye said branch, from thence running by a line of marked trees northwest nine hundred perches to a corner white oak standing in ye woods near the head of a branch which runs into Susquehanna river opposite to ye lower part of James LeTort's plantation: thence down ye said branch by ye courses thereof, three hundred and twenty perches to ye river: thence down ye same, fifteen hundred perches to ye place of beginning, containing two thousand acres."[7]

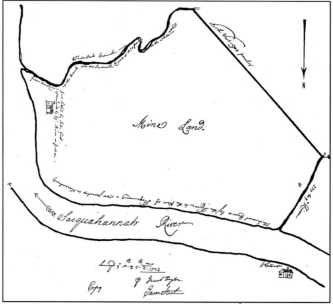

The Newberry Tract [8]

In contemporary terms, the Sawanna (Shawnee) Indian town was located near Columbia in Lancaster County and the creek on the opposite (west) side, which was then White Oak Branch, is now known as Kreutz Creek. Therefore, the survey began at the point where Kreutz Creek empties into the Susquehanna River just south of Wrightsville in York County. The lone settlement on the west side, belonging to John Grist, was vacant at the time of the survey due to the arrest and eviction of the squatter the previous year.

Grist, in defiance of the Board of Property, crossed the river in 1719 and built a cabin where Wrightsville is now located. This led to a complaint by the Native Americans, repeated warnings from the Commissioners of Property, and subsequent action by the Governor. According to the minutes of a Council held in Philadelphia on August 17, 1721, this action including the burning of his home, the imposition of fines, and his incarceration in a Philadelphia prison.

Grist promised to act respectably, pay a fine, and guarantee to vacate his settlement within a month. By the time the Newberry Tract survey was completed the following April, the only evidence remaining of the first settlement west of the Susquehanna was a notation on the draft documenting where his cabin was previously located, indicating it was currently being occupied by "Captain Beaver, an Indian."[9]

From the initial reference point, the first survey line ran about three miles southwest along the winding Kreutz Creek to a point near where Stoner's Station was located along the York-Wrightsville railroad in the 1800s. Today, the "marked white oak standing on the bank of a small meadow" would be about three-quarters of a mile south of Route 462 where Ducktown Road crosses Kreutz Creek.

The second line ran northwest two and three-quarters miles to the head of a creek, now called Dugan Run, at a point where it crosses Codorus Furnace Road, halfway between Chimney Rock Road and Millstone Road. Ironically, this was near the 1760s location of Grubb's Ore Bank, a productive mine not for the copper that Governor Keith had once hoped for, but rich iron ore.

From there the survey line ran down the course of Dugan Run exactly one mile to the Susquehanna River, and followed the curving shoreline east and south for a distance of four and three-quarters miles to the point where it began.

On April 16, 1722, the Commissioners of Property met in Philadelphia to discuss the duplicate and conflicting surveys conducted by their office and by Governor Keith. The governor was in attendance in an attempt to defend his unauthorized survey of vacant land west of the river. The minutes of the meeting record the council's uneasiness and distrust of Keith's motives with the following account:

"The commissioners having some days ago been informed that the Governor, (Sir William Keith) was gone toward Susquehanna and had taken Jacob Taylor with him, which gave them some apprehension of a design he might have on a parcel of land on the other (west) side of Susquehanna, where supposed to be a copper mine, whereupon they thought it expedient to send James Steele with a warrant under their hands and seals, dated the 5th ins., directed to himself and Jacob Taylor, authorizing them to survey and lay out for the use of the trustees (till the mortgage money and interest due thereupon should be paid and the property then revert back to the heirs and devisees of the late proprietary) the quantity of two thousand acres of land, enclosing within the lines of survey the land whereupon is supposed to be ye copper mine. James Steel accordingly set out with ye warrant and met with Jacob Taylor at Conestoga, who readily accompanied him over Susquehanna, where, after some opposition made by one John McNeal, by the Governor's express order, as he said, they proceeded on the survey on ye 10th inst. and finished the same on the 11th."[10]

Keith attempted to justify his secret survey by telling the Commissioners he was hoping to forestall the intrusions of settlers from Maryland into Chester County[†] in order to placate the Native Americans. Although the security of the local tribes was Keith's public justification, his intentions to secure mineral rights for himself were clearly obvious. As the meeting minutes relate, he told the council:

[†] *At the time, Chester County included the present counties of Lancaster and York. In 1729, Lancaster County was formed and included the land west of the Susquehanna River. York County was split from Lancaster County in 1749.*

"Upon some information I lately received that the Indians were like to be disturbed by the Secret and Underhand Practices of Persons, both from Mary Land and this Place, who under the pretense of finding a Copper Mine, were about to Survey and take up Lands on the other side of the River Sasquehannah; I not only sent up a Special Messenger with a Writ under the lesser seal to prevent them, but took this Occasion to go towards the Upper parts of Chester County myself in order to Locate a small quantity of Land unto which I had purchased an original Proprietary Right; And understanding further along the Road, that some Persons [Philip Syng] were actually come with a Mary Land Right to Survey Lands upon Sasquehannah, fifteen miles above Conestoga, I pursued my course directly thither, and happily arrived but a very few hours in time to prevent the Execution of their Design. Having a Surveyor General of this Province along with me in Company, after a little Consideration, I ordered him to Locate and Survey some part of the Right I possessed, viz; only five hundred acres upon that Spot on the other Side Sasquehannah, which was to prove a Bone of Contention, and breed so much mischief, and he did so accordingly upon the 4th and 5th days of this Instant April, after which I returned to Conestoga, in order to discourse with the Indians upon what had happened."[11]

Keith wanted the Commissioners to believe he was merely espousing the original intentions and policies of William Penn towards the Native Americans. Furthermore, he told them the tribes were contemplating going to war over the intrusions by Maryland settlers and he felt he had to take immediate action. Governor Keith reinforced this fact by informing the Council that he held a council with the chiefs the morning following his survey, relating to them that he had secured the lands himself to prevent any further intrusions.

In reality, his urgency to secretly survey the area was prompted by his discovery that others had the same objective. The chance meeting on the road with Philip Syng on April 4, when Keith found out that a Maryland Warrant had already been issued, was the very same day that he hurried across the river with Jacob Taylor to begin his survey. He knew the Maryland Warrant had not yet been executed, and Keith moved quickly in order to forestall Syng's plans.

Keith challenged the legality of the Commissioner's survey Warrant and produced an Executive Order he had issued a month prior to his own survey. The order indicated certain stipulations agreed to between the governors of Maryland and Pennsylvania, strictly prohibiting surveys west of the Susquehanna. Keith's writ from March accented the ongoing power struggle between the Proprietors Council and the Governor, and documented his perception of how the complicated issues of land management in the colony should be dealt with. The order stipulated:

"... that no Surveys or Settlements should be made by any private person whatever, on the west side of the Sasquehannah by Rights from either Province, and thereupon, and for preventing any disturbance to the Indians, by means of such Surveys or settlements, impowering and requiring the said Joseph Pidgeon, and his Deputies, to make diligent enquiry and search after any Person or Persons, who under the pretence of Land Rights from Mary Land or from this Province shall presume to survey or settle any lands within ten miles distance of Sasquehannah to the Westward, and not only to forbid all persons to survey as aforesd., but by force to restrain them."[12]

Governor Keith obviously felt that he had the authority to mandate land policy, a power that the Proprietors Council also claimed. Insomuch as he had just completed a survey of his own on the west side of the river, his order to prohibit them seemed hypocritical, but was used as his justification for his agent John McNeal to challenge James Steel when he attempted to carry out the survey for the Council on April 10. Keith complained to the Commissioners that Steel, "without paying the Regard due to the Governours Authority expressed in the sd. Commission had pretended to Survey Land over the River Sasquahannah, notwithstanding the Person or Person deputed by virtue of sd. Commission had forbid him, which action as it appeared a Contempt of the Governour's authority, and might be of unhappy Consequence with the Indians, as being contrary to what the Governr. in his Treaty two or three days before had stipulated with them. He was obliged to take notice of it and call the sd. James Steel to an account for it."[13]

After insinuating to the Council that they had no authority in ordering their survey, Keith implied that hostilities were imminent unless they allowed him to administer the land west of the river and deal with the Native Americans as he saw fit. The governor then questioned whether or not the Council had even given James Steel instructions to be on "his" land. The commissioners made it clear that they had indeed issued the Warrant for their survey, and if Steel had behaved disorderly and contrary to any legal order of the governor, they should not have to justify his actions to Keith.

Whether the survey made by Governor Keith was for his own personal gain or for the protection of Native American lands, it directly conflicted with the survey completed by the Pennsylvania Council, who was seeking to protect the financial interests of Penn's heirs. The Council could not begin collecting taxes, and Penn's heirs could not begin profiting from the settlement of the area, until it was officially surveyed by their office. They would then have to acquire the land from the local Native Americans and issue Patents before any rent could be collected.

In the end, the fact that Pennsylvania laid claim to the Accomac area was further complicated by the actions of Maryland in the period immediately before, and after, the survey of the Newberry Tract by Pennsylvania. Less than a month after Keith's surreptitious survey on April 5th, and only two weeks after the Council's survey, John Dorsey, a Deputy Surveyor for Baltimore County, Maryland, conducted a survey "by virtue of a warrant granted unto Philip Syng and Thomas Browne both of the City of Philadelphia in the Province of Pennsylvania out of his Lordships Land Office bearing date of March 28, 1722."[14]

Syng & Co., in conjunction with the Maryland Proprietors, had been prospecting and operating mines further south along the Susquehanna and became interested in the possibility of copper, iron and silver resources in the Accomac area about the same time as Keith and the Council set their sights west of the river. Not intimidated by the warnings of Governor Keith during their chance meeting on April 4, Syng continued with his plans to have the area surveyed.

The Maryland survey of 200 acres, which Syng and Brown called "The Partners Adventure," was completed on April 24 and was clearly within the boundaries of the 2000-acre Newberry Tract. By the end of April, the provinces of Pennsylvania and Maryland had both executed survey Warrants which included the area where the Accomac would eventually be established, and the contention for other land in the area began to escalate.

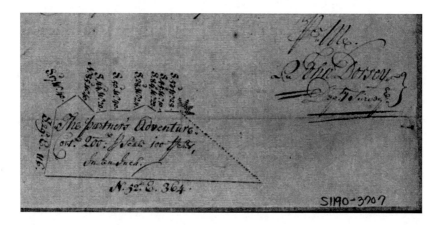

"Partner's Adventure, Phillip Syng and Thomas Brown, 200 acres"[15]
1722 land survey plat

Chapter 3

Accomac
The Summer of '22

"Heathens don't amount to shucks alongside of pirates"
... Mark Twain

In late May, 1722, about a month after Philip Syng surveyed the Accomac area under his Maryland Warrant, he returned to explore the area in hopes of finding promising mines. Syng had previously delivered ore samples from an exploratory mine on the property to Secretary Philimon Lloyd in Maryland, who noted in a letter to Lord Baltimore in London, "I have received at their hands 2 ps of Oar; the one copper and Iron and the other silver and iron."[1]

The discovery of copper and silver is doubtful based on the subsequent mining operations carried out in the centuries following Syng's first exploration of the property, but iron was most certainly found in abundance. The reports of finding other valuable metals were most likely an attempt to convince Lord Baltimore that the encroachment by Maryland on land claimed by Pennsylvania was justified and defensible.

When Syng returned to the area on the May 20, he was promptly arrested and taken before Francis Worley, a Justice of the Peace for Chester County, on a charge of surveying land within Pennsylvania's Newberry Tract. Depositions were taken during an inquiry the following day, and Syng was released pending the outcome.

Syng's opinions regarding who had a valid right to be on the land did not sit well with the local magistrate. Accused of lying, attempting to defraud Pennsylvania, inciting the Native Americans, and creating tension with Maryland, Syng was formally arrested on May 27 and jailed in Philadelphia. The charges were based on affidavits by witnesses taken at the May 21 inquest before Justice Worley.

"Whereby it appears that the said Philip Syng, upon the 20th inst., did say that the Tract of Land upon the West side of Sasquehannah, lately Surveyed by William Keith, Bart., Governour of this Province, did belong to him the said Philip Syng and Company, by a Maryland Title and That the said Tract of Land was lately surveyed by his Order & for his use by a Surveyor from Maryland, thereby endeavoring as much as in him lyes, not only to defraud the Propr. Of this Province of his just Rights, but also to create a misunderstanding between this Govmt. And its good neighbours of Mary Land, and to disturb the Indians settled upon Sasquehannah River under this Governmt, at this juncture, when it is requisite to give them all possible satisfaction."[2]

Philip Syng was called before Governor Keith and the Pennsylvania Council the next day, May 28, to answer these charges. The questions asked and the answers given reflect Syng's contempt for the proceedings:

"Q.   Have you surveyed any Lands by virtue of a Mary Land Right upon the West Bank of Sasquehannah, viz; that place know by the name of the Mine?

A.   *I have*

Q.   How much Land did you then Survey?

A.   *Two Hundred Acres*

Q.   By what Surveyor?

A.   *John Dussey [Dorsey], a Surveyor in Mary Land*

Q.   How came you to think that place was in Mary Land?

A.   *I was informed so*

Q.   When the Govr. Met with you on the 4th of April, at Pattisons, had you then made this Survey?

A.   *No*

Q.   Did not the Governeur then acquaint you that the place was not within the Limits of Mary Land, and that if you presumed to make any Survey then he would Committ you?

A.   *I do remember that the Gov. said if he had found us there it would have amounted to a severe Fine, but as to the rest I have forgot"*[3]

Philip Syng was born in Cook County, Ireland, in 1676, and learned the silversmith trade from relatives active in the guild of Dublin goldsmiths. In 1714 at the age of thirty-eight, he left Ireland with his wife Abigail and their son Philip, Jr., then nine years old. After landing in Annapolis, Maryland, they made their way to Philadelphia, and by 1720 opened up a shop near Market Place. During this time, perhaps lured by the prospect of copper and silver mines to the west, he began the process of applying for a survey Warrant.

Since the Pennsylvania Land Office was not yet issuing Warrants for the area west of the Susquehanna, Syng instead turned to Maryland. Understanding that both provinces laid claim to the same area, he decided to pursue applying for his survey Warrant through the provincial government of Maryland instead of Pennsylvania.

After obtaining the Warrant in March, having the survey completed by John Dorsey in April, being arrested in May, and spending time in a Philadelphia jail, Philip Syng had enough of Pennsylvania. By that time, his wife Abagail had died, and his son Philip Jr. was old enough to take over his workshop in Philadelphia. He moved back to Annapolis, Maryland in 1724, and immediately remarried. For the next eight years, Syng patiently waited for his Maryland Patent to be issued for the Partners Adventure survey.

His son, Philip Syng, Jr., was a well-educated gentleman and became a master silversmith in his own right. Producing some of the period's finest silver pieces, his most noteworthy accomplishment was the design of an elegant silver inkstand in 1752 that he called the Standish.* Delegates of the Continental Congress who signed the Declaration of Independence in 1776, and the Constitution of the United States in 1787, all dipped their quill pens into Syng's inkwell.

Following the multiple surveys in the Accomac area in the spring of 1722, Governor Keith became alarmed by the increasingly aggressive activities of Maryland and devised a plan to hinder further encroachments. Even though surveys had been conducted by both Maryland and Pennsylvania, official Patents had not yet been issued, and until they were, neither province legally owned the surveyed tracts. Keith's problem was the constraints imposed by the rigid policies of Penn's heirs, which would not allow the granting of Patents until the land was purchased from the Native Americans. Unless Keith was able to find a loophole to somehow gain official ownership, he knew Maryland would proceed to do so.

The solution to his problem was found in the original charter of Pennsylvania to William Penn, which allowed for the surveying of "manors" for use by the Proprietor and his heirs. In order to stem the tide of settlers from Maryland, Keith decided to approach the local tribes, express to them his concern that the rights promised them by William Penn were being threatened, and convince them that the only way to stop the loss of their land was to set it aside in the name of Penn's heirs.

On June 15, 1722, Keith held a council with the chiefs of the Conestoga, Shawana and Ganaway tribes at Conestoga in Lancaster County. He began his address by reminding them of their friendship and agreements previously made with William Penn. Through an

---

* *The Standish is on display at the Independence National Historic Park in Philadelphia, along with copies of the Declaration of Independence and the Constitution of the United States.*

interpreter, he then described the current threat from Maryland and proceeded to ask them for permission to survey a large tract on the west side of the Susquehanna for Penn's grandson Springett.

He advised them the survey was necessary in order to insure their continued use of the land as they saw fit, and to provide them a place to move when the east side of the river became too populated with settlements. In doing so, he subtly hinted to them that if they didn't agree to his plan, they would lose the use of their land forever.

"You say you love me because I came from your father, Wm. Penn, to follow his peaceable ways, and to fulfill all his kind promises to the Indians, you call me Wm. Penn, and I am very proud of the name you gave me; But if we have a true love for the memory of Wm. Penn, We must now shew it to his Family & to his Children that are grown up to be men in England, and will soon come over to represent him here.

Last time I was with you at Conestogoe, you shewed me a parchment which you have received from Wm. Penn, containing many articles of Friendship between him and you and between his Children & your Children; You then told me He desired you to remember it well for three Generations, but I hope you and your Children will never forget it.

That Parchment fully declared your Consent to Wm. Penns purchase and Right to the Lands on both sides Sasquehanna; But I find both you & we are like to be disturbed by idle People from Mary Land, and also by others who have presumed to Survey Lands on the Banks of Sasquehanna, without any Powers from Wm. Penn or his children to whom they belong, and without so much as asking your consent.

I am therefore now come to hold a Council & consult with you how to prevent such unjust practices for the future, And hereby we will shew our Love & Respect for the Great Wm. Penn's children who inherit their fathers Estate in this Country, and have a just right to the hearty Love and friendship of all the Indians promised to them in many Treaties. I have fully considered this thing, and if you approve my thoughts, I will immediately cause to take up a large Tract of Land on the other side of Sasquehanna for the Grandson of William Penn, who is now a man as tall as I am; For when the Land is marked with his name upon the Trees, it will keep off the Mary Landers and every other Person whatsoever from coming to settle near you to disturb you,

And he bearing the same kind heart to the Indians which his Grandfather did, will be glad to give you any part of his Land for your own use and Convenience, but if other people take it up they will make settlements upon it, and then it will not be in his power to give it to you as you want it.

Those who have any wisdom amongst you must see and be convinced that what I now say is intirely for your Good, for this will effectually hinder and prevent any Person from settling Lands on the other side of Sasquehanna according to your own Desire, and consequently You will be secure from being disturbed by ill neighbours, and have all that Land at the same time in your own power to make use of.

This will also beget a true hearty Love and friendship between you, your children, and the great Wm. Penn's Grandson, who is now Lord of all this Country in the room of his Grandfather. It is therefore fit & necessary for you to begin as soon as you can to express your Respect & Love to him; He expects it from you according to your promises in many Treaties, and he will take it very kindly."[4]

Keith made a good case and must have been very convincing. He threatened them yet made them feel safe, made them feel guilty yet empowered, and made promises he knew he could not keep. He insured them that if they agreed to his plan, no further settlements would occur, they would not be disturbed, and that they could have all the land west of the river that they wanted, when they wanted it.

Keith appealed to their honor, asking them to uphold their former agreements made with Penn, while he himself had no intention of living up to his end of the treaty. He knew that as soon as they gave their permission, the survey of Springetts Manor would immediately be ordered. Settlers would then be granted Warrants to survey within the manor, and after Patents were permitted by the Province, revenues would be generated for the Proprietors through rents and taxes.

Keith knew he had no real power to stop settlers from streaming across the river. The treaty with the local tribes for the survey of Springetts Manor was an attempt to give them the impression he was upholding the intentions of Penn's heirs with respect to Native American land rights. The only issue remaining would be to negotiate with them to relinquish their title to the land west of the Susquehanna, which he knew would come in due time. All he was asking for now was permission to survey, but he realized this would only be a temporary stepping stone to eventually taking over the lands permanently.

The following day, after considering the facts put before them by Governor Keith, the chiefs responded, realizing they did not have much of a choice except to agree with his proposal. From past experience, they understood if they did not allow Pennsylvanians to settle the land west of the river, Marylanders would occupy it by force. They also knew that settlers from Maryland would show no respect or consideration for their rights, or for their former agreements with William Penn.

They responded through their spokesperson, a chief named Tawenea, saying "They have Considered of what the Govr. proposed to them yesterday, & think it a matter of very great importance to them to hinder the Mary Landers from Settling or taking up Lands so near them upon Sasquehanna. They very much approve what the Govr. spoke, and like his Council to them very well ..."

" ... They ask the Govr. whereabouts & what quantity of Land does he propose to survey for Mr. Penn. It is answered, from over against the mouth of the Conestogoe Creek up to the Govrs. New Settlement, and so far back from the River as no Person can come to annoy or disturb them in their Towns on this side ..."[5]

Following his successful negotiations and the subsequent treaty, Keith wasted no time in preparing a survey Warrant for 75,000 acres west of the river. It was issued on June 18, two days after he received permission from the local tribes. The survey itself was started the very next day, expedited by the fact the Keith learned that more surveyors from Maryland were already on their way to the area. It was completed without delay two days later, on June 20, 1722.

The manor that Keith surveyed was to be named Springetts Manor because it was to be laid out for the use of Springett Penn, the grandson of William Penn. Penn died in 1718, and his son William passed away about 1720, so in 1722 when the survey was made, Springett was the rightful heir to the province.

The warrant states the reasons for the survey and outlines its boundaries: "And whereas, it is reasonable and agreeable to former Treaties with the Indians, that a sufficient quantity of Land upon the South West side of the River Sasquahannah be reserved in the Proprietors hands, for accommodating the said Indian Nations when it may be hereafter thought proper & convenient for them to remove their settlements further from Christian Inhabitants.

And lastly, Whereas, at a Treaty held between the Indians and me, at Conestogoe, the 15th and 16th days of this instant, They did earnestly desire & request me to Cause a large Tract of Land, right against their Towns upon Sasquehannah, to be surveyed and located for the Proprietors use only; Because, from his Bounty and Goodness, they would always be sure to obtain whatever was necessary & Convenient for them from time to time.

... and to survey or cause to be surveyed, marked and Located, the quantity of 70,000 acres or thereabouts, in the name & for the use of the Honble Springet Penn, Esqr., which shall bear the name and be called the Mannor of Springetsburg,...

... thence by a Line E.N.E. until you meet with the uppermost Corner tree of my Settlement called Newberry, from thence S.E b S.

along my head Line until you to come at my Southern Corner tree in the Woods; from thence down the Side Line of my Land E.N.E until you come at the river Sasquehannah ..."[6]

Even though the controversy concerning Keith's survey and the Proprietors subsequent survey of the same area had been settled in April, the Governor held on to the hope that the adjoining Newberry Tract would be for his exclusive personal use. As documented in the survey Warrant for Springetts Manor, Keith persisted in referring to the area as "my settlement" and "my land," and made sure the surveyors did not include his tract within the manor boundaries. The Manor of Springetts bordered the Newberry Tract to the south and west, and by using personal references as corner points, he hoped to give his claim genuine legal legitimacy.

Apparently, Governor Keith was eager for it to be publically documented that his reasons for the Springetts Manor survey were purely for the benefit of the Native Americans, as he twice mentions that it was being done to accommodate their needs. However, based on the fact that additional survey Warrants and temporary Patents for tracts within the Manor were issued almost immediately, it is obvious that the motives for the survey were more for protecting the interests of Penn's heirs than the interests of the Native Americans.

Since the survey Warrant for Springetts Manor was not sanctioned by the Commissioners of Property in Philadelphia, but issued under Keith's private seal, the Governor handled it much like his own secret survey of early April. Hoping to avoid another confrontation with the Council over surveys on the west side of the Susquehanna, and as an apparent afterthought, Governor Keith informed the Council in Philadelphia of his efforts in dealing with the Maryland problem. On June 18, the same day he issued the Warrant for the survey, he summarized his decisions and sent a letter to the Council while still in Conestoga.

"Finding the Indians, since I came here last here, to be very much alarm'd with the noise of an intended survey from Mary Land, upon the Banks of Sasquehannah, I held a Council with them at

Conestoga, upon Friday and Saturday last, wherein I proposed to them to Cause a large Tract of Land to be surveyed on the West Side of that River for the Proprietor, to begin from the Upper Line of my New Settlement six miles back & extending down wards upon the River as far as over against the mouth of the Conestoga Creek. They were all exceedingly pleased with this Proposition, and pressed to have it immediately done, which I fully designed as soon as I got home ..."[7]

In the same letter, he explained that following his council with the Native Americans, he was returning to Philadelphia when he learned that Marylanders were setting out the same day to begin additional surveys in the area. He immediately turned around and went back to Conestoga, determined to cross the river the next day and see that the survey of Springetts Manor began immediately. He also directed a company of militia to march to the area, where they were to challenge and turn away any surveyors from Maryland.

The Council received his letter and replied on June 20. Their tone is conciliatory in contrast to their criticism of the Governor and his actions only two months earlier when they clashed over his personal surveys of lands across the river. Ironically, the reply letter from the Council is signed by Richard Hill, Isaac Norris and James Logan, among others, who were the same Council members who wrote out their own Warrant for the Newberry Tract because they were "apprehensive of a design" the governor had in mind.

"As the Govr. has since his Accession to this Governmt. Given evident proofs of his Abilities in managing the Affairs of the Publick, We shall not here take upon us to form any judgment of his treaties with the Indians on matters with which We cannot at this distance be duly acquainted, But undoubtedly it will be of Service to keep the Nations of these people right in relation to any Incroachments made or intended by Mary Land, not can we conceive that it lies before us as a Council of State to Concern ourselves with Surveys of the Proprietors Lands. The Govr. has the best reason to be acquainted with his Powers and Instructions in those affairs to which we must wholly refer Him."[8]

The character of the reply is completely opposite to their skepticism of Governor Keith in April. After first acknowledging that his abilities in managing the interests of the Proprietors were beyond reproach, they concede the properness of his intentions, and finally absolve themselves from any further responsibility on their part for dealing with these types of issues. Clearly, their lack of interest was due to the fact that mineral wealth was not the basis for this new survey. Since it was supposedly being done on behalf of the Proprietors, they had no reason to oppose the survey and instead quietly agreed.

They continue in their response by expressing their hope that Keith would reach out to Governor Calvert, his counterpart in Maryland, and politely warn him of the consequences of allowing further encroachments. However, they made it clear that if Maryland forcibly proceeded with surveys, Keith's response to them should only be "by all methods that can safely & justifiably be used among Subjects to the same Sovereign."[9]

As both Pennsylvania and Maryland were accountable to the British Crown, they were careful to include the reference to the Sovereign, so that Governor Keith would understand that any retaliatory action against Maryland would be in effect against Britain. In a patronizing way, and avoiding the harsher words of war, they expressed their trust that Keith would continue to do the right thing and exercise caution in his dealings with Maryland.

"And we doubt not but the Governour in his prudence will always have this in view, that no hasty steps be made which may involve us in greater Difficulties and lead us into Inconveniences which we might when too late wish to have recalled."[10]

Following the completion of the 2,000-acre Newberry Tract survey in April, and the 75,000-acre Springetts Manor survey in June, the land containing the Accomac as well as all the surrounding land, was now officially surveyed and claimed by Pennsylvania. However, Patents were still prohibited, as no treaty with the Native Americans relinquishing their ownership of the land had yet been reached.

Although there would be many more years of conflict over surveys and settlements in the area, Governor Keith did attempt to make good on the suggestions made by the Council and reached out to Governor Calvert of Maryland.

Less than a week after the Springetts Manor survey, or Keith's Survey as it has become known, the governor wrote a letter from Newberry to Governor Calvert on June 23. He informed him of the treaty he negotiated with the Native Americans, his Warrant, and the subsequent survey of Springetts Manor. He explained that his decision to execute the survey immediately was based upon finding out that a survey Warrant had been issued by Governor Calvert, and that men and horses were on their way from Maryland.

"Now Sir, tho' I did not by any means give credit to all this Relation, yet knowing the weakness and former attempts of some of your people of whom I have formerly complained to yourself, who justly bear the character of Land Pyrates, I was resolved to put it out of the power on this occasion to embroil us by their ridiculous projects..."[11]

When Keith lobbied with the Native Americans only a week earlier, he presented his proposed survey in light of their best interests, in order to protect them, and to guarantee their use of their land west of the river. Keith clearly stated that he, along with the Proprietors, acknowledged the rights of the Native Americans to use the land at their convenience. He called the Native Americans "brothers," himself a "true friend." However, with Calvert, he was more worried about what the local tribes might do and assumed a more derogatory and superior tone. He indicated to Calvert that the survey was his only way for "quieting the Indians, as well as to prevent the mischief which might happen upon any of your People's presuming to encroach upon what the Heathens call their own Property..."[12]

Governor Keith finished his June 23 letter to Governor Calvert with a diplomatically worded reminder that he felt it rather obvious that the area in question was clearly within the limits of Pennsylvania. He also was careful to place the blame on others, and not Calvert, for the misconception that the area was within the borders of Maryland.

"Perhaps some ignorant, or should I rather say designing people, will endeavor to perswade you that this place is upon the Border of Mary Land; Whereas in Truth, there cannot be a clearer Demonstration in anything of that nature, than it is about twelve miles to the Northward of Philadelphia, and I am sure I nee'd not say no more to convince you at least I have good Reason to insist upon its being within the Limits of this Province, without all manner of Dispute."[13]

Despite the polite exchanges between the governors, Maryland persisted in attempting to execute further survey Warrants in the area in the ensuing months. Some were successful, others left incomplete, and a few were prevented from even starting. The frustration of not knowing exactly what constituted the boundary between Pennsylvania and Maryland is evident in a July 19 letter from Maryland Secretary Philemon Lloyd to Governor Calvert. In it, he reviewed what had happened to Phillip Syng earlier in the year.

"I know not by what means the Pennsylvanians had notice of it, but before our surveyor went up, they had posted souldiers all about the woods So that our officer dared not to go and execute the warrant. As soon as Sing Roach &c went up, a warrant was issued out by Sir William [Keith] and Sing was taken upon the mine: thence carried to Philadelphia and committed to the city goal [jail], as you will see by the inclosed papers which I have purposely transmitted that the rigorous methods of these people may be known ... I design however to make a survey there with all imaginable secrecy, but should be heartily glad if a proper instrument were sent over for the taking of the Latitude of the place, or that some publick directions were given to the Government for making and exact discovery of the line of 40 North."[14]

Chapter 4

Coyle's Ferry
Sunday, May 22, 1881

Just after midnight, when late Friday night faded into early Saturday morning and the black of the sky melded into the river, John finally headed home from Marietta. The moon proved to be an unreliable guide, shirking its navigational duties by retreating behind the scuttling clouds all too frequently. Rowing mainly on intuition and alcohol, he was making quick work of the trip despite the amount of cheap liquor he had just thrown down in the assortment of hotels on Front Street. His mood was foul and getting worse with every stroke, and the fact they had refused to continue serving him only increased his agitation. What gave them the right to decide it was time for him to stop drowning his anger?

His head dizzy with jealousy, John stopped rowing and began drifting lazily with the downstream current, the slow circular motion of his boat keeping pace with the spinning in his head. The last few days wore heavily on him, and he had come to the conclusion he needed to do something drastic, even desperate, to make Emma understand that she belonged to *him*. Suddenly aware that he had floated well past the ferry, he snapped back to reality with as much attentiveness as he could muster. He was almost down to the Point, where the river took a severe right-angle turn south towards Wrightsville. A break in the clouds illuminated the sheer face of Chiques Rock looming high on his right, and he heard the low rushing sound of water close below him.

The mile-wide river constricted as it rounded the sharp curve, and the escalating current began pulling him towards the rocks which extended across the width of the river on the other side of the bend. The faster he went, the faster his heart raced, thinking about running the low rapids in the dark, drunk. The underlying rocks usually hid just below the surface and didn't show themselves until late summer, but with the lack of rain so far in May they were already exposed. They presented a real danger to boats heading downstream, especially ones out in the middle of the night and piloted by intoxicated oarsmen.

The night was dark as pitch and the third-quarter moon which hung low in the sky provided barely enough reflection on the water to illuminate the danger ahead. Forcing aside his preoccupation with Emily and ignoring the rage that was slowly consuming him, John instinctively jerked sharply back on his left oar to turn away from the approaching rapids.

A stabbing pain raced through his thumb and index fingers, making him wince and cry out. Momentarily distracted by the sharp spasms in his hand, John stopped rowing and the boat resumed drifting on a collision course with the rapids. The crippled fingers continually bothered him, and he didn't have the strength to make the turn as quickly as he had needed. John strongly back-stroked the right oar to compensate and the small boat responded and pointed itself dutifully towards the safety of the York County shore.

Rowing frantically to put as much distance between himself and the rapids as quickly as possible, he noticed a fire brightly burning at the bend in the river, near where the rocks tumbled down to the water's edge. To his left, the shadowy hillside that towered above him followed the river for miles, passing behind the ferry and down to the Point which now lay in the direction he was heading. It had once been a part of the same ridge which continued across the river, but the endlessly flowing water had eroded its way through, leaving behind only the line of low rocks in the river and the sharp precipice of Chiques Rock on the Lancaster County shore. The flames provided a guiding light for him, and John angled the boat towards their flickering glow.

There had been a shallow cave at the Point until the railroad construction crew blasted the cliff face as a part of the short-lived plan for a rail line that was to be run up the Coyles side of the river. Although the cave was now gone, demolished into rubble, the spot was still a popular place for the locals John's age from both sides of the river to congregate on Friday nights.

"ACCOMAC BOAT" ON SUSQUEHANNA RIVER, ACCOMAC, PA.
The Point , between Coyle's Ferry and Wrightsville, ca. 1909
Collection of Author

Their loud talk floated easily out across the water, the boy's boisterous chatter mixing with the garish laughter of the girls. He could tell it was the same crowd that occasionally rented the pavilion in the old saw mill from his father for parties, and John never felt a part of their world. Besides asking the guys if they got lucky when they took their girls for walks in the woods behind the house, he didn't really know what to talk to them about, so he generally steered clear of them, as he planned to do now.

Not wanting to get too close for fear he would be discovered, John turned back up the river well before reaching the shore, depriving them of the opportunity to recognize him and launch their snide insults. He most likely had been heard when he cried out in pain, and realized how wild-eyed and desperate he would look, frenetically rowing across the river, emerging from the dark as if pursued by something unseen. They were probably looking out over the water right now, watching for him, and he imagined their amusement.

It would be just one more reason for them to consider him crazy, and in his current desperate and drunken state, it wouldn't take much provocation for him to stop and fight. He got his small revolver from his hip pocket and twirled it around on the trigger finger of his good hand, thinking about how good it would feel to confront them.

As he distanced himself from the Point and their voices began to fade, he pocketed his gun and glanced up the river towards the ferry house. There was a single faint light glowing from a lamp hanging on the front porch, and he realized he was rowing out of one difficulty and straight into another. His father usually waited for him when he was late coming home, and tonight would most likely be no exception.

They had quarreled earlier in the week and it had been a nasty drawn-out affair. Mr. Coyle would be especially angry tonight because John neglected the ferry all day, leaving it to his father to run back and forth across the river. Dreading the next installment of the argument, which he knew would happen as soon as he got home, John slowed the boat and allowed his thoughts to wander back to the past few days.

It all started at dinner on Thursday evening when John, his father, mother, and several of the semi-permanent residents gathered to eat at the big farm table in the dining room on the first floor, next to the tavern room. Emily served the shad and boiled potatoes, both in steaming abundance.

For the last several months the shad were running heavy, and John had been bringing home a steady supply almost every week. It was a favorite dish of the Coyles and their boarders, and fresh Susquehanna Shad was always in demand in the tavern as well. Whatever they couldn't eat or sell, John's mother salted, smoked, or dried, and they enjoyed the fish through the winter months.

Shad was a local delicacy, and only plentiful from April through June when the fish made their annual pilgrimage from the Chesapeake Bay upriver to spawn. The number of fish that made it as far as the Coyles had been declining since the low-head dam was built across the river in 1839 between Columbia and Wrightsville, and with the extremely low conditions this particular May, shad fishing at the ferry was practically non-existent.

Although good for canal commerce, the six-foot-high dam effectively ended the ability of the shad to move unimpeded into the northern branches of the Susquehanna in Pennsylvania and New York. It was a constant source of controversy and frustration for nearby residents who counted on the shad for a livelihood, or just a decent meal. When the Columbia Dam was completed, shad fishing practically disappeared from the upper Susquehanna, and was limited to the forty-three miles of the river below the dam. Located about a mile below the covered bridge, the dam diverted a predictable, constant volume of water into the Susquehanna and Tidewater Canal which ran along the river on the York County side, beginning in Wrightsville and heading south into Maryland.

Built of wooden cribs filled with river stones, the dam created a slack water basin so that the mule teams on the bridge could pull canal boats laden with coal, lumber, grain, and iron across the otherwise shallow width of the river from the Pennsylvania Canal, which ended in Columbia on the opposite shore. The Columbia Dam remained in place for fifty years and was allowed to disintegrate when canal operations ceased following the flood of 1894. The shad population rebounded for a short time, but following the construction of the Holtwood Dam about fifteen miles north of the Maryland line in 1910, shad fishing in the Susquehanna was effectively finished.

John rose shortly after 5 o'clock Thursday morning and had gone straightaway to the barn to hitch his horse to the small spring wagon for a fishing trip in Wrightsville, conveniently timing his entrance when Emily was doing her morning milking. She was startled by his sudden entrance, as she normally had at least an hour to herself before the others in the house were up and moving about.

"What are you doing sneaking up on a girl like that? You scared me half to death, John Coyle!" Emily cried. John teased her for being so scared, and Emily scolded him back, asking what he thought he was doing skulking around so early in the morning like a criminal.

Proclaiming he was going for shad, and boasting of all the fish he would bring home, John said "I'd be a fine catch for you, Em!" and threw his seines into the back of the wagon. He leaped up to the seat, lashed at the horses, and tore through the open barn doors, pounding down the lane and raising a billowing cloud of dust in his wake.

He made good on his promise, having no trouble catching several long strings of heavy fish off the top of the dam. Although the state made fishing within a half-mile of the dam illegal, enforcement was practically non-existent and John never paid any attention to the rules. The shad were easy to catch with throw nets due to the low water and he was back before noon. After Emily cleaned and boned enough fish for dinner, Mrs. Coyle fried the filets in butter and boiled them in fresh cream, with scallions from the garden behind the house.

Once Emily served everyone, she sat down and ate her dinner quietly, trying to gauge the mood of their conversation. There were days when they almost seemed to be a regular family, but they were few and far between. Most times there was no conversation between John and his parents, and other times simple questions flared into full-fledged arguments with little or no provocation.

Sensing today to be one of the more peaceable variety, Emily waited until she was done clearing the table of dirty dishes before asking Mrs. Coyle if she could have the following day off. The request wasn't well received and John thought it humorous. He snickered under his breath and was thankful that his Mother's wrath was being directed at someone else for a change.

Mondays were normally the day that Emily didn't have to work, but she had received an out-of-town letter the day before from William Overcash, a friend from Chambersburg, who was arriving by train early the following morning. He was hiring a carriage at the Hellam Station and riding out to the ferry to spend Friday with her, and Emily wanted to have the day free to show him around.

Predictably inflexible about such things, Mrs. Coyle complained that she would end up doing all the work, since Friday was the day they had to cook and bake for the weekend patrons at the tavern. Emily was politely insistent, pleading with Mrs. Coyle and promising to work the following Monday to make up for the lost time. Finally, after an endless tirade about how much work Emily actually accomplished on a good day, Mary Ann relented and agreed to let her have the day off, as long as she got up earlier than usual to get her milking and other morning chores done before she gallivanted off all over the countryside with her "gentleman friend."

Emily went into the tavern room to clear the tables left by the rafting pilots that had come in for drinks and some of Mrs. Coyle's boiled shad, and John followed closely behind. They were alone, and the rosy twilight slanting into the room cast an eerie glow. The sun set directly up the river and the large deep windows across the front of the inn caught the last dying rays of the day. He didn't speak as she lit the coal oil lamps on the bar and on each of the tables, but Emily could tell he was upset and guessed the cause of his accusing stare.

"Why do you look at me so?" she finally asked, and with a reply as razor-sharp as his look he shot back "Who is he, Em?" "Why, he's just an acquaintance from home," she said, feeling it necessary to add a contemptuous "if you must know." Incensed by her tone, John growled "You're damn right I want to know, I don't want him hanging around here – or you." Emily angrily replied "You don't own me John, and he's a sight nicer than anyone else I know."

Emily rushed out of the room and up the stairs, slamming the door to the bedroom she shared with Mrs. Coyle. Leaving him with more questions than answers, John yelled after her "Who is he, Em?" but got no response. He stood motionless, alone with his suspicions, watching and waiting for her to come back down and straighten things out. Surely it was not what it seemed, how could it be? How could she do this to him? She would explain that it was all a misunderstanding and tell him he was the only one for her and that he had nothing to worry about. She just had to. Didn't she? *Damn her. Damn her to hell.*

Realizing she was going to say no more, at least for the night, he soon retreated to his own room at the other end of the house and locked the door, not wanting to be disturbed. Crawling on top of his bed without bothering to remove his clothes, he curled up facing the wall, withdrawing from the world and into his own thoughts.

John spent a sleepless night tossing and turning, his bitterness growing along with the pain in his head and eating away at the little remaining reason he possessed. He usually just disappeared into the hills when he began feeling like this, sometimes for days at a time. But first, John decided he would follow Emily and her visitor the next day, and see for himself exactly what was going on.

When Friday morning finally came, John felt as if he hadn't slept at all and woke with a severe headache. As he listened to the house slowly come to life, he lay as still as possible to see if it would subside. Emily had gotten up earlier than usual, as she had promised Mrs. Coyle she would, and gone to the barn to get her morning chores done. His mother rose a short while after, moving slowly down the hall past his room and creaking down the back stairs to the kitchen.

He heard her put the kettle on the stove, heating water for his father so he could wash and shave. The heavy front door of the cast iron stove groaned open as she added more wood to the firebox and then closed with a bang. After the water was hot and the kettle began to whistle, he heard her climb back up the stairs and go to his father's room at the rear of the house. John fell back asleep, awaking again when his father tramped down the stairs and out the back door on his way to the barn.

The excited noises of the stock getting their breakfast, and the familiar sounds of his mother making their own, slowly invaded his drowsy stupor, urging him to get up and start the day. Once the irresistible smell of bacon reached him, he yielded to the temptation and slowly rolled over. Pulling himself up, he sat sleepily on the edge of his bed with his still-pounding head cradled in his hands.

Gradually, John recalled the argument with Emily the night before and remembered she was spending the day with the stranger from Chambersburg. Worried that he had slept too long and had already missed them, he jumped off the bed, instantly wide awake.

Quickly lacing his boots and splashing some cold water from his washbowl on his face, he bounded down the stairs to the kitchen.

His parents were the only ones in the kitchen, and were just sitting down to the eggs and bacon being pulled off the stove. Fearing the worst, he frantically asked where Emma was. "She's still in the barn, and better not be hurrying through her work," was his mother's curt reply. In a few minutes Emily returned to the house, and grabbing the perpetually hot kettle of water simmering on the stove, she went straight to her room to get cleaned up for her day off. Quickly eating his eggs and ignoring his bacon, John took the opportunity to hurry out to the barn to tack up his horse.

After throwing the frayed blanket and saddle on his bay stallion and sliding the headstall behind his ears, he placed the bit and led the horse around the barn, giving him a chance to relax before tightening the cinch. Satisfied that he would be ready to ride in a moment's notice, he led the confused horse back into his stall and tied the reins off. Rushing back into the house through the back door, he arrived in the kitchen only a moment before Emily came back downstairs.

She was wearing her best dress, a fashionable three-quarter length affair that John thought immodest. Not wanting to start something and possibly give her any clue of his plan to follow them, he bit his tongue and made no comment. She glanced at him, waiting for his expected sarcasm, and when it didn't come she looked away with a puzzled expression.

The dress was pale blue, with bright red trim around the waist and along the bottom edge. She had purchased it the previous fall on a rare shopping trip to York with the very first money she earned from the Coyles, and this was the first opportunity she had to wear it. Except for the few times she put it on and admired herself in the small mirror above her washstand, the dress had remained carefully folded in her clothes chest, waiting for a special occasion such as this.

As nice as the dress was, it contrasted sharply with her well-worn high-button brown boots. She had tried to clean them as best she could, but realizing they would soon be dirty again as soon as she walked outside, she soon gave up. They were her only shoes high enough to extend up beyond the hem of her skirt, and except for her low work shoes, were the only other pair she owned.

Her dark hair was clean, freshly brushed, and tied with a red ribbon that matched the trim on her dress. She had an excited look about her and was ready to meet the day, whatever it brought. John watched her pace back and forth from the kitchen to the front porch, anxiously waiting for her guest to arrive. Timing his own exit with one of her trips to the porch, John quietly left the house and went to the barn. Hiding himself behind the open door, he anxiously awaited.

After a few minutes, he heard the sounds of a carriage coming down the road by the creek, the thin iron bands of the wheels clicking loudly on the stones. As it stopped between the house and barn, John slid further back into the shadows, peering out between the cracks in the boards. Emily must have heard it as well, for as soon as the newcomer pulled up his horse, she ran down the steps and across the road, meeting Overcash as he stepped down from the carriage.

"William, it's so wonderful to see you!" she cried as he lifted her and spun her around. Setting her back down, he studied her and replied "Let me look at you, seems like you're grown up all of a sudden." "It hasn't been that long!" she laughed, taking his arm and steering him away from the barn.

As they walked past the house, and out of earshot, John went out the other end of the barn and climbed behind the house and apple orchard. He managed to get in front of them, and hunkered down behind some large rocks near the road, waiting for them to pass. Although he couldn't hear what they were saying, he could see they were talking in earnest.

"How are you, Emily? Are they treating you right? Your sister Annie wrote me and told me that you were having troubles. Why do you stay?" His questions tumbled out one after the other and he seemed genuinely concerned. She hesitated before answering him, not wanting it to seem like she couldn't handle herself living on her own. "I like the place well enough, but Mrs. Coyle can be a bit much to take, and John is a constant annoyance. He's just not right, and has such a temper. He scares me with his queer talk."

"If you don't feel safe, come back home to your grandfather's with me. And I don't like the sound of this Coyle fellow." She *was* occasionally frightened, she told him, and tired of all the drinking and fighting in the house. She confided to Overcash that she had talked to Mrs. Coyle a few months earlier about leaving and had been threatened not to even consider it. Emily thought they wanted her to marry John so they could secure her services permanently, and she wanted no part of that. Reassuring Overcash that she would take his advice if John continued to bother her, she finally said "I'm just not ready to leave, but I'll run away shortly if I can do no better."

As they neared the rock where John lay hidden, their conversation turned back to the day at hand. On their left was the river, and on the right the cleared fields and orchards belonging to the Coyles. Beyond this point, the road narrowed and wound between the hillside and the river, continuing on around the Point to Wrightsville. The trees created a dark canopy over the road, shrouding it in shadow.

Emily stopped suddenly, hesitant to enter the gloominess, and suggested they go back to his carriage and take a ride upriver to Wild Cat Glen. "You'll love it there," she said, thinking to herself that it would brighten her suddenly somber mood. John remained hidden behind the rocks until they were almost back to the house before he made his way across the hill to the trees behind the smokehouse.

Parting once they reached the barn, Emily went back into the house, and Overcash untied the carriage and waited for her by the hitching rail. She returned a few minutes later, bringing a small basket of food she had hastily thrown together. After they climbed into the carriage and started up the river road toward the falls, John ran into to the barn and mounted his patiently waiting horse.

Wild Cat Glen, a favorite spot for the locals from both sides of the river, was two miles upstream from the Coyles. The wagon road ran in front of the ferry along the winding shoreline, past Wild Cat Glen and on to the iron furnaces at Codorus. Wild Cat Run originated in a small lake about a mile from the river and tumbled 100 vertical feet in a series of scenic falls before emptying into the Susquehanna.

In the hot summer months, Wild Cat was a destination for excursion parties from Marietta, Columbia, and Wrightsville. On weekends, the grounds were used for "pic-nics, private and public, social and Sunday School, mutual and money-making – for love and pleasure, for recreation and money."[1]

Where the falls cascaded down the last rocky ledges, crossed the road, and flowed into the river, a series of boardwalks, ladders and steps had been crudely constructed to allow the crowds to scale the height of the hill. Once at the top, adventurous picnickers and campers had plenty of wilderness area to explore.

"The Glen Wild Cat Falls, Marietta, Pa"
Collection of Author

At the top of the falls where the land leveled off, a large clearing provided room for tent platforms and hand-hewn log benches. Under tents and canopies, groups such as the Lancaster Medical Society and the Freemasons regularly held encampments, complete with entertainment and plenty of food. Religious camp meetings replete with music and sermons were also common at the Glen. It was a favorite location of the Masons, who held week long encampments every year, with a typical bill of fare "embracing Meats, Soups, Fish, Eggs in every style, relishes and entrees. The dessert list embraces all the delicacies of the season."[2]

On a high point on the edge of the creek gorge, an overlook called Eagle Rock provided climbers a fantastic view of the river and the Donegal Valley in Lancaster County on the other side. A narrow trail followed Wild Cat Run back to its source, and grassy areas around the lake provided plenty of private places to gather. John had been there many times, rowing over from Marietta when the Coyles lived across the river, and riding or hiking there once they moved to York County when he was nine. Like most boys from the area, he craved adventure and tramped the woods all summer, exploring every creek, rock ledge, and cave.

The previous February, John had discovered a bee tree near the falls and proceeded to cut it down. Since it was winter, the bees were lethargic and he only suffered a few stings on his arms and face. The 100 pounds of honeycomb he was able to sell at twenty-five cents a pound to a nearby beekeeper netted him enough money to buy an old revolver from a canalman in Marietta, and he carried it in his hip pocket almost all the time.

Emily and William were already well up the road before John started along behind them. After crossing the creek by the ferry landing, he turned away from the river on the defunct old road to York, laid out in 1750. It led up the hill behind the old ferry house ruins and ran parallel to the river on top of the ridge for about a quarter of a mile. From there it veered left and wound through farmland and woodlots for about three miles until it met with the main road to York.

The old road was no longer heavily used since it had been rerouted in 1800 when James Anderson IV owned the ferry, but it was still occasionally travelled by local farmers to access the river. Where the road began to bear left away from the river, John paused by the stone cabin of a small-time farmer who scratched out a living on the rough ground at the top of the hill. No one was about, and John could see down to the road that ran along the river, watching the progress of Emily and James as they approached the first bend.

He let his horse take a drink out of the trough and took a long sip himself with the tin cup hanging by the well, lingering long enough to insure that he maintained a safe distance from the carriage below. He stayed straight instead of turning left towards York, and worked his way back down the hill to the road on the latticework of logging paths that crisscrossed the hillside.

Cloaked by the veil of dust trailing behind the carriage, he wasn't worried about being discovered. Stopping his horse when the couple reached the falls, he watched as they dismounted and tied off at the rails along the road. Carrying the picnic basket and blanket Emily pulled from the back of the carriage, they walked up the rough wood planks to the first steps and disappeared from John's view.

Once again, he turned his horse off the river road and climbed a steep switchback that would lead him up and behind the top of the falls. The previous fall, a lumber gang had worked near the iron furnace, cutting logs into ties for the new rail line being laid in Marietta, and they had boarded for a few weeks at the Coyles. John had delivered the lunches that Mrs. Coyle made for the laborers each day, and learned the shortest route to the clearing at the summit.

After reaching a dense copse of hemlock near Eagle Rock, he looped the reins of his lathered horse over a nearby branch and crept to the edge of the clearing, waiting for Emily and her companion to appear at the crest of the falls. A small group of men at the far end was working on the large canopies being erected for the Decoration Day encampment the following weekend, and John knew several of them from Wrightsville and Marietta. Not wanting to be recognized, he stayed well hidden in the deep brush.

Overcash soon appeared along the creek and stepped into the clearing, turning and taking Emily's hand to help her over the last rise. They sat on a nearby bench which was built out of leftover lumber from the tent platforms, and chatted in animated tones for about an hour. John realized he couldn't get close enough to hear what they were saying, and he had to be content with just watching.

John had never seen Emma so happy, and a deep envious resentment began to rise within him. He spent the next several hours crouched in one spot or another, shadowing their movements as close as he was able. After leaving the clearing, they walked to the lake and back, finally taking their picnic basket and heading to Eagle Rock to enjoy their lunch and the panoramic view.

John returned to the house early in the afternoon with the images of what he witnessed at Wild Cat smoldering in his mind, constantly reigniting his jealous temper. It was not just his wild imagination this time; he had seen it with his own eyes and heard it with his own ears. Emma making love to the fellow from Chambersburg, walking with her arm locked in his and laying her head against his shoulder. He watched them sitting close on Eagle Rock at the top of the falls, laughing and talking like they had known each other all of their lives.

Their low whispers had been drowned out by the constant sound of the cascading falls, and although he was not able to hear most of what was said, John could tell by the flirtatious tone of her voice that she was being playful. Once, when they were descending the uneven wooden walkway through the steeper part of the glen, Emily slipped and was caught up in his arms. She hesitated a moment before withdrawing from his embrace and exclaimed in a coy voice loud enough for John to discern, "Mr. Overcash, what would people think?"

John had been very close to them at the time, watching from the deep overgrowth right next to the boardwalk, and although he wasn't sure what anyone *else* would think, it was perfectly clear to *him*. He had seen and heard enough, and sneaking away, he made his way back to the barn.

Pacing in tormented circles, kicking at the ground and chasing the invisible demons hammering around in his head, he cursed himself for not carrying his revolver along when he followed them. His horse, patiently standing in the open barn door watching him, began pawing at the ground in sympathy, seeming to understand his torment. John led him back into his stall and tossed some grain in his feed bin. In a rage, he removed the saddle and hurled it across the barn, where it smacked the wall and landed in the dirt with a thud.

The saddle knocked over the log he used as a chopping block, and the long-handled ax that had been wedged in the top careened across the ground, barely missing his leg and landing by the cow stall. Reaching down to retrieve it, he remembered he had promised to finish splitting a stack of firewood for Benjamin O'Bryan that afternoon over in Marietta. Although John wasn't in any frame of mind to do much of anything productive, let alone work, he gathered his splitting wedges and gloves and left the barn. Shuffling up the road to the ferry landing, he tossed the tools in one of the smaller rowboats and started across the river.

Over the past few years, John worked off and on doing odd jobs for O'Bryan and he had been working at this particular one for several weeks. He was anxious to get it over and done with, now that he was busier with the ferry and had little time to himself. The last thing he wanted to do was spend all his free time working.

O'Bryan, an elderly neighbor of his Aunt Kate, was an ex-canal boatman who had lost a foot several years before when it was crushed between his freighter and one of the canal lock gates. He was the only man in town that John could identify with, a rowdy spirit with a mischievous streak as wide as his own. They struck up a conversation one day and John felt they had something in common, since he considered himself crippled as well. He liked the old man's tales of rough life on the river, and John's silliness amused O'Bryan, so the pair had an oddly mutually beneficial friendship.

It wasn't steady work by any means, but the taverns and hotels in town appreciated the pocket change that John earned and just as quickly spent. Besides, O'Bryan distilled some of the best White Lightning around, made from corn and aged very little. It was strong stuff and had a kick, and John was in the mood to drown his rage in something stronger than the low-proof watered-down excuse for whiskey they passed off as good liquor at the public houses in Marietta.

As he neared the far shore, he became more determined to start drinking right away, and less inclined to attack the waiting woodpile. He was working on a plan, and a good plan required strong drink. Tying off his rowboat to the dock at the foot of Perry Street, he walked the several blocks along Front Street to Gay Street, then turned away from the river and went up through the center of town toward his Aunt Kate's house.

Kate always listened to him, and although she rarely said exactly what he wanted to hear, she would know what to tell him to do to win Emily back from this unexpected suitor. She was in the back yard hanging out laundry when John barged through the gate. When she turned around and said "Good morning, John, how are you now?" he realized that it wasn't his Aunt Kate, but another neighbor, Mrs. McCann. "Not very well, Mrs. McCann, not very well at all," he replied. When he asked where his aunt was, Mrs. McCann told him that Kate was laid up sick and she was helping out for a few days.

Noticing that he looked upset and anxious, Mrs. McCann asked "What's that matter with you now Johnny?" Blurting out "Well, I can't stay at home," he began pacing back and forth, wringing his hands in despair. "Why do you talk that way?" she asked, and beginning to cry, John replied "Me and Emily Myers the maid was to get married, and my mother ain't agreed, and I can't stay at home." "Why Johnny, she loves you and you love her, why don't you go and get married? That is the best advice I can give you." John turned to walk away and Mrs. McCann called after him "Look here, Johnny," but all he said was "I daresn't talk about it," and kept walking.

After leaving his Aunt's house and hearing Mrs. McCann's advice, John was even more resolved to propose to Emma again. He wasn't quite sure why he had lied to Mrs. McCann about marrying her, as he had never talked to either of his parents about it. But, he hadn't wanted to tell her why he was really upset or admit that he had been following Emma and her visitor. He wanted to get Mrs. McCann's opinion, which he had, but was embarrassed about his sudden show of emotion. At least marrying Emma would solve all his problems and get everyone else out of the picture. He had proposed to her before, but this time he was more earnest and determined than ever.

First, he had to get some whiskey from O'Bryan and head to the river bank to get his head right. Then he would go home and have a talk with Emma. Find out who this Overcash fellow was and what she meant to him. And make her see that there was nobody else for her but him.

O'Bryan lived near the north edge of town, a block from his Aunt Kate, on a large lot with some decaying outbuildings and a small barn behind the house that had seen better days. John had grown up just down the street, and before the Coyles purchased the ferry and moved across the river, he had known the alleys of Marietta like the back of his hand.

Emily's grand-uncle Simon Myers also lived on Gay Street, and although John hadn't known Emily when he lived in Marietta, he had known Simon. Myers never tolerated John's antics, and like most of the other people in town, he considered Coyle crazy. Simon was sitting on his front porch and John waved in his wild way as he passed. Ignoring him, Simon turned and walked the other way. Smiling to himself, John mused "Someday you'll be my relation, old man!"

He found O'Bryan sitting on his porch in a tall-back caned rocker, sipping on a glass of his best vintage. John asked for a shot, but the old man didn't answer him right away, apparently deep in thought. After a moment, he explained that he had his eye on some fresh ripe strawberries up the road on James Duffy's farm and had asked him for some several times. Colonel Duffy, a wealthy landowner, tobacco farmer, and businessman, was generous with those of his own station in life, but for O'Bryan, an Irishman of less than upstanding morals, he had nothing but disdain and was not inclined to share his crop of plump red berries. O'Bryan had just returned from Duffy's and was still angry about how he had been brushed off.

James Duffy had worked hard all his life, and obtained everything he possessed through his social connections and diligent effort. His father, also James Duffy, was instrumental in the development of Marietta, constructing many of the roads and turnpikes, as well as sub-dividing and establishing Irishtown at the west end of town. Like his father, the Colonel had the reputation of being a shrewd businessman, building up the Marietta Hollow-ware and Enameling Company, establishing a line of canal boats, and serving on various committees and commissions. He was friends with many important politicians and public figures across the state, and held many fancy gatherings on his large farm. Senators, judges, and other wealthy businessmen were regular visitors on the Duffy farm.

James Duffy 1818-1881 [3]

Although an Irishman himself, Duffy had little respect for the likes of O'Bryan, living in squalor off his pension and disability from the Canal, and spending it on nothing but liquor and tobacco. When O'Bryan approached him about getting some of his fine fruit, Duffy had dismissed him, telling him that he could just as well grow his own.

After O'Bryan explained what had happened, John told him "I wouldn't have asked him to share in the first place. I'd just find a way to get them." O'Bryan gave him a sly look and said, "Tell you what Johnny. I have a deal for you." With a wink, he proposed that if John were able to get him some of those strawberries, perhaps he could part with more than a shot of his best White Lightning.

If it were anyone else but Colonel Duffy, John would have instantly jumped at the challenge. But, it was from Duffy the Coyles purchased the Ferry in 1863, and his father had gone back to him on several occasions when things were tough, borrowing money and using the property as collateral. Although John knew he'd be recognized if seen pilfering the strawberries and would get in serious trouble at home, perhaps even jeopardizing the ferry, the temptation and promise of liquor was too much for him and his malicious instinct prevailed.

John left O'Bryan grinning on the porch, and walked up the road past Duffy's large farm. He was familiar with the layout, and also with the many large dogs that camped out on the front porch. Whenever anyone walked near the house, the dogs would begin barking wildly, alerting the house that someone was about. The first thing John had to do was to figure out how to distract the dogs. Once they were out of the way, the strawberry patch at the edge of the front yard would be easy pickings.

A scheme quickly formed in his head, and he hurried back to O'Bryan's house to get the requisite props. He asked for two empty feed bags and a length of cord rope, and seeing that he had the old man utterly confused, he decided to keep him in the dark concerning his plan. Securing the needed supplies, he started on his way back to Duffy's with O'Bryan calling after him, "If you get yourself caught, boy, I don't know ye."

As John approached Duffy's farm lane, he was careful to stay on the far side of the road so as not to alarm the dogs. When he reached the corner of the pasture, he ducked into the fencerow and moved down the line of trees until he got to the field where the Colonel's string of fine horses was grazing. He figured that if he created a commotion among them, the dogs would come running to investigate and would be distracted long enough for his thievery. And the best way he knew to start a lot of horses running was to get one going. If he could do that, the rest were sure to follow.

He spied a mare with a young colt near the edge of the pasture and climbed over the fence, slowly approaching the wary animals. When he got near enough, he slipped one of the empty feed bags over the colt's head and quickly tied it fast around his neck with the rope. Giving the horse's flank a sharp slap, he quickly retreated back over the fence and retraced his route up the fencerow. John knew there was no stopping a horse race, and was counting on the other animals being spooked at sight of the strange horse in their midst.

Meanwhile, back in the pasture, the temporarily blinded colt started bucking wildly, trying to shake the stifling cover from his eyes and mouth. He began a frantic dance, circling around the field prancing and snorting, and the other horses dashed the opposite direction as John had predicted. The disoriented colt heard them running away and tried to chase after them, which caused them to turn once more. The dogs and Colonel Duffy, hearing the pandemonium, came running from the house to investigate and John was home free.

The dogs began chasing the bagged horse, which in turn was chasing the rest of the horses, and soon they all were going around and around the pasture in perpetual pursuit. John casually walked through the front gate and filled his empty sack with as many red juicy berries as he could grab. Turning and nonchalantly walking back out the way he had come in, he sauntered down the road towards his liquid reward. He could still hear Duffy's excited shouts as he tried to get control of the situation in his back pasture, and John grinned with the thought of the scene he had created.

When he got back to O'Bryan's house, he turned over the contraband berries and told him how he had managed to carry it off. The old man had a good laugh and slapped him on the back, congratulating him on his success. Hobbling into the small shed at the back of the house on his one good leg and a cane, he soon emerged carrying a stoneware jug of whiskey, turning it over to John as promised. Sitting on the porch, they shared a swallow from the jug, and John left O'Bryan with his strawberries and a smile on his face. He could always attend to the log pile another day.

Walking back through town, John crossed the railroad tracks along Front Street and found a quiet spot in a small grove of thick trees between the canal and the river's edge. The smell of honeysuckle was strong, and he sat with his back against an old locust tree and closed his eyes. He often sat alone along the river, or in the hills behind the ferry, trying to work through what was bothering him. When he got angry, or frustrated, his head would begin to pound and his thoughts would get confused. Over the past ten years, the pain had progressively been getting worse and more frequent, and he found that strong drink and solitude was as good a cure as any. After an hour or so, he tossed the empty jug aside and headed for Front Street to continue his therapy.

He spent the rest of the day and night going from one hotel to another, getting beer and whiskey wherever he could, however he could. After exhausting the little money he had in the Rail Road Hotel and the Eagle Hotel, he moved on. There was no shortage of places in Marietta to get a drink, and with rafting season in full swing, men were lined up at every bar two deep. Front Street had more than its fair share of saloons, hotels and brothels, all catering to the menagerie of characters working the canal or coming down the river on lumber rafts.

He resorted to getting drinks and slipping out before paying at the Swan Hotel and Nagle's Hotel, finally ending up at the Steamboat, where he managed to beg and borrow enough for a couple of shots before they threw him out too. He didn't remember how he found his boat in the dark, or how he managed to untie it and get in without getting soaked, but he found himself rowing back towards home, and Emily, more angry than when he had arrived.

A shot rang out from the Point, where the rowdy partiers were getting carried away and shooting out across the river. The noise brought John back to the present, and he realized he was almost back to the ferry. The coal oil lantern hanging at the top of the steps illuminated the full length of the long porch, and John could see that his father was not in sight. However, he was taking no chances and rowed as stealthily as he could past the house, not wanting to raise anyone in the house or the dogs that slept in the barn.

Crossing the yard, he went to the back of the house and hid his pistol in a small wooden cigar box he kept in a shallow depression under a flat rock near the garden gate. John entered the dark house through the kitchen door and stood motionless for a few minutes, listening for anyone still awake waiting for him. Hearing nothing, he took off his boots and climbed the back stairs, carefully avoiding the steps that creaked with the slightest footfall. Moving quietly down the hall past his father's room, John stepped into his room and eased the door shut. Falling into bed in a drunken haze, he slowly spun into the dark and fell asleep.

John never heard the call for breakfast or lunch, and only awoke late in the day when someone pounded loudly on his door. He opened his eyes, closed them just as quickly, and managed a feeble "go away and leave me alone." The Saturday afternoon sun filtered through the broken slats in his shutters, casting uneven stripes on the wall above his bed, and making his head hurt even more. He squinted at the patterns it created, struggling to remember the words that he had so carefully planned the previous day to say to Emily.

When he finally managed to get downstairs, his father was nowhere in sight, and John was hoping that he hadn't realized what time he had come in. His mother and Emily were getting ready to go out in the garden to work, and John asked Emily if he could have a word with her. Mrs. Coyle went out the back kitchen door, and Emily stayed behind, turning to face him. "What did you do yesterday Em?" Ignoring his question, she cast a critical glance at him, taking in his disheveled and wide-eyed appearance, recognizing the all too familiar hung-over look. "What's going on with you and that fellow? I have a right to know."

This wasn't going at all as he had planned, and the words he had laid out in his mind slipped away from him, slowly being replaced with angry thoughts. "John, it's really none of your business, but if you must know, William is my cousin from Chambersburg. I don't know what you thought, but I really wish you would leave me alone today. You look a sight." With that, she turned on her heel and followed his mother into the yard.

John slammed open the door and stormed after her, almost knocking over Sallie Hendricks as she rounded the corner of the house. Sallie worked on and off for Mrs. Coyle, and today was the day they were planning to set the vegetables. She didn't like John one bit, and quickly stepped back and let him pass. His mother was already in the garden, and Emily was just opening the gate to go in, almost stepping on the stone where his hidden pistol lay.

John called to Emily not to go into the garden, yelling "Don't do it Em, I'll tear the clothes right off your back if you go in." Catching up to her and grabbing her arm, he swung her around and snarled "Em, you're ornery, you know it? You're sure an ornery one." Jerking herself free she cried "I know I am, but don't make me more ornery than I am, John Coyle!" She slammed the garden gate shut, leaving John outside, and hurried over to where Mrs. Coyle was working.

John turned and stormed back into the house, leaving a stunned Sallie Hendricks staring after him. Emily, clearly shaken, turned to Mrs. Coyle for support, but in a quiet voice heavy with warning, all she said was "Em, you'll give John impudence until he'll put out your light some day." No more was said, and they set to work on the planting.

John retreated back upstairs and remained locked in his room until Sunday afternoon, when he heard voices and went to see who was downstairs. William Hetrick, a neighbor from Hellam, was in the kitchen visiting, and apparently had been there for quite some time as evidenced by the stack of dirty plates and the empty coffee pot. He had come to get a boat but changed his mind, and ended up spending the entire afternoon talking to Mr. and Mrs. Coyle and Emily.

When John came into the kitchen, he was dirty and unshaven, and still had on the same clothes he had been wearing for the past few days. As he entered the room, the conversation suddenly stopped and they looked at him warily. John was immediately suspicious and glanced at Hetrick to see if he could tell they had been talking about his confrontation with Emily in the garden the day before.

Realizing that it was almost 4 o'clock and he had better be getting home, Hetrick rose to leave. John was curious to find out what was said about him, and told Hetrick that he wanted to accompany him part of the way. While Hetrick excused himself and thanked Mrs. Coyle profusely for the several pieces of pie, John quickly pulled on his boots and together they left and started up the road along the creek towards Hellam.

Hetrick was on fairly good terms with John and noticed that he looked haggard and troubled. After walking about a hundred yards, they stopped and sat on one of the large rocks at the edge of the old dam. The dam was built to divert a constant flow of water to the saw mill from the creek which flowed through Accomac Glen, and a spillway had channeled the water across a long wooden sluice and on to the large water-wheel on the side of the mill which powered the blade. The sluice was long gone, and the dam was beginning to crumble, but it was one of John's favorite places to sit and think.

They sat in silence for a few minutes, listening to the water rushing over the spillway, before John finally spoke. "The maid won't hold connection with me, and if she refuses me again, by damn, I'm going to shoot her. I swear it." Taken aback by the sudden outburst of emotion, Hetrick said "why John, you shouldn't shoot her, you would be hung." John simply replied, "No, I won't," and Hetrick wasn't sure whether he meant that he wouldn't shoot her, or that he wouldn't be hung. Either way, John's words concerned him.

John also confided to Hetrick that Emily had written letters to other boys and that he had ripped them open and read them before they were sent. Never knowing what to believe, Hetrick soon tired of the talk and told him that he had better be moving along.

He left John sitting on the rock alone, with his legs dangling off the edge, his elbows on his knees, and his head in his hands. *I love her,* John thought, *and the only way to have her is to marry her. I've asked a lot of girls to marry me, but this time I mean it. I really mean it.*

"'The Glen,' Accomac, Pa.," ca. 1906
Collection of Author

Chapter 5

Accomac
1723 - 1771

"Children's children are the crown of old men;
And the glory of children are their fathers"
                                           ... PROV, xvii, 6

Following the territorial controversies in 1722, the disputes with Maryland over the land west of the river continued on and off over the following year. Finally, a temporary truce was reached between Lord Baltimore, Proprietor of Maryland, and Hannah Penn, widow and executrix of William Penn, in an effort to protect the settlers and for "Quieting of the People."[1]

The 1723 agreement directed "... that for avoiding all manner of Contentions, or Differences between the Inhabitants of the said Provinces, no Person or Persons shall be disturbed or molested in their Possessions on either side, nor any Lands to be Surveyed, taken up, or Granted in either of the said Provinces near the boundaries which have been Claimed or Pretended to on either Side ..."[2]

Apparently the agreement was never adequately communicated, much less enforced. Since the document did not actually define a specific border between the provinces, Warrants and surveys continued to be issued and executed by both sides. The conflict occasionally escalated into violence, arrests, kidnapping, retribution, and the burning of homes. The period was filled with contradictions, with politicians diplomatically bantering back and forth while settlers bitterly fought for their very lives. It was characterized as "... arrests and recriminations on one side and now on the other, the two governors making respectful representations to each other, and their officers using any but respectful means to settle a question which kept the countryside in a state of open war."[3]

In March of 1730, English-born Thomas Cresap assumed a right of land under a Maryland Patent, bringing settlers into the Accomac area with assurances from Maryland that permanent land grants would be issued. He built a log house[*] for his family on the west bank of the river four miles south of Accomac and proceeded to clear the land for crops. He called his tract "Pleasant Garden" and established the Blue Rock ferry across the Susquehanna. Since Cresap had settled on the northernmost parcel of land currently held under a Maryland Patent, he was appointed a Justice of the Peace and was given the rank of Captain in the Maryland militia.

Cresap was by no means an innocent victim of the conflict. Under orders of then Governor Ogle of Maryland, he was receiving arms from Annapolis to carry out the removal of Pennsylvania German settlers in the area, and was assisting the authorities in their attempt to replace them with Maryland settlers. His wife was no less devoted to the cause than her husband and carried "a rifle, two pistols, a tomahawk, and scalping knife, and, in her boot, a small dagger."[4]

Cresap's tactics included the raiding and vandalizing of farms, the killing of livestock, and on one occasion, the murder of a deputy who attempted to arrest him. He was reported to have abducted six German settlers while they were digging a grave for a dead child, on charges of improving land without authorization of the Maryland Proprietors or paying the required quit rents.

It is little wonder that "he focused upon himself the hatred of more than a generation"[5] of Pennsylvanians. This hatred eventually led to a siege of Cresap's homestead by a group of armed men led by Sheriff Samuel Smith of Lancaster on November 24, 1736. His house was set ablaze, and he and his family were fired upon while attempting to escape the flames. After a fourteen-hour siege, Cresap was arrested and jailed in Philadelphia where he was held until the following year. When the "Maryland Monster" was led through town, Cresap was

---

[*] *A historical marker indicating the site of Cresap's house is located along Long Level Road (PA Route 624,) four miles south of Wrightsville.*

asked what he thought of Philadelphia. He replied "this is one of the prettyst towns in Maryland."[6]

Thomas Cresap was only one of many settlers in the Accomac area to receive Patents from Maryland during the period in which both provinces were to be abstaining from issuing them. A full ten years after the original surveys by both provinces were completed in the area of Accomac, Maryland finally made good on the Warrant of Philip Syng and granted him a Patent to the 200-acre "Partners Adventure" on December 9, 1732.

Syng's Patent was the first official Patent issued within the original Newberry Tract by either province for the land that John Coyle eventually purchased. When Philip Syng died in Annapolis in 1739, he left one-half of his estate to his eldest son, Philip Jr., including the Partners Adventure. During the time it was owned by the Syng family, the land was never settled, no improvements were made, and no producing copper mines were ever discovered.

Finally, on October 11, 1736, the Proprietors of Pennsylvania received from the Five Nations of the Iroquois the deeds for the lower Susquehanna lands, which included the Accomac area. Twenty-three chiefs of the Mohawk, Oneida, Onondaga, Cayuga, Tuscarora, Delaware and Shawnee tribes gathered in Philadelphia, and the Treaty of the Five Nations granted to John, Thomas, and Richard Penn "all the said river Susquehanna with the lands lying on both sides thereof, to extend eastward as far as the heads of the branches or springs which run into the said river Susquehanna, all lands lying on the west side of the said river to the setting of the sun."[7]

As soon as the treaty was ratified and the land officially owned by Pennsylvania, the process of issuing Warrants for surveys and Patents for land grants began in earnest. However, the deeding of the land west of the Susquehanna by the Five Nations further complicated the continuing debates between Maryland and Pennsylvania because both were now issuing Patents within the same area. Eventually the two provincial governments brought their cases to the High Court of Chancery in London in 1737 to petition for a permanent solution.

On August 18, a preliminary Royal Order from King George II dictated that neither Maryland nor Pennsylvania was authorized to grant any further Patents within the confirmed territory of the other. The problem remained that neither province knew exactly where their confirmed territory began and where the boundary of the other ended.

The Order stated "That the governors of the respective provinces of Maryland and Pennsylvania, for the time being, do not, upon pain of incurring his Majesty's highest displeasure, permit or suffer any tumults, riots or other outrageous disorders to be committed on the borders of their respective provinces; but that they immediately put a stop thereto, and use their utmost endeavors to preserve peace and good order amongst all his Majesty's subjects under their government inhabiting the said borders, his Majesty doth hereby enjoin the said Governors that they do not make any grants of any part of the lands in contest between the Proprietors respectively ..."[8]

Apparently the Crown was tired of dealing with the situation and the provinces were eager to comply. Both governors issued public proclamations relaying the contents of the Order and entered into an agreement the following year to establish a temporary line on their shared border. This eight-part agreement in 1738 commissioned a survey to settle the boundary issue, and defined the conditions regarding authority which were to be followed until its completion.

The provisional line was not intended to displace any of the settlers currently occupying the disputed areas, but was to serve only as a line demarking the area in which future grants were to be suspended. Maryland was not to issue Patents north of this line and Pennsylvania was to refrain from issuing them to the south.

Both provinces also agreed that once a permanent line was established, any Patents issued prior to the date of the Order were to be considered legally binding grants, even if they fell within the eventual boundaries of the other province. This clause turned out to be instrumental in determining who would be the first legal owner of the Accomac area.

The Royal Order of 1737 remained in effect for the next twenty-two years until July 4, 1760, when a formal agreement for a permanent survey line was reached between Lord Baltimore of Maryland and Thomas and Richard Penn, the surviving Proprietors of Pennsylvania. No time was wasted putting the plan in motion, and local surveyors began marking the boundary immediately. Progress was slow, and the Proprietors became impatient for results. By 1763, they felt the work was not advancing quickly enough and decided to replace the team of surveyors. On August 4, 1763, Charles Mason and Jeremiah Dixon were employed to "mark, run out, settle, fix and determine all such parts of the circle, marks, lines and boundaries"[9] between the two provinces.

Mason was a world renowned astronomer who had worked at the Royal Observatory at Greenwich and Dixon an equally well-known English Surveyor, and together they represented the best resources the Crown had to offer. Without delay, Mason and Dixon left England for America, arriving in Philadelphia in November of 1763.

They immediately "proceeded to measure on its meridian fifteen miles from the parallel of the most southern part of Philadelphia, the north wall of a house on Cedar Street occupied by Thomas Plustead and Joseph Huddle,"[10] the agreed upon beginning of the east-west parallel between the two provinces. They began moving slowly west along 39 degrees, 43 minutes, 18 seconds latitude, placing a marker stone every mile, with a special Crownstone being placed every fifth mile. Measurements were taken with instruments especially designed for the survey.

The marker stones, quarried and cut in England, were between three and five feet in length and weighed 300-600 pounds each. They were transported along the survey line by horse and wagon and placed in the ground using specially constructed timber tripods. According to their final report made after the survey was complete, "... every five mile stone having on the side facing the north, the arms of the said Thomas Penn and Richard Penn graved thereon, and on the side facing the south, the arms of Frederick Lord Baltimore graved thereon, and the other intermediate stones are graved with the letter P on the north side, and the letter M on the south side."[11]

By June 22, 1765, the surveyors had reached the banks of the Susquehanna and were ordered to proceed "as far as the provinces of Maryland and Pennsylvania were settled and inhabited."[12] They crossed the river and commenced laying their line through the area which had been so hotly contended for the previous forty years.

Mason and Dixon eventually ran their survey line 233 miles from the Delaware River westward, cutting their way through the remote and unexplored wilderness of Pennsylvania. In October 1767, they were forced to stop near Mount Morris, thirty-six miles short of completing their goal, when their local Native American guides refused to go any farther. Making their way back to Philadelphia, Mason and Dixon were discharged on December 26th, 1767, a little over four years from when they began. The survey cost the Calverts and Penns over £3,500 to complete, but finally provided a defined border between their two provinces.

A Warrant had been issued by Lieutenant Governor James Hamilton on May 21, 1762, to resurvey the boundaries of Springetts Manor, but was delayed six years due to the uncertainty of the Pennsylvania-Maryland border. Once the Mason-Dixon survey was completed in 1767, James Tilghnian, Secretary of the Land Office, wrote to Surveyor General John Lukens, and requested that the re-survey, known as "Hamilton's Survey" or the "Survey of 68"[13], was to be completed as soon as possible.

Although the re-survey encompassed only 64,500 acres as compared to the original 1722 survey which contained 75,520 acres, it clearly included the former Newberry Tract surveyed by Governor Keith and therefore the Accomac area as well. Three significant issues instigated the 1768 resurvey of Springetts Manor. First, when the original survey was completed in 1722, it did not include the town of York, which was not laid out until nineteen years later in 1741. By relocating the western boundary eight miles further west, York was centrally located within the manor.

Second, the Royal Order of 1738 dictated that prior grants issued by one province were to be honored, even if it was determined that the Patent fell within the other province's eventual boundaries. The largest Maryland grants were within the 1722 survey, and by moving the southern line five miles north and the western boundary eight miles to the west, most of the large Maryland grants were excluded and more unpatented land was available to Pennsylvania.

Lastly, the land office had never authorized the original 1722 survey, as it was performed by Governor Keith without their approval. It had never officially been returned and filed, so there was no permanent record, and there were questions concerning its legality. In order to clearly define the rights of Penn's heirs to the land, the resurvey of 1768 was ordered to put the issue to rest.

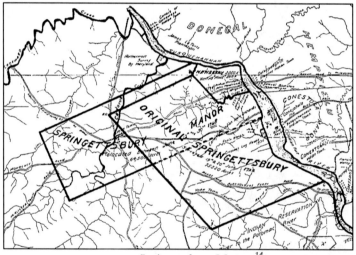

Springettsbury Manor [14]

The establishment of the permanent boundary between Maryland and Pennsylvania, and the new survey of Springetts Manor, firmly defined the Accomac area as belonging to Pennsylvania. However, due to the terms of the Order of 1738, Syng and Brown would retain their ownership of the "Partner's Adventure," the land granted to them by Maryland in 1732.

Directly across the river from the Partners Adventure, the land was relatively flat compared to the rolling river hills on the west side. Since Pennsylvania already had legal ownership of the land on the east side through a previous treaty with the Five Nations, Patents for the fertile land along the river were already being granted by the time surveys were only being started on the west side.

Trade with the many Native American settlements up and down the Susquehanna was a brisk business, and by 1722 there were more than fifty licensed traders established in the area.[15] Among them were Robert Wilkins and his four sons, William, Peter, Thomas and John, who bartered kettles, blankets, cloth, and other goods for furs and crops with the tribes living along the Potomac River and the Great Valley of Virginia. In 1718, Wilkins purchased a 318-acre farm along the east side of the river and gave it to his son William.

Several years later, the Reverend James Anderson answered a call to serve the Presbyterian Church at Donegal, a few miles north of the river, and purchased the land adjoining William Wilkins's farm. The ferry crossing at Accomac owes its existence to this enterprising and controversial minister from Scotland.

Born in Scotland in 1678, educated at Edinburgh under Principal Sterling and ordained in 1708, Reverend Anderson sailed to the colony of Virginia in 1709, excited to settle and begin his ministry. However, being a Presbyterian of strict orthodoxy, he was not well received and found the Virginia governor unfriendly to any faith other than the established Episcopalian Church of England.

Finding Virginia inhospitable to his beliefs, he moved northward to New Castle, Delaware, and became a member of the Philadelphia Presbytery in 1710. For the next seven years, Reverend Anderson split his ministerial duties between his home church in New Castle and several others in the surrounding area, periodically travelling great distances to preach. On December 5, 1712, at age thirty-four, he married nineteen year old Suit (Sodt) Garland, the daughter of one of the church founders where he was installed.

In December, 1716, an initiative began in New York City to form a Scotch-Presbyterian congregation in the growing city of about 6,500 inhabitants. However, the movement lacked organization and a leader. Anderson, who happened to be in New York City for a month in the summer of 1717, encouraged the embryonic congregation and was persuaded to preach to them on several occasions.

The reaction to Anderson's preaching was unanimously positive, and the congregation selected two of their original founders, Thomas Smith and Gilbert Livingston, to extend a call to the members of the Presbytery of New Castle requesting Anderson's reassignment to New York. He accepted the position as the city's first Presbyterian pastor after "much deliberation and counsel, and was favorably received by the people calling him."[16] In late October, he gathered his wife and two children and moved to New York City.

Unlike the predominantly Scotch-Presbyterian congregation Anderson served in New Castle, two philosophically different groups existed within the church in New York; the strict orthodox Presbyterians and the more liberal Congregationalists. Although Anderson seemed initially optimistic, the enthusiastic reception of the new minister was short-lived and conflict began almost immediately between Anderson and the congregation.

Ironically, this was especially evident with Smith and Livingston, both Congregationalists, who had obviously failed to ascertain the theological philosophy of Reverend Anderson before so fervently extending their call for him. Had they realized his strict adherence to Presbyterian order and his tendency to dominate all church affairs, they most likely would not have pursued their request for Anderson quite so aggressively.

Of the four original founding members of the church in New York, Livingston and Smith were of English ancestry. The other two, Patrick MacKnight and John Nichol, were of Scotch-Irish descent.

Predictably, the escalating disagreements within the congregation fell along both spiritual and ethnic lines, with the English Congregationalists on one side opposing Anderson, and the orthodox Scotch-Irish Presbyterians on the other supporting him.

The conflict with Anderson gained momentum during 1720 with Livingston and Smith formally complaining to the Synod concerning his appointment and subsequent performance. After realizing the he was a man of "stern orthodoxy, of firm and decided opinions, and open and fearless in the expression of them,"[17] and clearly in opposition to their own Congregationalist beliefs, they presented their complaints, but Anderson prevailed.

In addition to alienating a large portion of his congregation, his strict adherence to Presbyterian discipline did not sit well with the church Trustees. In their Journal of Transactions, they describe the situation with Anderson "who sometime after his coming to New York affected a domination which English Presbyterians had not been used to, and intermeddling in the Temporalities of that Congregation and the disposition of Publick Money (with which ministers ought to have no concern), a breach ensued, and the people were divided and scattered and the church fell into extreme poverty and Disgrace till at length after nine years, Mr. Anderson was obliged to remove."[18]

During his turbulent years in New York City, seven more children were born to Reverend Anderson and Suit, including his son James. The controversy concerning his ministry began to take its toll on Anderson and his family, and he finally decided he had enough of New York City. He requested that he be allowed to accept another call, and at the Philadelphia Synod meeting on September 23, 1726, it was noted "That Mr. Anderson, (according to his desire,) be left at his liberty to remove from New York, and to accept a call from any other people, as Providence may determine; and the congregation of New York be at liberty to call another minister, (in an orderly way,) as soon as they shall pay up what arrears appear justly due to Mr. Anderson."[19]

Anderson must have been proactively planning a move for some time. On his way to the Synod meeting in Philadelphia, he stopped and preached to the congregation in Donegal, Pennsylvania, and obtained from them a preliminary vote to accept him as their minister. The next day on September 24, "a call from the people of Dunegall to the Rev. Mr. James Anderson, being presented to the Synod, the Synod recommended said call to Mr. Anderson for his consideration about it."[20]

In all probability, the offer was not a coincidence, and Anderson most likely sought out the offer to serve at Donegal. However, nothing could happen immediately. The New Castle Presbytery, under whose jurisdiction the Donegal church fell until 1732, would have to approve the terms of the offer, as well as provide a signed list of financial subscriptions[†] and a formal salary offer.

Compared to the fast-paced environment in New York, the pastoral surroundings along the Susquehanna River must have appealed to Anderson, and he looked forward to accepting the call. Before returning to New York, he acquired a 305-acre plantation from the trader Peter Allen, about a half-mile east of where William Wilkins had established his riverfront farm in 1718. With the exception of a few acres of meadow, the farm was covered with timber.

Anderson remained in New York for another ten months until the New Castle Presbytery made a decision. "The Rev'd Mr James Anderson lately of New York and desireing to be admitted a Member of this Presb was Accordingly embraced. The Sd Mr Anderson having at our last Synod Received a Call from ye People of Donegall which he then took under Consideration & now the Representatives of Said People desireing that Mr. Anderson might declare himself with respect to Sd Call, which Mr Anderson freely accepted."[21]

The Presbytery voted at the end of August 1727 to install Anderson, and he was free to move to Donegal. In September, Anderson relocated his wife and nine children to the farm he purchased the previous year and soon recognized the potential of his

---

[†] *Members of Presbyterian congregations signed subscription forms, specifying the amount pledged towards the minister's salary each year.*

neighbor's farm along the river as a strategically important ferry location. The earliest documented use of Wilken's farm as a crossing place was the spring of 1727, when Presbyterian missionaries from Donegal used it to visit settlers "along the Conewago on the west side of the river."[22] Anderson, in his dealings with clergy travelling to the west through Donegal, would have realized that a ferry could be profitable in the right hands.

More of an entrepreneur than a farmer, Reverend Anderson offered to trade his 305 acres with that of William Wilkins, throwing in "about 20 pounds to boot."[23] The proposal was accepted in late 1727, and Anderson immediately moved his family to their new farm. He wasted no time in improving the property, and soon built a large farmhouse on the flat land furthest from the river.

W.U. Hensel, speaking at the Marietta, Pennsylvania centennial celebration on September 4, 1912, observed that "in those days worldly wisdom and business thrift were not deemed qualities incompatible with spiritual leadership and the clerical office."[24] Reverend Anderson would have needed to raise cash to pay his note on the Wilkins property, "and not all by preaching, marrying, baptizing and burying his own congregation."[25] Needing to supplement his income, he made the decision to establish a legitimate ferry crossing.

Anderson's shrewd business acumen provided him with the foresight to see the profit that could be made off his new property. His development of the area began a period of economic and commercial growth which lasted almost a century, and four generations of Andersons, before ending with a dramatic collapse.

He immediately began improving the informal crossing, and transported the occasional passenger, horses, and wagons across the river on flat boats. However, without a formal Patent for the operation, and having no ownership of any land on the west side of the river, Anderson was limited in how far he could develop the use of the site as a ferry. At this point, Pennsylvania was still not granting Patents for land across the Susquehanna, and it would be another ten years before Anderson could move forward with his plans.

Reverend Anderson had finally found a place to call home, as the majority of his new congregation in Donegal shared his Scotch-Irish roots. They were an "energetic, liberty-loving, religious people, strongly attached to the Presbyterian faith; and all possessed some worldly means."[26] Anderson became one of the most prominent Presbyterian ministers in America at the time, and travelled to churches all along the Susquehanna River. Anderson was well-liked, and contrary to the opinions of his former New York congregation, he was regarded as "a man of talents, learning and piety, a graceful and popular preacher."[27]

Reverend James Anderson [28]

Anderson's growing congregation at Donegal flourished, and a few years after he arrived, he led an initiative to build a new church building. The original log church, built around 1722 near a spring at the head of the Chicquesalunga Creek, was replaced by a stone church[‡] which still stands today.

[‡] *Donegal Presbyterian Church is located on Donegal Springs Road in Mount Joy, Pa.*

Anderson's interest in his congregation soon extended beyond serving just their religious needs, and the Reverend actively helped settle land title issues for members of his congregation, "which then included nearly the whole population of Donegal township."[29] Many people occupied land without Patents and some refused to continue paying quit rents to the Proprietors.

Due to their inherent dislike of the proprietary system that oppressed them in Ireland and Scotland, and also because they felt their property improvements made up for any unpaid taxes, many settlers were discontent with the way land issues were handled. During frequent visits to the Philadelphia Land Office to plead with the Commissioners on behalf of the members of his congregation, Anderson helped arbitrate many disputes between the Provincial government and the settlers who were claiming legal title to land in the Donegal area.

Anderson also faced difficulties regarding the title to his own riverfront property, which he had occupied since 1727. The official survey Warrant was not issued until September 2, 1732, and the survey was conducted the following year. Anderson finally received the Patent on September 17, 1736.

For his first ten years at Donegal, Anderson tended to the needs of his congregation, and his growing family, with the last two of his eleven children being born on the riverfront farm. Suit passed away on Christmas Eve in 1736, and Reverend Anderson scrawled a notation on a leaf of his bible referring to the death of "a very beautiful woman by small-pox."[30] Quickly rebounding, the charismatic minister married Rebecca Crawford from Donegal one year later in 1737.

Although Reverend Anderson had been actively operating the ferry on a small scale since 1727, he knew he had to eventually secure a legal right to keep it in service. Once the majority of land issues of his congregation had been settled, he was able to refocus his attention on developing his own plans, and submitted the application to the Province for a ferry Patent in 1737.

Anderson had an advantage over many Presbyterian ministers of the early 1700s, as he personally owned the farm where he and his large family lived. Normally, the congregation provided a "glebe," or land that was available for use by the minister, for farming or renting out as they saw fit. However, since he owned property and had plans for expanding his holdings, his financial needs were also more significant than most ministers.

His plans depended on his congregation fulfilling their pledges and his ability to collect his salary from all the subscribing members of his church. Reflecting his own personal situation, Anderson composed a 2,000 word address, or Overture, which described the financial plight of Presbyterian ministers of the time, and which he hoped would foster changes in the way that ministers were compensated.

Unfortunately, the Overture was not read by most ministers to their congregations for fear of alienating those who they served. And, the Presbytery did not follow through by making the payment of the minister's salary an obligation of the congregation as a whole instead of the responsibility of individual members. As such, the financial situation of ministers changed little. However, Anderson continued to prosper despite his Overture not reaching those who he intended.

—————⟫⟫⟫—————

Due to the vehement protests of John Wright, who had been operating a thriving ferry three miles downstream since 1730, the granting of Anderson's ferry Patent was continually delayed. Wright's Ferry was the nearest alternate river crossing, and the threatened competition from Anderson created a point of contention for Wright. Anderson's Patent application became the first of many conflicts between the two ferries over the next decades.

The main road west from Lancaster and Philadelphia led directly to Wright's Ferry, and before Anderson began his operation, there was virtually no competition in the nearby area. However, for people coming from New England, New York and the northeastern regions of Pennsylvania, Anderson's Ferry was a more convenient crossing point.

Once travelers reached the relatively flat terrain of Donegal from the northeast, they faced a choice. To use Wright's Ferry, they would have to cross or circumvent the rocky Chiques ridge. Or, they could simply continue on the road heading straight towards the river and cross at Andersons. In addition, Anderson's Ferry was usable more months out of the year, as it was deeper and less rocky than at Wright's Ferry, where the river was wider and the water often low.

After Wright built a new ferry house and began using larger flat-bottomed boats, their business increased and frequent delays became common. Parties wishing to cross at Wright's Ferry sometimes had to wait for several days, and "it was no unusual thing to see from one hundred and fifty to two hundred vehicles of various kinds waiting at the ferry-house for their turn."[31] Wagons were numbered with chalk and had to wait their turn before being taken across the river.

As a result of the long delays at Wright's Ferry, the number of people diverting their wagons to Anderson's Ferry grew, and an increasing number of people began using the road which passed by his farmhouse.[§] This road formed the eastern border of Anderson's property and led directly to the river crossing.

In the meantime, while the ferry Patent was being held up at the Land Office in Philadelphia, Anderson began looking into opportunities for acquiring land on the west side of the river, opposite his property in Lancaster County. Since Philip Syng and Thomas Browne had already been issued a grant from Maryland in 1722 for the land directly across from Anderson's Ferry, he instead secured a Patent for a thirty-five-acre tract of land contiguous to the Partner's Adventure on June 1, 1739.

[§] *The road leading to the ferry eventually became PA Route 772 and is still known as Anderson Ferry Road.*

The summer following his purchases on the west side of the river, Reverend Anderson fell ill after returning from a trip to Virginia. He developed pneumonia, and sensing that he had little time left to live, he hastily made out a will on July 14, 1740. He dictated his wishes for his large estate, including the riverfront farm, the thirty-five acres across the river, the ferry operation, and three slaves.

In it, Anderson said "I give and bequeath to my dearly beloved wife, Rebecca Anderson, the half of this plantation whereupon I now live, including the house, barn, run to or about the place where Bank's house and improvements was, with some land at the riverside bottom, during her natural life; also I give an bequeath to her assigns forever the third part of my moveable estate and ye use and services of the negro wench Dinah while she and Dinah lives. In the next place, I give and bequeath to my son James the other half of this plantation to him, his heirs and assigns forever, to the possession of which he is to enter when at age or marries, and that piece of land over the river opposite to the place I also give to him and his heirs forever. I have payd and have a warrant in lien under the hand of the Receiver General and paid for the patent to Mr Peter's to him and his heirs and assigns forever. I also give and bequeath to him the negro man Pline to him and his heirs forever; this in the meantime my will is that he pay one-half the mortgage and quit rent yearly till all the mortgage be payed ..."[32]

The majority of his large estate was split between his second wife Rebecca and his son James. James had just turned nineteen at the time the will was written, and he was to inherit half of his father's farm in Lancaster County, all of the land on the west side of the river, and the pending ferry rights. As documented in his father's will, payment for the ferry Patent had already been made to Richard Peters, the Secretary of the Province, and was still on hold pending the resolution of the conflicts with John Wright. As long as the younger James began paying half the mortgage notes and taxes, the valuable property was his.

The negro man Pline, also left to James, was most likely the same slave that had been in the Anderson family since the Reverend Anderson's first marriage to Suit twenty-seven years earlier. The terms of her father's will, a trader named Silvester Garland, stated "to my daughter Sodt Anderson I give and bequeath the house and lot adjoining my own dwelling house ... and one negro boy called Plim."[33]

Anderson's daughter Susannah was the only other of his eleven children to receive any specific tangible property, that being one of his three slaves. Anderson's final wish for his son Thomas, nine at the time the will was written, was that he be taken care of by his step-mother Rebecca. As far as the rest of his children were concerned, they were left to split the remaining two-thirds of his belongings.

Only two days after writing out his will, Reverend Anderson passed away on July 16 at age sixty-two. He was buried alongside his first wife Suit in the small fenced cemetery in front of his church at Donegal Springs. His grave is marked with a large flat red sandstone tablet with the inscription:

> *"Here lyeth the body of the*
> *REV: JAMES ANDERSON*
> *late Pastor of Dunnigall*
> *who departed the life ye 16th of*
> *July, 1740, aged 62 years*
> *also*
> *His wife, SUIT ANDERSON*
> *who departed this life ye 24th of*
> *December, 1736 aged 42 years."*[34]

His son James, thereafter referred to as James Anderson, Sr., remained on the family estate and operated the ferry from the east side of the river after his father's death. Not wishing to follow in his father's theological footsteps, the Reverend's enterprising son aggressively moved forward with developing and expanding the ferry. On March 5, 1741, he married Ruth Bayley, and their first son, James Jr., was born the day after Christmas the same year.

Anderson, Sr. finally received news that the ferry rights his father had applied for five years previous had been approved. Although the crossing had already been in operation for about fifteen years without legal authorization, the Patent was a valuable saleable asset that insured that the ferry could be passed down to future generations, or be sold if necessary.

Richard Peters, the Secretary of the Province of Pennsylvania, confirmed the fears of John Wright and granted the ferry Patent on November 17, 1742. "James Anderson's petition for a Ferry was presented to Mr. Thomas Penn and he gave me verbal orders to make out the Patent; it is not within the limits of another Grant, and a new County Road is ordered to be made to it, as it lies the most convenient for the New Town of York, to the great mortification of John Wright, whose Ferry will be much hurt by this, for it must by its situation be the principal Ferry on the Susquehanna."[35]

It was obvious to those crossing at Anderson's Ferry that an improved road was needed to connect the ferry landing on the York County side to points further west, including the new town of York, which was laid out the prior year in 1741. At the time, the ferry put in on Anderson's thirty-five acres just north of the eventual location at Accomac, and the only road leading from the landing followed a rough route along the river's edge to Wrightsville. However, it would be another seven years before the process to construct a new road began.

In the August Quarter Session of the York County Court in 1748, a petition signed by settlers in the "townships of Hallam and Donegal was presented to the court at Lancaster for a road from Anderson's ferry to join the road from John Wright's ferry to York."[36] York County, recently split from Lancaster County in August of 1749, ordered a survey and approved the building of the road in 1750. The route followed a meandering course through rolling farmland and timber and remained in place until a new, straighter route was laid out in 1800.

The road, known today as Accomac Road, climbed steeply from the river to the top of the ridge, bisected the Partner's Adventure tract of Philip Syng, Jr., and connected with the Monocacy Road[**] in

---

[**] *This portion of the Monocacy Road from Wrightsville to York eventually became PA Route 30, and subsequently PA Route 462.*

the center of the modern day Hellam Borough. The Monocacy Road, originally laid out through York County in the early 1730's, followed an old Native American trail and was the main east-west road connecting Wrightsville to the new settlement at York.

The 1750 Accomac Road as it nears the Susquehanna
Collection of Author

Shortly after obtaining the ferry Patent, James Sr. built a large ferry house called Anderson's Ferry Hotel on his Lancaster County farm at the end of where Perry Street is now located in Marietta. Following the successful example of Wright's Tavern, Anderson Sr. realized the economic advantages of providing food, lodging and drinks for the travelers waiting to cross the river.

In the terms of his father's will, James Sr. inherited only 129 acres of Reverend Anderson's original 305-acre farm. His tract bordered the river, but did not extend to the flat land further north which included the family home. This portion was left to his step-mother Rebecca and was subsequently deeded to his brother Thomas in 1755 when Rebecca passed away. In 1758, Anderson Sr. purchased the remainder of the original 305-acre tract from Thomas for £330, and now owned his father's entire original farm.

Following brief service in the French and Indian Wars in Western Pennsylvania, James Sr. continued to prosper. His plans included building an inn and tavern on the west side of the river, but the thirty-five acres he owned included only enough flat land for the wooden ferry house. Needing to expand, he purchased the 200-acre Partner's Adventure from Philip Syng, Jr. on November 20, 1759, for £100. This tract, which would eventually become Accomac, had never been developed or occupied by Syng during his ownership.

Further increasing his holdings on the west side of the river, Anderson, Sr. surveyed and purchased an additional 288 acres a few miles further north and another 200 acres contiguous to the east side of the Partner's Adventure in 1763. He held the 288 acres only a few years before selling it, and the 200-acre plot was resurveyed, subdivided and sold over the ensuing years.

James Anderson, Sr. now had substantial land holdings on both sides of the Susquehanna, and continued to operate the ferry until June 18, 1771, when he sold the two properties on the west side of the river to his thirty-year-old son, James Anderson, Jr. In a somewhat disproportionate transaction, he sold his father's original thirty-five-acre tract for £1,100 and the 200-acre former Partner's Adventure for £200. These tracts included the ferry landing in York County and the other improvements that had been made over the previous thirty years.

James Anderson, Jr., was married five years to Jean Tate, and had three children, including three year old James Anderson IV. Now owning the land on the west side of the Susquehanna, he began taking an active part in the operation of the ferry and managing the hotel on his family farm on the Lancaster County side of the river. As he and his father discussed construction plans for the west side of the river, the first rumblings of the American Revolution began to be heard across the country, and their attention was temporarily turned elsewhere.

<u>Chapter 6</u>

Accomac
1771-1800

"The American Revolution was a beginning, not a consummation"
... Woodrow Wilson

In 1772, the year after purchasing the two tracts of land in York County, James Anderson, Jr. also acquired his father's 129 acres along the river in Lancaster County. The token amount of five shillings (about one dollar), compared to the £1,300 paid for the 235 acres on the west side of the river, was really just a formality to allow the property to officially be deeded to James Jr. This left James Sr. with the remainder of the original Anderson farm and family home, purchased from his brother Thomas in 1758.

"This indenture, made the 22d day of July, 1772, between James Anderson and Ruth, his wife, of the Township of Donegal, yeoman of the one part, and James Anderson, the younger, son of the said James Anderson, of the same township, yeoman of the other part, witnesseth that the said James Anderson and Ruth, his wife, for and in consideration of natural love and affection which they have and bear towards the said James Anderson, the younger, their son, and for his better preferment and advancement in the world and in consideration of the sum of five shilling lawful money of Pennsylvania to them in hand, paid by the said James Anderson, the younger."[1]

Included was "the ferry on and across the said River Susquahannah now and heretofore had and used to and from the said Tract of Land or some part thereof with the Benefits Advantages Profits Tolls and Emoluments belonging to and Arising from the said Ferry..."[2] Adding the Lancaster County property to his purchases of the west shore properties the year before, James Jr. now had control of the ferry and the landings on both sides of the river.

To finance the development of the ferry or to repay prior financial obligations, possibly the £1,300 he owed to his father for the land he purchased in York County the previous year, James Jr. mortgaged the newly acquired 129 acres only five days after purchasing them. Perhaps taking advantage of his grandfather Reverend Anderson's reputation and contacts within the Presbyterian Church, he entered into a mortgage agreement with the "Corporation for the Relief of Poor and Distressed Presbyterian Ministers and of the Poor and Distressed Widows and Children of Presbyterian Ministers."

The Corporation was formed in order to supplement the inadequate financial support ministers received from their congregations, and was granted a charter from Thomas and Richard Penn in 1759. It had the distinction of "being the first life insurance company in America, it is also the first business corporation chartered in America."[3] In exchange for annual premiums, the Corporation made lump sum payments or annual annuities to disabled Presbyterian Ministers and to their widows and children when they died.

The Corporation was a separate entity from the Presbyterian Synod and as such managed their own funds and investments in order to meet their financial obligations. Designed "to give perfect security to the subscribers and to make their investments largely productive,"[4] the Corporation made unsecured loans in the form of judgment notes, as well as writing mortgages secured on real estate.

On July 27, 1772, James Anderson, Jr. and his wife Jean signed a mortgage agreement for £1,200, giving the Corporation temporary ownership on paper for the acreage along the river in Lancaster County. The one year mortgage deed specified James Anderson to pay "six hundred pounds on the aforesaid Twenty Seventh date of July which will be in the year of our Lord One thousand Seven hundred and Seventy three in one intire Payment."[5]

It was a common lending practice in colonial America to require the borrower to put down 50% of the loan amount, with the balance and interest due in one payment within a one-year period.

However, it was not until shortly after his wife Jean died in 1777 that James Jr. finally satisfied the mortgage.

Perhaps using some of the borrowed money, James Jr. moved forward with his construction plans on the west side of the river. About 100 yards east of the intersection of the road from York and the existing wooden ferry house, he built an imposing two-story stone house and inn to serve passengers and boarders. Although the exact date of construction is not known, it is thought to have been built between 1772 and 1775.

The next several years were prosperous, but Anderson's personal success was overshadowed with the increasingly frequent news of the growing conflict with the British. Around the colonies, Committees of Safety were formed and meetings being held to draft complaints against taxation and other oppressive measures imposed by the Crown. Late in 1773, shortly after the birth of Anderson's fourth child, and the last with his wife Jean, tensions in America boiled over when patriots in Massachusetts dumped 342 chests of tea overboard in Boston Harbor.

In 1774, local committees were formed in York and Lancaster counties to officially protest continued British rule. The first meeting of the Continental Congress in Philadelphia was held in the fall, and the revolutionary spirit spread quickly to the Susquehanna River. Militia duty was still voluntary, and several companies were mustered into service in the townships along the river.

Events unfolded quickly in the northern colonies following the firing of the first shots of the war in Lexington and Concord in the spring of the following year. By 1776, George Washington had been appointed Commander-in-Chief and several important battles had already been waged in the New England states. On July 4, 1776, in Philadelphia, the Declaration of Independence was approved and signed shortly thereafter, using Phillip Syng, Jr.'s silver inkwell.

The lingering question of proprietary ownership of land by Penn's heirs was finally settled in 1776. The newly formed Commonwealth of Pennsylvania took possession of all unsold land within the boundaries of the province, paid Penn's heirs £130,000 to abdicate all rights of ownership, and ordered all unpaid fees and quit rents to be paid to the Commonwealth. The year closed with Washington's crossing of the Delaware River to capture Trenton, New Jersey, eventually chasing General Howe back to New York. The British spent the winter in New York City, while Washington watched warily from New Jersey.

Early in February 1777, Anderson's wife Jean passed away and James Jr. found himself a widower at age thirty-six, with a young family of four, a sizeable amount of valuable property, and his country in turmoil. He had little time to mourn, as the Pennsylvania state government soon thereafter adopted the "Act to Regulate the Militia of the Commonwealth of Pennsylvania" on March 17. Under the act, militia service became compulsory and all white males between the ages of eighteen and fifty-three who were capable of bearing arms were required to enroll. Ministers, teachers, servants, and certain elected officials were exempt. James Anderson, Sr., at age fifty-six, was beyond the maximum age required to serve, but both he and his son James Jr. took the Oath of Allegiance in July of 1777.

Although enlistment was now mandatory and the militia was no longer a volunteer force, in most other aspects it resembled today's National Guard, with the only obligation being that of conducting monthly training and drilling sessions. If needed for active duty, militia units were called up by the state to serve rotating tours of up to sixty days. The militia was organized at the municipal level, usually along township lines, and infantry companies of 80-100 men were formed from local neighborhoods. The men chose their own company officers, and James Anderson, Jr. was elected Captain of 1st Company, 4th Battalion, Lancaster County Militia.

Even though militia officers held military rank the same as regular Continental Army personnel, they remained civilians. They were responsible for insuring their units turned out for exercises, providing state-issued arms, and finding substitutes for those who declined to serve. When a Company was called for active duty, the

Captains delivered written notices to each man's house or place of business, indicating where and when to report.

For the remainder of the summer, James Jr. worked on recruiting and organizing his company of men from the surrounding farms and villages. He wasted no time in drilling them and obtaining the arms and supplies they would need in the event they were called up for active duty. The timing of his efforts was fortuitous, for the British had just begun to move on their objective of capturing the colonial capital at Philadelphia.

Over the previous winter, the British had formulated a plan to attack Washington's forces from two fronts. General Burgoyne would march from Canada, capture Albany and isolate New England from the rest of the colonies. Howe was to capture Philadelphia, but with Washington still blocking his way in New Jersey, he was forced to find an alternate route from New York City. In mid-July, he launched a massive flotilla of 265 ships and 17,000 men from New York and followed the Atlantic coast south, leisurely navigating up the Chesapeake Bay and landing at the head of the Elk River in Maryland. Howe paused for several weeks until late August, when he began his march northward into Pennsylvania and towards Philadelphia.

One bright Sunday morning in early September, a rider pounded up to the Donegal Church on a lathered horse and rushed inside. Interrupting the service, he proceeded to inform the congregation that the British Army under Lord Howe had moved from New York City to the Chesapeake Bay with the intention of invading Pennsylvania. The war, which had seemed so remote only a year ago, was now at their doorstep.

The minister rose to the occasion, and challenged by the patriotism of the congregation, led them outside to gather around the large oak tree in front of the church. According to the contemporary plaque mounted next to the bronzed stump, "Their pastor, Rev. Colin McFarquhar had been accustomed to offer prayers for the King of England. Pastor and Congregation gathered under this historic tree, and together joined hands, and under its shade pledged their loyalty to the cause of liberty and the founding of a new nation in this western land." The Revolution finally reached the Susquehanna, and the local militia companies were soon called up in response.

Although James Anderson, Sr. never saw active duty, he served in the General Assembly from 1778-1780 and was deeply involved with the cause. James Jr., however, was soon ordered to gather his militia company along with other units from Lancaster County. They marched to Chester County in the late fall of 1777 to help defend Pennsylvania from Howe's movements toward Philadelphia.

As James Jr.'s attention became focused on the war effort, his motherless children were looked after by his parents, siblings and extended family living on the family farm. Likewise, he had little time left to devote to his business interests and in 1777 decided to lease the ferry in order to be able to dedicate his efforts to serving his country.

Richard Keyes, who ran a smaller river crossing two miles upstream, leased Anderson's Ferry in 1777. He took charge of the inns, the maintenance of the boats, and the ferrying of passengers, until James Jr. returned from his tour of duty in 1778. While at Andersons, Keyes leased his upstream ferry to Christian Winiker in order to attend to the Anderson's larger, more prosperous operation. Some years later he sold his former crossing to Winiker, whose German surname eventually became corrupted to Vinegar. Vinegar Ferry was not officially chartered by the Commonwealth until 1867 and only exists today in the name of the road leading to the crossing.

The autumn of 1777 was not encouraging for the American colonies. The British controlled New York City, and the Americans lost Fort Ticonderoga in upstate New York in July. Lord Howe, after landing at the head of the Chesapeake Bay, marched towards Washington's troops gathered around Philadelphia in early September. Washington suffered defeat at the Battle of Brandywine on September 11, with 700 killed or wounded and 400 captured, and a little over a week later, the Continental regulars suffered another 300 casualties in nearby Paoli.

Following Washington's losses at Brandywine, a British occupation of Philadelphia seemed inevitable. Continental Congress hastily vacated the capital city on September 19, traveling north to Bethlehem to avoid British patrols, then south through Reading. They fled first to Lancaster, where they adjourned after staying in session for only one day. The delegates discovered there was a shortage of rooms in Lancaster's inns, and deciding that the enemy still posed a significant threat, they crossed the river to York, putting 100 miles and the Susquehanna River between themselves and the British. They settled into every inn and tavern, and even some private homes, and resumed the business of the government.

Philadelphia, then America's largest city, fell unopposed to the British on September 26 and the mood of the nation fell with it. Washington attacked the British at Germantown on October 4, but was once again was defeated and lost another 500 men. The following month, Anderson's 1st Company was called to active duty.

Over the winter of 1777, while Anderson and his men were occupied near Philadelphia, Richard Keyes witnessed many of the historic crossings to take place at the ferry. A majority of the members of Continental Congress, including John Hancock and John Adams, crossed the river on flatboats at Wright's Ferry since it was on the main road from Lancaster to York. However, others from New York, Boston, and New England chose to cross at Anderson's.

During the nine months that Congress resided in York, delegates and military couriers regularly travelled back and forth between the colonies and the capital in exile. Over the winter, the ferry crossing at Anderson's was used more frequently than the one at Wright's, due to the narrower width and "on account of the condition of the water and ice."[6] With the British firmly in control of the eastern coastal waterways, these crossings became the most critical transportation links within the colonies.

Although the news from Philadelphia was disheartening, General Gates was waging a successful battle against the troops of British General Burgoyne in New York. Marching south from Canada as a part of Lord Howe's two-pronged plan, Burgoyne met Gates at Saratoga, New York. In a series of well-placed skirmishes just thirteen days after Washington's loss at Brandywine, Gates was able to surround Burgoyne, who surrendered his 5,800 officers, artillery, and thousands of small arms on October 17.

With the remainder of Burgoyne's force retreating back into Quebec, the British made no further attempts to conquer the middle states and separate New England from the rest of the colonies. This was a major defeat for the British, and General Gates wanted to personally report his success to the Continental Congress in York.

In Lancaster and York, celebrations spontaneously erupted following the reading of unofficial reports of the battle at Saratoga. Taverns overflowed, church bells tolled, militia paraded, and overjoyed patriots fired shots in the air. Following the difficulties that General Washington experienced holding back the British under General Howe in Brandywine and Germantown, Gates' victory at Saratoga was a cause for celebration. Turning the tide of the war and boosting confidence in the Continental Army under General Gates, the victory also served to bolster the growing wariness of Washington's command.

On October 31, official news of the surrender reached the Congress in York with the arrival of Colonel James Wilkenson, a messenger sent by General Gates. A committee, including Samuel Adams, began work that same night to draft a resolution to commemorate the occasion. Saratoga, in addition to restoring the confidence of many members of Congress, served to solidify France's allegiance and commitment to the American cause, and was a reason to give thanks. The resolution was adopted the next day in a short session on Saturday, November 1, following the election of Henry Laurens to replace John Hancock as president of the Congress.

The proclamation recommended "to the several States, to set apart a day for thanksgiving, for the signal success lately obtained over the enemies of these United States ..." and "sets apart the 18th of December, for solemn thanksgiving and praise ... that with one heart and one voice, the good people may express the grateful feelings of their hearts ..."[7] This proclamation was the first of several which eventually established the national holiday of Thanksgiving.

After many weeks of debate, the final draft of The Articles of Confederation and Perpetual Union, more commonly referred to as The Articles of Confederation, was approved on the evening of November 15 by the Second Continental Congress while in York, earning the city the designation as the first capital of the United States. The day before, William Ellery, a Representative from Rhode Island and one of the signers of the Declaration of Independence, made the trip to York to participate in the vote, and recorded the following journal entry, "1777, Nov. 14, stopped at Lititz and on the 15th crossed at Anderson's Ferry at noon and reached York in the afternoon."[8]

General Gates, making his way to York in January of 1778 to meet with Congress, also crossed with Richard Keyes at Anderson's Ferry. He spent a night on the east side of the Susquehanna with Colonel Alexander Lowry, whose Lancaster militia battalion had served at Brandywine. Since Lowry owned a large estate less than a mile from Anderson's Ferry, he frequently hosted travelling dignitaries. At Anderson's the next morning, Gates "crossed the river at this ferry while on his way to Congress then in session at York."[9]

Many other important political and military figures, including Baron Von Steuben and Marquis de Lafayette, crossed at Anderson's Ferry while James Jr. was on active duty. Lafayette, a French military officer, voluntary aide to General Washington, and Major General in the Continental Army, was serving with General Washington at Valley Forge when he was informed that he had been placed in command of a campaign to invade Canada.

Lafayette, only twenty at the time, was initially hesitant about accepting the appointment, but Washington convinced him otherwise, assuring Lafayette that it would never materialize. Lafayette proceeded to York to meet with Congress and General Gates to begin planning the expedition.

Gates, capitalizing on his new found popularity with Congress after his capture of Burgoyne and the growing apprehension concerning Washington's ability to defeat the British, had convinced Congress to approve the campaign. They gave Gates the authority to carry out his plan as the newly appointed president of the Board of War. He drafted the orders for the invasion and proceeded with informing General Lafayette of his appointment.

While in York, Lafayette publicly reaffirmed his devotion and support of General Washington, effectively ending the movement of Gates and others to replace Washington as Commander-in-Chief. Congress agreed, and Gates became anxious to put as much distance between Lafayette and Washington as possible. He insisted Lafayette leave York at once for Albany, New York, where the operations against Canada were being organized.

After leaving York and heading east on February 3, 1778, Lafayette stopped at Anderson's Ferry before crossing the river and heading north to Albany. Here he wrote several letters to Henry Laurens, the delegate from South Carolina who had been elected President of the Continental Congress the previous November.

Referring to his trip to New York, Lafayette wrote "I beg your pardon my dear sir of the impropriety of this letter, but I only have a minute, and I must make an incursion into the boat with all possible rapidity ... Anderson ferry at three o'clock in a great hurry ... Marquis delafayette"[10]. In his second letter to Laurens also dated February 3rd, he stated that he "crossed the Susquehanna at Anderson's Ferry" and "the river was full of ice"[11]

After Lafayette crossed the river, he turned northeast, arriving in Albany on February 17. Over the following week, he found the army in disarray and rampant discontent among the troops. Congress realized the serious nature of the conditions and finally informed Lafayette to delay the invasion plans, effectively ending the campaign just as Washington had predicted the month before.

Meanwhile, while Richard Keyes was busy tending to the activity at Anderson's Ferry generated by the Continental Congress in York, Anderson Jr.'s militia company was occupied over the winter of

1777-1778 watching over Philadelphia from Valley Forge. Chosen for the ample water supply, abundant wood for building and burning, and defendable terrain, Valley Forge was used as a command center for the Continental Regulars as well as for militia units. Although the militia did not see a large degree of combat, it had been deployed in early September to guard some of the lesser crossings of the Brandywine Creek during Howe's advance from the head of the Chesapeake.

James Anderson's men, along with the other units called up over the winter, supported Washington's effort in various ways. After the British occupation of Philadelphia in October, the militia companies, under the command of General John Armstrong, operated in the area between the Schuylkill and Delaware rivers in an attempt to blockade Howe's troops in the city. Patrolling in small independent units and remaining mobile, the primary duty of Anderson and his men would have been to assist in securing and holding all the roads leading out of Philadelphia.

The Lancaster County militia would also have helped to disable local gristmills and collect cattle in an attempt to reduce the availability of food supplies that civilians loyal to the Crown may have been tempted to take into Philadelphia. Other militia patrols were charged with disrupting communications between General Howe and the surrounding areas. Aside from the occasional clash with British outposts and scouting parties, the winter was spent without any major encounters with the enemy.

After surviving the harsh winter conditions in Valley Forge, the militia units from Donegal returned home following their sixty-day tour of duty. Anderson most likely arrived back at the ferry at about the same time Lafayette crossed on his way to Albany on February 3, for he married twenty-one year old Margaret Chambers on February 19 and began rebuilding his former life. The arrangement for management of the ferry with Richard Keyes was ended, and James Jr., then thirty-seven, once again resumed control of the ferry operation for the next several years. With a thriving business and accommodations on both sides of the river, the future looked promising for the Andersons.

Over the next twenty years, James Jr. and Margaret added ten more children to their family, and as his obligations at home grew, Anderson had less time to devote to managing the Ferry and taverns on both sides of the river. In 1784, his mother Ruth passed away and his father, James Anderson, Sr., was starting to decline in health.

Perhaps as a result of these family issues, Anderson Jr. leased the operations to Jacob Strickler and began to assume fewer responsibilities in the day-to-day operation of the ferry. The competition with Wright's Ferry, which had begun in 1742 with the issuing of Anderson's ferry Patent, began to escalate. At stake were the fees paid by the many wagon teams carrying goods between Philadelphia and the markets west of the river. In addition, travelling parties stopped to eat in the taverns or stay overnight at the inns, and competition for this type of revenue served to fuel the rivalry.

John Wright had been the first to receive a Patent in 1730, establishing his ferry three miles south of Anderson's. In 1787, in an effort to attract additional business, Wright reduced his tolls and advertised the superiority of his operation in the *Pennsylvania Chronicle*, the first weekly paper published in York. On November 27, Jacob Strickler, who was operating Anderson's Ferry at the time, wrote in response to his competitor's advertisement:

"The subscriber cannot think of passing over the illiberal and unjust publication of Messrs. John Wright and Joseph Jeffries, in the York Chronicle of the 21st instant, in which they say that he will deceive concerning his ferry at Anderson. I think that Mr. Wright knows nothing of a ferry, nor what constitutes it, and is in no wise calculated to be a ferryman; and that Mr. Jeffries is illiberal and unjust, must appear to the public, to be greater deceivers that they are apprized of, for reasons best known to myself, I will not animadvert on this subject; but the public may rely that I have a better and safer ferry than theirs, and travelers will find that they can go sooner, from Lancaster to York by crossing at this ferry, than at Wright's; and notwithstanding that they have laid wait on the roads, and have induced all that they could, that since occupying that noted ferry, formerly called Anderson, that I have put over the river Susquehanna, 10 wagons and persons to their one. I now say that my boats are new and good, and that are equal if not superior to any on the river Susquehanna, and sufficient on both sides of the river. I expect the indulgence of the generous public, and remain their humble servant."[12]

Not willing to let the editorial battle rest, John Wright issued a rebuttal in the December 8 issue:

"As there have many ill-natured falsehoods appeared in an Advertisement of the 27th November last, signed Jacob Strickler, intending to injure the character of this ferry, and its keepers. The subscribers do not think it worth their while to enter into particulars respecting the author; but, beg leave to inform the public, that the Great Western Road through Lancaster and York, is much shorter and better this way, than any other and the passage of the river perfectly safe; they have a sufficient number of good boats, and make every exertion to forward travelers. They have lowered the price of the ferriage of a four-horse wagon to three shillings and nine pence, and that of a man and horse to six pence[*], and all other things in proportion. That they will strive to accommodate in the best manner in the tavern way any persons who please to favor them with their custom."[13]

---

[*] *Three shillings and nine pence was worth 62 cents in 1787 and six pence was worth 8 cents. It is unusual for Wright to have quoted British units, as Congress adopted the dollar as the monetary standard in 1785, two years prior the Chronicle editorial.*

In another account depicting the intense competition between Wright and Anderson, Bishop and Mrs. Reichel, who crossed on May 22, 1780, recorded the crossing in their travel diary. "In the sixth hour we reached Anderson's Ferry, where the Susquehannah is 1 ½ miles wide. On the side from which we approached there is a high sandy bank, and the wheels of Conrad's wagon sank to the axle in the sand, and were freed only after one and a half hours of work with levers and extra horses. On the other side is a high stony ridge. We were fortunate as to get our two wagons and three riding horses across within two hours, by means of two Flats, which are too small for a river of such considerable size; but frequently travelers are detained here for an entire day. Each crossing only takes ten minutes, and they race with each other. But they had to cross over and back three times, and the loading and unloading takes as much time as the crossing. Here they charge $56.00[†] for taking over a six-horse wagon, and $8.00 for a horse and rider; at Wright's Ferry, where the Susquehannah is two miles wide, the charge is $90.00 for a six-horse wagon, and $12.00 for a horse and rider."[14]

As Wright and Anderson skirmished over toll rates and customers, another battle was being waged in Congress which had the potential to substantially impact both ferries. After the British left Philadelphia in June of 1778, Congress vacated York and the seat of government returned to Philadelphia until 1783. Massive protests by Revolutionary War veterans demanding back pay for their service prompted Congress to hastily relocate to Princeton, New Jersey. From there they moved to Annapolis, Maryland, then to Trenton, New Jersey, and finally to New York City.

After the ratification of the Constitution of the United States in 1789, the Residence Act was passed in 1790, and the attention of

---

[†] *The stated fees must have represented cents rather than dollars. Compared to the tolls before and after 1780 at Andersons and Wrights, 56 cents would have been a reasonable rate for a wagon and horses, not 56 dollars.*

Congress turned to finding a permanent home for the United States government. This began one of the longest and most hotly-contested debates ever to be seen in Congress.

The criteria for determining the location of the capital city varied. Some members felt that it should be located in the geographic center of population, wealth, or territory. This led to lengthy arguments as to where this actually would fall, as the centers of those three factors ended up fixing three different locations, and were constantly changing.

Pennsylvania Congressman Thomas Hartley, a resident of York, advocated Wright's Ferry on the Susquehanna as the ideal location for the capital. Bolstered by members who claimed that Wright had placed his ferry at a location that would be "the center of population for years to come"[15] and "the hub of the universe,"[16] the idea gained popularity. However, others questioned how the center would be calculated after the Ohio Territory was settled.

Other members of Congress insisted that an easy connection to the Atlantic Ocean was the most important criteria in determining the location of the new capital. Northern members favored a site far above the Mason-Dixon Line, while their southern counterparts touted the advantages of their climate, eventually recommending a location on the Potomac River near Georgetown.

Not only did Congressman Hartley champion choosing Wright's Ferry based on the soil, water, and beauty of the place, he also appealed to the appetites of Congress by remarking "if honorable gentleman were disposed to pay much attention to a dish of fish, he could assure them their table might be furnished with fine and good from the waters of the Susquehanna."[17]

In addition to Wright's, Hartley also proposed York as a possible permanent site for the capital. At the beginning of the debate, he favored Wright's due to the initial requirement of a location on the Susquehanna, but at the same time he was also advocating York, since it had already once accommodated Congress. Hartley was asked by Congressman Richard Lee about the distance from York to the ferry, and whether the Codorus Creek could be made navigable. Hartley assured him that York could accommodate the capital, to which Lee replied "Then why not go at once to Yorktowne? Why fix on the banks of a swift river when it is possible to occupy the shores of Codorus creek?"[18]

In hopes of influencing Congress, residents of Wright's Ferry renamed their town "Columbia," in honor of Christopher Columbus. They also enlisted George Washington as a champion of their campaign to become the capital. President Washington, along with representatives from New England and New York, favored Wright's Ferry, due to its "beauty, security, and other natural advantages,"[19] and the proposal gained momentum and eventually passed in committee.

Finally, a vote was called in the House to select a commission to find a suitable location at Wright's Ferry, allocate funds, and purchase land for the buildings. The bill passed the House of Representatives by a narrow margin and went on to the Senate, where it lost by a single vote. Columbia's bid to become the capital of the United States had come to an end.

After additional debates on both sides of Congress, the decision eventually came down to a matter of finances. Among the many other subjects that deeply concerned Congress was the issue of whether or not the federal government would pay for the debt incurred by the states to fight the Revolutionary War. The northern states were in favor of the assumption of the debt by the federal government and the South was not. Conversely, the South was for locating the capital on the Potomac River while the North was not.

In a political compromise, Alexander Hamilton, then Secretary of the Treasury, induced a few northern members to change their vote on the location of the capital, and convinced several southern members to switch sides on the issue of the war debt. Everyone seemed satisfied, and the location on the Potomac was set in stone. Congress moved back to Philadelphia for the next ten years while the capital buildings were being erected, and the idea of establishing the seat of the federal government along the Susquehanna was permanently abandoned.

Had the capital of the United States been established at Wright's Ferry, it would have greatly affected the local economy and changed the face of the river forever. In another bid for fame, Columbia was briefly in contention to be named the state capital of Pennsylvania in 1812, losing out to Harrisburg due to its central location in the state.

In 1790, James Anderson, Sr. passed away at age seventy at the family farm in Lancaster County. He was buried alongside his father, the Reverend James Anderson, his mother Suit, and wife Ruth, in the cemetery at the Donegal Church.

His grandson, James Anderson IV, then twenty three, began taking a more active role in the business concerns of the farm and ferry. He married Mary Bayley on New Year's Eve in 1795, having one child before Mary passed away in 1797. The following year, on March 28, he married Mary McQueen, and their first child together, James Anderson V, was born nine months later on December 12. Following in the tradition of his father James Jr. (fourteen children), his grandfather James Sr. (eight children), and his great-grandfather Reverend James Anderson (eleven children), James IV also fathered a large family of ten children.

James Anderson, Jr., did not live to see the dawning of the nineteenth century. In 1799, he passed away unexpectedly at age fifty-eight on New Year's Eve, the same year his last child Eleanor was born. James IV now owned and controlled the extensive land holdings on both sides of the river, along with the prosperous ferry operation. However, he did not share with his paternal ancestors the same desire to preserve the Anderson farm and estate. He was a "man of enterprise and progress,"[20] and had other plans for developing the land that his father owned, and that he inherited.

The legal transfer of ownership to James Anderson IV from his father's estate was a complicated issue. Up until that point, the land in Lancaster County had clearly been deeded from the Penns to

Reverend James Anderson (1736), passed to James Anderson, Sr. through the Reverend Anderson's will (1740), and sold by James Anderson, Sr. to James Anderson, Jr. (1772).

Likewise, on the west side of the Susquehanna in York County, the land had been purchased from the Proprietors by Reverend Anderson (1739), from Phillip Syng, Jr. (1759), and others (1763), by James Anderson, Sr. These properties were subsequently sold to James Anderson, Jr. (1771).

With the extensive land holdings owned by James Anderson Jr., it would seem logical for him to have made accommodations for the disbursement of the property upon his death, but he died intestate without a will. The Orphans' Courts of Lancaster County and York County were left to settle the estate when he passed away in 1799.

The Lancaster and York courts ruled that the entire estate was to be vested in James Anderson IV as the eldest son of the deceased, with the condition that he pay (or secure notes to pay) his step-mother, living sisters, step-brothers, and step-sisters, their respective shares of their father's estate. In Lancaster County, the property was appraised at £3,295 (approximately $15,000 in 1800) and in York County, the various land holdings were valued at £1,740 ($7,800).

Anderson IV was bound by the court order to pay his step-mother Margaret the interest on the value of the lands during her lifetime, and after her death the principal amount of her share was to be distributed among the surviving children. In addition, he was required to pay his sisters Margaret and Ruth, his step-brothers Thomas, John, William, Chambers, and Garland, and his step-sisters Jane, Mary, Elizabeth and Eleanor (one year old at the time) their proportionate share of the value of the estate. At the time of his father's death in 1799, his brother Joseph Tate and step-brother Michael had already passed away with no heirs, and they are not mentioned in the Orphans' Court orders.

As with most financial transactions of the time, little cash changed hands and promises to pay the shares from the estate were simply secured with notes. Although this sufficed at the time of the court order, the fact that Anderson IV did not actually satisfy these notes, and therefore never received formal releases from the other parties, would come back to haunt his widow for years to come. But, by merely issuing promises for the required amounts ordered by the court, control of the property was firmly placed in the hands of James Anderson IV.

On the east side of the river in Lancaster County, James IV had ambitious plans for the 129 acres of land he inherited. However, these plans would eventually prove to be his financial ruin. The development of the area over next twenty years would forever change the character of the riverfront, and eventually "... he was overtaken by reverses, the result of circumstances beyond his control, and thus the estate, which had descended through three generations, passed from the family."[21]

Chapter 7

Coyle's Ferry
Saturday, May 28, 1881

The flowers slowly spread out on the surface of the water, some swirling back into lazy eddies along the river's edge and others catching the swifter current and setting a course downstream. The lighter lilacs and snowballs drifted away from the heavier peonies and iris and soon looked like the flocks of white birds that floated down the Susquehanna in the early spring. Emily stood on the river bank in front of the inn, watching her morning's handiwork slowly fade away in the distance, her frustration and helplessness mounting as they eventually disappeared from sight.

The day's earlier events frightened her even now and served to steady her resolve to leave the Coyles for good as soon as she was able. The quarrel with John started innocently enough that morning as she was making her floral crosses for the graves in Wrightsville, and she never imagined it would escalate into such a confrontation. Emily was planning to meet Kate Emsweiler at the upper end of town early Monday morning to join in the Decoration Day parade, and John was not at all happy about it. He wanted to go across the river to Marietta where the festivities were more elaborate and insisted that Emily go with him.

The morning started off bright and sunny and full of promise, and as soon as Emily finished her regimen of chores, she hurried into the garden to gather the flowers she needed for her mission. Most of the younger children who joined the GAR veterans, fire companies and dignitaries in honoring the Civil War dead simply gathered loose flowers to place on the graves, but Decoration Day held a special meaning for Emily.

Decoration Day, casually observed on various days in the three years following the cessation of fighting in 1865, was officially proclaimed a holiday by General John Logan, national commander of the Grand Army of the Republic, a veteran's organization for the Union Army. In Washington, DC, on May 5, 1868, he issued General Order 11, declaring:

"The 30th of May, 1868[*], is designated for the purpose of strewing with flowers, or otherwise decorating the graves of comrades who died in the defense of their country during the late rebellion, and whose bodies now lie in almost every city, village and hamlet churchyard in the land. In this observance no form of ceremony is prescribed, but posts and comrades will in their own way arrange such fitting services and testimonials of respect as circumstances may permit."[1]

Emily's father died of the wounds he received in the war and she missed him terribly. Every year she made it a point to do something special on Decoration Day by fashioning small arrangements, wreaths or sashes for the graves of the fallen soldiers. This year she was planning something different, and was making as many fresh floral crosses as she could.

The Viburnum bush behind the inn was huge, with hundreds of white pom-poms that looked like snowballs. Mrs. Coyle also had a lilac bush and several clumps of bright pink peonies, and there were purple and white iris growing all along the bank of the river up the road near the ferry landing.

After moving in with the Coyles the previous October, Emily wasn't sure where she was going to find all the flowers she needed for her annual Decoration Day tradition, but when spring came and she saw how many were growing at the ferry, she was ecstatic. Mrs. Coyle, in an uncharacteristically generous gesture, said she could have as many as she could cut, and Emily was planning to outdo herself this year.

---

[*] *Memorial Day was observed on May 30 until the Uniform Monday Holiday Act (P.L. 90-363) was enacted in 1971, when it was changed to the last Monday in May, insuring a three- day weekend for Federal employees.*

Emily carried a wooden bucket of water as she moved from bush to bush, filling it with cut flowers. After it was full, she went into the barn, dumped them in the water trough and went back for more. She soon had the trough full and the barn was filled with their fragrance. Emily loved the smell of flowers, and looked forward to weaving the flowers together onto the crude cross frames she had made out of sticks tied together the day before. Cutting the flowers was hot work, and the mercury was already showing 80 degrees, compared to the cool temperatures in the 60s the previous few days.

At breakfast the day before, she had come across an editorial in the Columbia Spy which one of the passengers had brought back with them from across the river. The writer had expressed his fear that Decoration Day would soon fade from memory and eventually pass unobserved by anyone. But, he optimistically hoped that as long as the surviving veterans of the Grand Army of the Republic continued to honor the graves of their comrades, the tradition would live on. And, if they passed it to their children, the day would become an occasion for all to visit the cemeteries to pay respect to their loved ones whether they fought for the preservation of the Union or not. His words struck a heartfelt chord with Emily and affected her deeply, and she was even more determined to make this Decoration Day a special one.

Emily was excited about attending the local celebration the following Monday in Wrightsville, and had been anticipating the rare trip to town for weeks. She was especially looking forward to seeing Captain Frank Magee, the handsome and distinguished Chief Marshall of the parade and featured speaker at the ceremony.

Captain Magee, a Wrightsville native and Civil War veteran, was a popular local figure. After serving as the public school superintendent until 1871, he was elected to the State Legislature for a two-year term. By 1881, he was the local Justice of the Peace, the borough surveyor, president of the Wrightsville Hardware Company, director of the Wrightsville Iron Company, and secretary of the local school board. As the captain of the Wrightsville Grays National Guard detachment and commander of GAR Post 270, he was the obvious choice for leading the Decoration Day ceremonies.

Captain Frank Magee [2]

Magee was married and had two children, Robert and Helen, both near Emily in age. Emily had forged a sisterly friendship with Helen immediately after moving in with the Coyles, and visited with the Magees as often as she could. Since her father had also served in the Union army, Helen was especially sympathetic to Emily's plight as a war orphan. The Magee's farm was a few miles west of the ferry and Frank made it a point to stop and say hello to Emily whenever he passed Coyle's Ferry on his way to and from the farm. Since Emily's closest relative was her sister Annie in Harrisburg, she had adopted the Magees as her surrogate family.

For the past week, the GAR had been busy decorating Wrightsville with flags and banners. Red, white and blue fans hung at every window and bunting had been hung across the main street at each intersection. One of the boarders at the ferry outlined for Emily the plans for the upcoming Decoration Day ceremonies, and she was looking forward to making the most of the festivities.

All businesses were closing at noon, and everyone was to gather near the toll gate at the west edge of town. A procession consisting of GAR Post 270, the town council, the fire company, the School Board, citizens, and school children would proceed down Hellam Street under the marshalship of Captain Magee. The end of the parade was the Fairview Cemetery, where the children would be stationed with their flowers at the graves of the Civil War veterans.

Following a three-shot volley from the Wrightsville Grays, the flowers were to be placed on the mounds and the crowd would regroup at the entrance to the cemetery. The services were to open with the singing of "America" and be followed by remarks from Captain Magee and a rendition of "The Night before the Battle." The main speaker was George McElroy, a Civil War veteran and prominent lawyer in York. The ceremony would close with the Doxology, and be followed by a community picnic along the banks of the river.

Emily baked four strawberry pies for the picnic with berries from Mrs. Coyle's garden and they sat cooling in the kitchen as she gathered her flowers, filling the inn with their sweet fresh-baked scent. The strawberry crop was abundant, and Emily had picked quart after quart the past several days. Mrs. Coyle usually took some of her berries across the river to Marietta to sell to the grocer or exchange for other things she needed, but because there was no shortage of berries the prices had come down drastically. John had seen plump juicy ones offered on the streets a few days previous, two boxes for a quarter. Since Mrs. Coyle wasn't planning on sending any over at those rates, she agreed to give some to Emily for her pies.

Emily had lived in Chambersburg since she was six with her grandfather Samuel Myers, where her Decoration Day ritual consisted of placing her floral creations on the graves of some of the local soldiers who had served with her father. He was buried in Harrisburg, and Emily had not been able to visit his grave since she had moved in with her grandfather. Ever since her father's passing, Emily spent the holiday quietly each year, and she was eager to participate in the big public celebrations in Wrightsville with her friends for a change.

After gathering enough flowers from the garden and along the river, she went into the barn and eagerly began working. Dipping into the trough and taking out a handful of flowers, she carefully intertwined them into the stick crosses. With a sharp knife, she cut the ends of the long stems off even with the edges of the framework. As she finished with the last one, John walked into the barn.

She heard him come in and turned excitedly to show him what she had made. Knowing she would never be able to take all of the flowers to town herself, she was planning to ask him to take her to Wrightsville in the wagon early the next morning. However, the look on his face told her he was still upset about the previous weekend and the visit from her cousin. After he sarcastically said "What are you making *those* for Em?" she knew there was going to be a confrontation.

Trying to counter his mood, she lightly exclaimed "Getting ready for Decoration Day!" "Why bother, you're coming with me to Marietta, aren't you?" John immediately shot back, and Emily decided to ignore his question. She had been expecting it for a few days, ever since she read about the controversy in Marietta about the business closures on Monday.

All the dry goods and hardware stores, along with the banks and other business establishments were planning to close, with the exception of the hotel bars and saloons. Most people felt that it was disrespectful, but with a brisk trade expected, the saloon keepers were thrilled. John, of course, was eager to go to the ceremonies in Marietta as a result, and was simply using the day as another excuse to drink.

The ensuing argument was one of the worst they ever had, with John insisting that she accompany him, and Emily persisting in telling him no. She could tell that he wanted to show her off to the boys in Marietta, and the thought of anyone thinking that they were in love angered her to no end. He desperately pleaded with her, but Emily was adamant that she would have no part in his plans. She eventually turned her back to him and started gathering up her crosses when he grabbed her by the shoulder and spun her around.

Emily lost her balance and fell to the barn floor, watching in horror as John started kicking at the flowers. He picked up a handful and stalked out of the barn and down to the river's edge, where he proceeded to rip them apart and toss them into the water. When he came back the barn, she pleaded with him, but he picked up another bunch and started back out the door. She grabbed desperately at him and he roughly pushed her away, and the look on his face told her it was no use. She ran after him yelling for him to please stop, but "I told you you're going with *me*" is all he would say.

One by one he tore apart every one of her crosses and unceremoniously dumped them into the river, ignoring her continued protests. Finally storming back into the house, he left her standing by the water's edge, sobbing and wondering how he could have sunk so low. Coming to the realization that she needed to make a change in her life, she came to two conclusions. First, she was even more determined to go to Wrightsville on Monday, even without the flowers. And, vowing she would leave the Coyles for good as soon as possible, she came up with an idea where she could get help.

Emily had confided in Helen Magee on many previous occasions about her problems with John. She would see Helen in town and would talk to her about the incident that morning and enlist Helen's help in persuading her father to find her a position at his hardware company. Smiling at the thought that maybe Helen would offer to let her move in with them, she turned and made her way back to the inn.

Emily could hear John and his father yelling at each other behind the house, arguing about getting the tobacco set in the field. Time was wasting, according to Mr. Coyle, but John was in no mood to hear about it. He had worked with his father the last couple of days on the corn crop, from the afternoon until late into the evenings, and loudly protested against doing any more chores. After a few more minutes of shouting, which most certainly could be heard across the river in Marietta, the men came back into the kitchen.

As John started up the back steps to his room, Mr. Coyle turned to Emily and said "Since *he* won't give me any help, can you can come out and give me a hand?" She thought the work may help take her mind off her ruined flowers, and replied "Of course, if *he* can't do it, I'll come along." This infuriated John, since he most certainly *could* do it, he just didn't *want* to. Emily followed Mr. Coyle outside, and John trailed quietly behind them.

He waited until they had gone through the garden gate and into the orchard beside the inn. Reaching under the rock near the gate, he took out his hidden cigar box and pulled out his small pistol. Making sure it was loaded, he shouted after them "When are you going to start minding what I say?" and fired the pistol over their heads. Mr. Coyle grabbed Emily and pulled her to the ground and looked back at John in amazement and anger.

He hadn't realized that John even possessed a pistol, and had been careful to hide his own guns following several incidents over the past few years where John had threatened to kill himself. Boiling over with rage, Mr. Coyle returned to the house and grabbed the pistol from John's hand. After realizing it was not one of his own, he demanded to know where John had gotten the gun. Instead of answering, John glanced menacingly at Emily and went back into the house and up to his room, slamming and locking the door behind him.

Although it was not the first time that John had threatened him, Mr. Coyle was shaken up over what had just happened. He told Emily that there would be no more work that day and went in the kitchen to calm down Mary Ann. He found his wife crying and wringing her hands in worry, and he tried to console her, absent-mindedly laying the pistol on the wood box beside the stove.

After retreating to his room, John lay on his bed, trying to give his head a chance to stop pounding. It had been bothering him on and off for the past week, ever since the episode with Emily and her assumed beau had sent him on another one of his drinking binges the previous weekend. With the exception of a few trips across the river, he had spent the better part of the week in his room, ignoring the repeated knocks on his door and only going down to get things to eat from the kitchen after every one else was in bed for the night.

His blowup that morning with Emily weighed heavy on his mind. He had been giving a lot of thought lately on how to make Emily understand how serious he was about marrying her. Now that he had caused another scene, he realized his plans were probably ruined for good, and feared he was sinking back into one of his depressive moods. As he tried to calm his rage and frustration, his thoughts drifted back to the events of the past few days.

Two days earlier on Thursday morning, Ascension Day, John had gone across the river with his father to help transport a wagon laden with cut timber to Marietta. The water was fast, and hard to handle for just one person, and they had to use their biggest flatboat to accommodate the team of horses and the wagon. He normally would have given his father a hard time about helping, but had agreed to go along for his own ulterior motives.

After they reached the far shore and the boat was unloaded, he told his father he had some things to do and to go back home alone. He wanted to check in at the Post Office to see if a package he was expecting had arrived, and didn't want his father around to ask any questions about it.

In late April, John had noticed several advertisements in the newspaper about a cure for a personal problem he had been wrestling with for years. Although the "secret disease" that afflicted John was something his parents had attempted to get him treatment for from several doctors in Marietta, nothing seemed to help and he was growing desperate. Thinking that it may help him conquer his problems and win Emily, he had sent off for a copy of the article and had checked in at the Post Office every chance he had for the past couple of weeks.

Although masturbation is not categorized as a disease today, in the late 1800s it was thought to cause anything from laziness to death, draining the body of its essential life-force. John had been "dubbing off," as his friends called it, for years, and the captions splashed across every issue of the Columbia paper caught his eye, proclaiming "Startling Discovery! Lost Manhood Restored," and "Manhood; How Lost, How Restored." In an era filled with worthless tonics, patent medicines and elixirs promising to cure any and all ailments from toothaches to female complaints, John felt a couple of three-cent stamps was a small price to pay to remedy his addiction.

Drs. J.N. and J.B Hobensack of Philadelphia promised relief to "those suffering from that fatal practice, self-abuse and seminal emissions, which destroy both body and soul and cause consumption, mental and physical debility, nervousness, epilepsy, impaired nutrition of the body, lassitude, weakness of the limbs and neck, indisposition and insincerity for duty and labor, dullness of appreciation, loss of memory, aversion to society, love of solitude, timidity, self-distrust, dizziness, headache, affection of the eyes, and sexual incapacity, the consequences of youthful indiscretion."[3]

Another classified ad announced "a just published new edition of Dr. Culverwell's Celebrated Essay on the radical cure (without medicine) of Spermatophia or Seminal Weakness, Involuntary Seminal Losses, Impotency, Mental and Physical Incapacity, Impediments to Marriage, etc, also Consumption, Epilepsy and Fits, induced by self-indulgence or sexual extravagance, &c. The celebrated author, in this admirable essay, clearly demonstrates from a thirty years successful practice, that the alarming consequences of self-abuse may be radically cured without the dangerous use of internal medicine or the application of a knife; pointing out a mode of cure at once simple, certain, and effective, by means of which every sufferer, no matter what his condition, may he cure himself cheaply, privately, and radically. This lecture should be in the hands of every youth and every man in the land."[4]

Anyone that knew John would have agreed he suffered from lassitude, mental incapacity, insincerity of labor, aversion to society and occasional fits. He was well aware of his own headaches and dizziness and certainly didn't want any more impediments to marriage. So, the promise of a cheap cure-all delivered in a plain brown envelope seemed like the perfect solution, and he had purchased the stamps and envelope when he had been in Marietta in April.

After leaving his father at the dock, he walked to the Post Office and found his package waiting for him. Judging by the look on Postmaster Abraham Cassel's face, the thick wrapper with the return address of The Culverwell Medical Company had given away the contents. *So much for the plain brown envelope* he thought, and suddenly embarrassed, John snatched it from Cassel's hands and rushed out the door. He stumbled as he ran down the steps, causing laughter from the Postmaster inside and the children outside who had seen him fall. John ran back towards the river to find a quiet spot to discover the answer to all his problems.

On his way down Front Street, he met up with John Warfield, one of the Coyle's neighbors from across the river. Warfield lived on a farm a few miles from the ferry, and was in Marietta with a business partner from Wrightsville. They owned one of the many saw mills along the river and were in town to purchase some of the lumber from the rafts that had come down that week. Although their mill was already running at full capacity, with stacks of cut boards piled high in their warehouses and outside along the river, they couldn't pass up a chance to cash in on some of the incredible deals that were to be had in Marietta.

There was a glut of timber that year, and all of the local lumber mills were already taxed to their limit. Now that the river had fallen to safer levels, rafting season was back in full swing and at least 1,500 rafts of timber had already reached Marietta, with at least double that number still en route from Lock Haven further up the river. Such a surplus of lumber was causing a dull market, with most buyers having already purchased all they wanted. Those who failed to sell early were now sitting on thousands of board feet of lumber that they were eager to unload at a cheap price.

Warfield had come from Wrightsville on Monday, and had spent the last several days negotiating and consummating several significant lumber transactions. He and his partner were heading back across the river after they were done their business at the bank, and John asked if he could catch a ride back to the inn with them.

Warfield agreed, and said John was welcome to come along if he could be at the dock in fifteen minutes. He had also offered a ride to several rafters he purchased lumber from and told them to meet him at the boat if they were interested. The hotels in Marietta were overflowing with lumber dealers and rafters and were not able to keep up with demand for meals, with one serving over five hundred in a single day. Warfield told the lumberman about the incredible home-cooked food served at the less-crowded Coyle's Ferry across the river, and eager for a good meal, they accepted Warfield's offer. John figured he would be returning them to Marietta later that night; probably much less sober than they were at the moment.

Meeting Warfield and the rafters at the river, John tucked the envelope under his shirt to avoid the inevitable questions that he wouldn't want to answer. He helped Warfield row the men across the river to the inn, diverting the conversation from the bulge under his clothes to the upcoming bass fishing season. It was due to start in less than a week on June 1, and the pilots were disappointed that they would already be gone back upriver by then. John told them of some fine bass he had already caught while shad fishing off the dam in Wrightsville, and promised the men if they stayed in Marietta till the next Wednesday, he would take them out fishing.

They soon reached the far shore, and after saying his thanks to Warfield for the ride, John showed the men to the tavern room. Leaving them with Emily, he hurried up to his room to open his package, but as soon as he closed the door, his mother knocked on his door telling him that dinner was ready and insisting that he come downstairs. John hurriedly stuffed the unopened envelope between the thin mattress and the lattice of ropes holding it, and went down for some of the home-cooked food the raftsmen were so excited about.

His father cornered him right after lunch, and the rest of the day they worked together on the hillside behind the house, pulling the immature shoots of corn out of the ground and burning them in a pile behind the smokehouse. The cut-worms had been especially problematic for the past few weeks, and many of their plants had already been chewed off close to the ground. Other stalks still had eggs on them, and without the benefit of modern insecticides, they had no choice but to destroy their first planting and get more in the ground as soon as possible. His father had been planning to set their tobacco, but instead had John working until dark on the corn crop.

By the time they finished working and had eaten supper, John was so tired that he forgot completely about his hidden package. He stumbled up to his room, falling asleep in his clothes as soon as he hit the bed. He and Emily had actually been civil to each other at supper, talking about the Decoration Day preparations that John had seen in Marietta earlier that day. He had hinted at taking Emily with him, and she had decided to not tell him about her plans in Wrightsville just yet. As he fell asleep, he thought that maybe things were on their way to getting better with her.

John slept later than usual on Friday, waking at seven-thirty only after repeated calls from his mother. John Warfield was downstairs asking for him because he needed to be taken back across the river. The bank in Marietta had closed at noon the day before due to the Ascension Day holiday, and Warfield was not able to finish all his business. Since John was still dressed from the night before, he quickly splashed some cold water on his face and shuffled down the steps and onto the porch. Warfield was pacing back and forth down the road by the landing, impatient to get started.

Warfield was already waiting in the boat by the time John got to the dock and they quickly untied the ropes and started across the river. Deciding to confide in his passenger, Coyle blurted out "I have trouble." Curious, Warfield asked what was bothering him and John answered "I would tell you, but you might blow on me." Warfield reassured him that he would not and John continued. "I want to get married, and I haven't the means." Warfield then asked "Johnny, how can you expect to have a woman the way you are carrying on?"[5]

John told Warfield he had already proposed to Emily and added, "She refused me; but I am going to ask her again, and, by God, before any other man shall have her, I will shoot her!" Not taking John seriously, Warfield told Coyle that killing her "won't better it, she would be dead, and you would be hanged for it."[6]

Nearing the far shore, they saw a group of men gathering sand and stones, and John whispered "You should not talk so loud." Warfield said "I am not ashamed to be heard," and in a low voice John responded "John Warfield, I think I ought to be ashamed for I have become so low I don't care what becomes of me." Warfield replied "Johnny, there is no man got so low yet he could not raise his head if he wanted to."[7] John had no answer, and as they passed the men working near the shore, nothing more was mentioned.

John waited at the boat for Warfield to conclude his business at the bank, and watched the men drag the heavy bags up to the waiting wheelbarrows. He eventually became impatient and started walking towards town to see what was keeping Warfield, and soon met him coming down Perry Street toward the dock carrying a small brown sack. Warfield's business had gone well, and he had stopped and bought some pretzels to share with John for waiting so long for him. The ride back to the inn was a quiet one, with no more talk of Emily.

The rest of the day Friday was once again spent with his father in the fields, working on replanting corn until well after dinner. As was the case on Thursday, John was exhausted by the time he went to bed, and fell asleep immediately. Saturday morning came all too quickly, and his mother woke him around 6 o'clock. She had churned fresh butter earlier that morning and needed him to take some to Lindenmuth's store in Marietta, along with a long list of groceries to bring back.

He returned just before noon, just in time for dinner. Dropping off the groceries in the kitchen, he looked around for Emily and didn't find her anywhere in the house. He asked his mother where she was, and she told him that Emily had been out cutting flowers and was in the barn putting together arrangements for Decoration Day in Wrightsville. John was counting on her going to Marietta with him, and had already told the younger boys in Marietta that he would be bringing his girl with him to the parade. *Why she would be going to all that trouble unless she wasn't planning on coming along,* he wondered, and went out to confront her about it.

After the ensuing argument in the barn, something snapped and in a fit of rage he had thrown into the river any excuses Emily could use for not going to Marietta with him. As if her refusal to go with him wasn't enough, she then taunted him when his father asked her to help with the tobacco with her sarcastic "Of course, if *he* can't do it, I'll come along." He had decided to show her that he wouldn't be talked to that way, and had fired a shot over her head in the orchard to intimidate her.

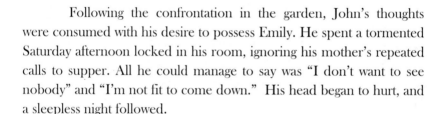

Following the confrontation in the garden, John's thoughts were consumed with his desire to possess Emily. He spent a tormented Saturday afternoon locked in his room, ignoring his mother's repeated calls to supper. All he could manage to say was "I don't want to see nobody" and "I'm not fit to come down." His head began to hurt, and a sleepless night followed.

Sunday was much the same, despite repeated efforts by both his father and mother to get him to come downstairs in the morning to eat, and later to go to town. He told them that he didn't want anything to eat and that he was sick, so they eventually stopped coming up to bother him. Emily was sent up for him at about 5 o'clock when supper was ready, and he laid still and quiet, ignoring her efforts. He heard her go down and tell his mother that she didn't think he was even in his room, and he had probably gone out and locked the door behind him so they would think he was still there.

Nicholas McDonald had been visiting with his parents all day, and John had listened to their conversation to see if anything was said about him. When McDonald returned from a late afternoon walk up the road along the river, he heard his father ask him if he had seen John anywhere, and the reply was that he hadn't.

Apparently they believed Emily's suggestion that he probably wasn't in his room any longer, and John heard their theories about where he had disappeared. His father guessed that he had gone to Marietta, and his mother supposed that he had gone off in the hills somewhere with a party that had some whiskey and that he had gotten drunk and was staying there until he was sober.

The reality was that John just didn't want to be bothered. Earlier that morning he remembered the mail he had picked up in Marietta on Thursday and had hurriedly stuffed under his bed when his mother came upstairs. He spent Sunday intently reading the information from cover to cover, and by the end of the day he was convinced he was almost beyond hope.

In the pamphlet, the Reverend Dr. Adam Clarke was quoted as saying "The sin of self-pollution is one of the most destructive evils ever practiced .... It excites the powers of nature to undue action, and produces violent secretions which necessarily and speedily exhaust the vital principle and energy, hence the muscles become flaccid and feeble, the tone and natural action of the nerves relaxed and impeded, the understanding confused, the judgment perverted, the will indeterminate and wholly without energy to resist ... and thus the victim drags out a miserable existence ... with a mind often debilitated even to a state of idiotism, his worthless body tumbles into the grave ..."[8]

As if that wasn't enough to cause him to despair, John learned that his "secret vice" robbed his brain of vital blood, caused his headaches, and made him act crazy. However, there was hope. He read and re-read the section on how the love of a pure and noble woman could cure him. He was convinced that if he asked Emily to marry him, and she accepted, he would be able to turn his life around. If she turned him down again, his life would be ruined forever. To him it was as simple as that. Yes or No. It was up to Emily.

Chapter 8

Accomac
1800-1824
The Rise and Fall of Marietta

"The love of property and consciousness of right and wrong have conflicting places in our organization, which often makes a man's course seem crooked, his conduct a riddle."
                                        ... Abraham Lincoln

James Anderson IV inherited substantial land holdings in both York and Lancaster counties following his father's death in 1799. By providing ferry service, overnight accommodations, and meals on both sides of the river, he was able to cater to a wide range of customers. Selling alcohol to the rafters, canal men, and other transient workers along the river also greatly enhanced his profitability.

River trade was steadily increasing with more lumber coming downstream every spring from the growing number of logging operations in northern Pennsylvania. The area was also rapidly expanding as a center for other industries as well. Saw mills processing raw logs into lumber, lime kilns producing plaster and whitewash, ore banks, and iron furnaces sprang up all along the river. Because of the booming economic growth, Anderson, along with others, realized that the vast empty farm land they owned was worth exponentially more to them if it were developed.

Additional development meant more traffic using Anderson's Ferry, and the poor condition of the road leading from the landing to York was a source of constant problems. Laid out fifty years prior, the rutted and rough path was in no condition to handle the growing numbers of wagons attempting to negotiate the steep climb at the river and the narrow winding track it followed after reaching the top.

Anderson and his neighbors in York County composed a petition and filed it in court on June 2, 1800. They complained that "the Publick in General labour under great Inconvenience for want of a good road from the road leading from the Borough of York to Wright's Ferry to Anderson's Ferry on the Susquehanna. That the road from Kleins Tavern commonly called the 'Two Taverns' to said ferry, is at Present used on very bad Ground and entirely too narrow and also extremely crooked, nor is it possible for the Supervisors of the township to open, alter or repair it, without the consent of the Persons through whose lands it passes, ... in consequence of which it is liable to be stopped up, or altered, at the Disposition or will of the Persons through whose land it passes."[1]

The petition requested that a commission be appointed to view the old road and to lay out a new course which would "not only shorten the distance between York and Anderson's Ferry very considerably as the same is at present travelled, but would be on much better ground than the present road."[2] All six members of the commission agreed and authorized a survey for a straighter route beginning where Canoe Run crossed the Monocacy Road, just west of present-day Hellam. It closely followed the line of the former road until it neared to within a mile of the river. The old route veered left across open fields and into the woods at the top of the hill high above the former ferry house, whereas the new road followed a shorter, more level path along the creek which led to the river near the stone inn.[*]

Jacob Strickler, during the time he leased the ferry operation from James Anderson, took advantage of the new road and the increased accessibility it provided. He began making improvements to the property, including tearing down the old wooden ferry house, building barns, and constructing a shad fishery and saw mill along the creek. The rocky slopes along the river below the inn were cleared as much as possible for orchards, and crops were planted on the hill behind the house.

---

[*] *With the exception of slight changes made at the beginning and end, the course of the 1800 road follows the current route of Accomac Road through Hellam Township.*

Fishing for shad was big business all along the river, and the fishery at Anderson's Ferry was one of the many on the lower Susquehanna. The short season lasted between April and June, and was signaled by the arrival of the Shad Fly (May Fly) and the blooming of the Shad Bush (Serviceberry). When the shad were running upriver from the ocean to spawn in the fresh water of the Susquehanna and its tributaries, there seemed to be an unlimited amount of fish available to both commercial fisheries and local fishermen. "They came in such immense numbers and so compact as to cause a wave or rising of the water in the middle of the river, extending from shore to shore."[3]

Several shad fishing techniques were used by commercial fisheries. The primary method used a long tightly-woven seine used to encircle schools of shad. When the fish were spotted, one end of the net was anchored on the shore or a floating barge, and the other end played out by a boat rowing quickly across the river. The boat would return to its starting point, making a large loop in the net. Using manpower or windlasses, the catch was hauled in to the shore.

The second method was gill fishing, where nets made of fine twine and larger holes were used to ensnare the gills of the shad swimming upriver. Fishing was done at night so as not to scatter the easily-spooked shad. One end of a 250-foot gill net was attached to a floating platform with a red lantern and a boat containing a net box was quickly rowed diagonally upriver against the current. The top of the net was lined with cork floats and the bottom was affixed with lead anchors to keep it hanging vertically towards the bottom of the river.

As the boat moved across the river, the gill net was played out hand-over-hand by the netman standing in the stern. When they reached the end, the net was attached to another platform with a lantern. The timing of the rowing and laying out of the net was critical for correct positioning. Once deployed, the oarsman would carefully row back along the length of the net and the gillman would run his hand along the top line of the net. When he felt the weight of a fish caught by the gills, the net would be lifted out and the shad flipped into the boat. The boat would then turn back for another run along the net.

Gill net fishing required strong rowing skills to allow the net to be deployed correctly and to guide the boat back along the net. The boatmen employed by Strickler were accustomed to navigating the river in all types of weather and water conditions, and were especially suited for this type of fishing. Anderson's Ferry was one of only two commercial gill-net fisheries on the Susquehanna.[4]

In the mornings, wagons lined up at the ferry landing waiting for the daily catch to come in. After the fish were unloaded and a supply taken to the house for use in the inn, the remainder would be sold wholesale, singly, or by the pair. Shad purchased in bulk were preserved by salting, smoking or drying and used throughout the year. After the fish were sold, the nets were hung to dry on long drying racks along the shore in order to keep them from rotting. Fishing continued as long as the river conditions permitted and the fish were running.

"The River Fisheries of the Atlantic States
Shad fishing at night on the Susquehanna River:
laying out the gill net"[5]

———~~~———

Over time, James Anderson IV began to focus his attention on ways to exploit the potential profit from the development of his empty land in Lancaster County. He devised a plan to subdivide a portion of his riverfront property on the east side of the river into lots and offer them by lottery, reserving the ferry hotel and the adjoining twenty acres for himself. In late November of 1804, Anderson advertised for his new real estate endeavor in the *Lancaster Journal.*

"Town of Waterford – The subscriber has appropriated a tract of land on the north side of the Susquehanna River, at Anderson's Ferry, for a new town, to be called Waterford, and wishes to dispose of the lots on the same by way of lottery. Waterford will be excellently situated on account of health; will afford an elegant prospect and good limestone water in abundance. It is laid out at right angles. Each of the upper lots are 206 feet in depth and 50 feet in width, fronting on a main street, and having a 16-feet alley in the rear. The water lots are 123 feet in depth and 40 feet in width, separated from each other by a 10-feet alley. All the lots will be clear of ground rent. The bank of the river is to be kept open for the use of the holders of town lots and for no other purpose whatever. No privilege will, however, be given that can affect the interests of the present ferry. A plan of the town may be seen at the home of Mr. Hugh Wilson, at Lancaster, and at Anderson's Ferry. The drawing of the lottery, it is expected, will commence in the month of February, or early in the month of March next. Tickets at $60 each may be had of Hugh Wilson and William Ferree, in Lancaster; of John Pedan, Chickies; of John Greer, Yorktown; and the subscriber at the Ferry. (Signed) James Anderson. November 16."[6]

Almost exactly one year earlier, David Cook adopted an identical plan for a portion of his 159-acre farm which adjoined Anderson's property to the east. He had announced that he owned a "tract of land adjoining Mr. Anderson's plantation at Andersons Ferry, and that he had laid out a town to be named New Haven, containing one hundred and one lots, which he intended to dispose of by lottery."[7] The lottery system seemed to have worked for both Anderson and Cook, and additional acreage of adjoining farmland was parceled off into lots by others over the next several years.

The lots sold quickly, fueled by the expanding lumber trade and the projected development of a turnpike to connect Anderson's Ferry with the city of Lancaster. Land speculators flocked to the area and the lots quickly escalated in price and were sold and resold many times. Of all the river towns founded along the Susquehanna in the early nineteenth century, none grew as fast as Waterford and New Haven. In a description of Marietta sixty years later, it was speculated "had the town increased in population, buildings, and appreciation of real estate from that time to the present [1875] in the same ratio, it would have successfully vied with Chicago and New York."[8]

Northern and central sections of Pennsylvania were being heavily timbered, and the cut logs accumulated over the fall and winter were floated down the Susquehanna in the spring. The wood was formed into rafts and brought downriver to be torn apart and milled, or purchased and consolidated by middlemen into larger quantities to continue on to the Chesapeake Bay. The seasonal teams of laborers and river pilots needed places to rest, eat, and drink, before going back up the river to pick up another load of lumber, and the area served as one of the major inland ports for the growing industry.

As the two adjacent towns continued to expand over the following eight years, so did the number of additional lots that were laid out on adjoining farms, including Cook's, Myers', Sharer's, Grosh's and Long's additions. Due to the increasing prosperity and the need for consolidated local government, Anderson and Cook procured a state charter for the consolidation of New Haven and Waterford. The two towns, and the multitude of subsequent additions, were incorporated as a borough in 1812 and renamed Marietta.

Local lore attributes the name "Marietta" as a concatenation of "Mary" and "Henrietta," the first names of the wives of its founders. Although both of James Anderson's wives were named Mary, David Cook's spouse was not named Henrietta. He was married to Mary McFarquhar, the daughter of Reverend Colin McFarquhar, who was the fourth permanent minister at Donegal Church after the Reverend James Anderson. Both David and Mary Cook are buried near Reverend Anderson in the burial ground at the church. Another theory attributes the name to two of James Anderson's daughters. Although he had a daughter Mary, he did not have a daughter named Henrietta.

The name may simply be a tribute to Mary Anderson and Mary Cook, as a familiar or pet form of the name Mary. Ironically, various word origins of the name "Marietta" cite definitions of "sea of bitterness," "sea of sorrow," and "star of the sea." As both Anderson and Cook were looking to develop Marietta as an important inland port of commerce on the Susquehanna, they may have viewed the town as a "star of the sea," but in reality the area had more than its fair share of sorrow and bitterness.

In the first year or so as a borough, all indications were that Marietta would continue to grow and prosper. As lots were sold, developed, and resold, the demand for new construction attracted a large number of laborers connected with the building trade, including carpenters, masons, painters, and plasterers as well as shopkeepers and merchants. Compared to the brick and stone buildings in other parts of Lancaster County, the majority of buildings constructed in Marietta during this period were built of wood, which was plentiful due to the amount of lumber being brought down the river and milled.

However, the lure of the new town also encouraged less reputable elements such as transient rafters and lumberman, land speculators, and gamblers. Whiskey was plentiful and brought in from the distilleries operating on almost every neighboring farm. "The place grew too fast; a large class of disreputable persons followed the stream of speculators who overflowed the place, and like birds of prey, lived off the earnings of others."[9] Along Front Street, many of the buildings were used as taverns, brothels and boarding houses for the migratory river population.

The following year in 1813, another subdivision was laid out immediately to the west of Marietta and became known as Irishtown. The 161-acre farm previously owned by Colonel Alexander Lowry, with whom General Gates had stayed on his way to visit Congress in York in 1778, was purchased by a group of investors consisting of John Pedan, James Mehaffey, and James Duffy, Sr. Even though it was generally regarded as a part of Marietta, the inhabitants of Irishtown resisted the inclusion of their town into the borough, and it was not officially incorporated until 1969.

Risking not only his personal wealth, but also the legacy left by the three generations of Andersons before him, James Anderson IV committed much of his own money into the development of Marietta and the surrounding area, investing in the hope that the town would become the economic hub of Lancaster County. In an attempt to divert more traffic from Wright's Ferry, Anderson spent several thousand dollars of his own money to construct a road up and over the rocky Chiques ridge, which lay between Marietta and Columbia. This created an easy way for travelers and wagons using the crossing at Anderson's Ferry to access the main road to Lancaster and Philadelphia. Although a new straighter road eventually replaced the one Anderson constructed, the Old Chickies Hill Road still follows a winding course up and over the ridge.

In addition, a charter for a bridge across the Susquehanna at Marietta was approved, which would have been the first in the area over the lower Susquehanna. With a permanent crossing linking his properties on both sides of the river, Anderson's prosperity, as well as Marietta's, would have been guaranteed. Confident that Marietta would be chosen as the site for the bridge, Anderson named the street forming the western edge of his original farm Bridge Street.

When the decision was made to construct the bridge at Columbia instead, the potential of Anderson's extensive investments in Marietta suffered a blow. Construction of the span began in 1812 and was completed two years later at a cost of $231,771, financed by the newly formed Columbia Bank and Bridge Company. Constructed of wood and stone, it was one of the longest covered bridges in the world. Standing on fifty-four piers, with a wooden roof, whitewashed interior, two carriageways and open wooden sides, it measured a little over a mile long at 5,690 feet.

The completion of the bridge negatively affected Wright's Ferry more than it did the crossing at Andersons, as the bridge was built directly beside where Wright's crossed the river. Tolls charged to use the bridge were slightly higher than those for using the ferry, but the increased convenience and virtual elimination of long waiting lines insured a steady stream of two-way traffic. Bridge tolls were $1.50 for a wagon with six horses, and six cents for pedestrians.

Had the bridge been constructed at Marietta instead, the reduction in ferry traffic would have impacted James Anderson, but he knew that any loss of ferry income would have been more than offset by the development of new commercial opportunities. With his extensive land holdings on both sides of the river, Anderson was in the best position to capitalize on the opportunities the new bridge may have presented, but soon realized his chances were now gone.

Anderson's plans to profit on the rapid expansion of Marietta were dealt a second blow in 1812. Fueling his speculation and greed even further was the prospect that nearby Columbia would be named as the permanent location of the Pennsylvania state capital, which Anderson anticipated would increase land values in Marietta as well. When Harrisburg was chosen instead of Columbia in October of 1812, many viewed the real estate boom with growing wariness, and Anderson began to realize that his substantial financial investments were not going to pay off as he had hoped.

The pace of development was much too rapid to sustain, and Anderson sensed the beginning of the end. On October 4, 1813, he sold the ferry rights, the hotel, the worthless bridge charter, and the twenty acres of land that he had withheld from the original lottery for $110,000 to Henry Share. This somewhat shady transaction, hastily made in an attempt to recover some of his recent financial loses, was to cause problems for both Share and Anderson's wife Mary, long after James Anderson's death.

By the articles of agreement, James Anderson agreed "that on or before the 15th of the same month of October, 1813, he would by good and sufficient deeds or instruments of writing, duly made and executed according to law, sufficiently convey and confirm the premises to Henry Share in fee" and that "he should have full possession on the 1st of March, then next ensuing, and have the privilege of going on the land in the borough of Marietta, at any time, to lay off and draft the same for building lots, so far as the lease with Snyder would admit."[10]

The property in the agreement included "all the lands that he the said James Anderson now holds in Hellam Township aforesaid, together with the fishery and ferry belonging thereunto, and all and singular the appurtenance whatsoever belonging or otherwise appertaining, and all the lands he now holds in the Borough of Marietta aforesaid not laid off into building lots together with the ferry belonging thereunto."[11]

In York County, the land included his great-grandfather Reverend Anderson's original thirty-five acres and the former two-hundred-acre Partner's Adventure of Philip Syng, which had been in the Anderson family since 1739 and 1759 respectively. These tracts were owned by his grandfather James Sr. and his father James Jr. before being passed to James IV. The valuable property contained the stone inn, the fishery and the ferry.

In Marietta, Lancaster County, the property consisted of the twenty acres and ferry hotel that Anderson had reserved when he laid off the original town of Waterford in 1804. On this plot, approximately 105 lots could be laid off and sold, and Share made it clear to Anderson that his intention was to do this as rapidly as possible in order to turn a quick profit. Anderson, who at this point was not willing to take the financial risk on developing additional lots in Marietta, realized that Share was anxious to purchase the property and offered it to him at an inflated price.

In his eagerness to recoup the extensive real estate losses he had sustained over the previous ten years, Anderson was less than honest with Share concerning the property. Share, in his zealous desire to turn a quick profit, was too careless in his pursuit of the opportunity and overlooked the many warning signs associated with the sale. In early October, Share and William Child, the cashier at Henry Cassel's bank, visited Anderson in his home in Marietta to discuss the deal. Anderson was ill at the time and confined to his bed, and called his friend Doctor Watson to serve as his witness to the negotiations.

In the hurried meeting, the agreements were read over several times and all the parties seemed satisfied with the terms. After they were reviewed, Doctor Watson leaned over to Anderson, who was resting in bed, and in a low whisper asked him if he knew what he had just done. Anderson replied that he thought he did, and Watson told him that if he understood correctly, he had just promised to make a clear title in a very short time. He asked Anderson if he had gotten releases from his step-mother and brothers and sisters, since they also had claim on the property that he had just agreed to sell to Share.

When Anderson IV inherited his father's estate in 1799, the Orphans Court had ordered that all the land holdings were to become his property, being the eldest son, provided that he paid the other heirs their share of the value of the property. At the time, Anderson had given notes for the required amounts, but had not yet paid them or secured the releases for their shares. As such, Anderson did not have a clear title to the land that he was in the process of selling to Share, and legally and ethically should not have entered into the agreement.

After Doctor Watson asked him if the liens were still outstanding, Anderson replied that he had not yet gotten the releases, but would send off immediately and get them. Not satisfied, Watson told him that he knew his step-mother Margaret as well as Anderson did, and didn't think she would willingly sign a release. Anderson assured him that he could convince her to release her claim.

Still concerned that there was some misrepresentation of the agreement, Watson asked Anderson if he ever told Share he didn't have the releases, and Anderson indicated he had not. Amazed this fact had been withheld, Watson told him he needed to be forthcoming while Share was still present, because if he was not, the deal could be ruined. Anderson was too embarrassed to tell Share himself, and using the excuse that he was too sick and exhausted, he asked Watson to tell Share for him.

Stepping out of Anderson's bedroom, Doctor Watson spoke to Share and explained that there was a step-mother and some brothers and sisters involved who also had a claim to the property and had not yet signed releases, but that Anderson would send off for them right away. Surprised that this was the case, Share expressed some hesitancy in continuing forward with the transaction. From the other room, Anderson spoke up and called "Yes, I will send Abel off tomorrow or the next day and get them, and at any rate, you shall be at no loss or no loser for want of them."[12]

Share seemed satisfied, but told Anderson that it was important to him to have clear title to the property because of his intention to immediately lay off lots and sell them. "You know for what I bought this property, that it was to sell again, and make as much out of it as I can, the times are good now, and the sooner I sell perhaps the better for me."[13]

Satisfied with the promises made by Anderson, Share signed the agreement and made arrangements for the deeds to be drawn up. Shortly afterwards, accompanied by Henry Libhart, Share again met Anderson at his house to execute the deeds. Finding out that the releases had still not been obtained, he once more expressed his dissatisfaction with moving forward. After the deeds were read, Anderson again told him there was no need to be uneasy, that he would get the releases, and that Share would suffer no loss. Satisfied once more with Anderson's assurances, the deeds were signed and the transaction was executed.

This would have been Share's last chance to abort the contract, but he let the opportunity pass. Years later, the Supreme Court of Pennsylvania would observe "If Mr. Share meant to make any objections to the title, on account of these incumbrances, this was the time for making it. He was not obliged to take the deeds until the incumbrances were removed. But with a full knowledge of all the circumstances in the case, and all the difficulties which might attend it, he expressed himself satisfied, and accepted the deeds."[14] Clearly, his rush to turn a quick profit clouded his better judgment, and this greed would cause problems for Share for many years.

Following the sale, Anderson made a half-hearted attempt to obtain releases from his relatives who had claims to the property. His servant Abel was sent to Cumberland County to find Anderson's siblings, step-brothers, and step-mother Margaret, but only received promises instead of signatures. Since Anderson had not yet made good on the promissory notes he had given each of them for their shares, it was not surprising he was unable to get anyone to release their claims to the property. Anderson neglected to provide any of this information to Henry Share, who blindly proceeded with his plans to lay off his new building lots.

The first hurdle for Share was the exorbitant $110,000 that he now owed Anderson. Since most real estate transactions of that era rarely involved exchange of actual cash, Share planned on giving Anderson notes for the property, which he would then satisfy as he sold the lots in Marietta and parceled off the acreage across the river. In order to pay Anderson, and perhaps to spread the financial risk of his investment, he formed a partnership with five other local landowners and real estate speculators.

On October 8, 1813, just four days after he signed the contract with Anderson, Share executed another agreement with James Mehaffey, John Pedan, Mathias Rank (Runk), James Duffy, Sr. and John Hane (Hoan). Mehaffey, Duffy, and Pedan were the same group of investors who had recently purchased and developed Irishtown, and were some of the wealthiest landowners in the area, at least on paper.

The agreement bound the six partners and their heirs to "pay or cause to be paid share and share alike of the aforesaid purchase money unto the said James Anderson in such manner and at such times as the said Henry Share contracted for the payment of the same."[15] Clearly looking for everyone to make a quick profit, the purpose of the partnership was for "better managing and carrying into effect whatever they may deem most advantageous to the disposal or improvement of the above mentioned property purchased from the said James Anderson."[16]

Understanding that subdividing and selling lots would incur additional expense, and that there was significant risk in the speculative purchase, the new partners also agreed "that they will pay share and share alike of all expences that may accrue or arise in any way in the management, disposal or improvement of the above mentioned property, and that they will pay share and share alike of all the loses that may accrue in any wise from the same and they will divide share and share alike of all profits if any arising from the said above mentioned property by disposing of the same in any other way."[17]

Each partner was liable for one-sixth of the purchase price of $110,000, amounting to approximately $18,333 per person. On December 28, Share received $18,875 (principal and interest from the date of the agreement) from James Mehaffey, Mathias Rank, and John Hane. Along with additional notes, a total of $60,000 was paid to Anderson, and a bond was taken out on the balance of $50,000. This bond was to be paid on March 15, 1815 with interest from March 1, 1814, the date that Share was to receive full possession of the property.

Share pressed forward with the laying out of lots, and offered them for sale at auction on December 11, 1813. However, many of the purchasers refused to pay after finding out there were still outstanding claims to the property. Showing better judgment than Share did when he purchased the land from Anderson, the buyers insisted on receiving clear title to the lots before signing any purchase agreements.

In order to recoup his mounting losses, Share proceeded to file suit in Lancaster County Common Pleas Court against several of the purchasers to enforce the payments due on the lots. The fact that the liens of Anderson's step-mother and brother and sisters had not been released prevailed, and Share was "uniformly defeated in those suits."[18] Since Share received no payments for any of the lots he sold, he was not able to satisfy the remaining $50,000 bond to Anderson on March 15, 1815, as he had agreed to.

After purchasing the property from Anderson, Share and his partners leased the ferry operation to various others who lived in the stone inn in York County and operated the ferry for them. Christian Grove was the operating tenant from 1813 until about 1819, followed by Christian Keesey, an innkeeper from Marietta. Becoming known as Keesey's Ferry shortly thereafter, it continued operating under that name for the next two decades until Keesey's death in 1842.

The same group of investors that joined Share in his venture pressed aggressively forward with the rapid development of the Marietta area, oblivious to the impending depression of real estate values. In 1814, a year after the purchase of Anderson's property, James Mehaffey, Mathias Rank, Henry Share and others were appointed commissioners to incorporate a company which hoped to erect a competing bridge over the Susquehanna near Marietta, using the charter they had obtained in the agreement with Anderson. Share and Mehaffey were also involved with several of the turnpike companies developing roads in and around the area, and Share constructed several mills of his own near Marietta.

Most significantly, Share, Pedan, Mehaffey and Rank were appointed commissioners of the newly formed Marietta and Susquehanna Trading Company, which took over the private banking business Henry Cassel founded in 1812. Up until this point, banking houses were privately owned and unregulated. On March 21, 1814, "An Act Regulating Banks" was passed by the Commonwealth of Pennsylvania and Lancaster County was allowed to have five banks "one to be called the Marietta and Susquehanna Trading Company."[19]

Following the organization of the new bank, stock was issued, notes printed and investments made in real estate to back the notes. Taking over some of the outstanding notes for the money owed James Anderson for the purchase of the ferry and land in York and Lancaster Counties, the Marietta and Susquehanna Trading Company was now a full partner in the wild land speculation fever gripping the area.

When the real estate crash in Marietta happened, it came quickly, and "in 1816 a wild speculation in real estate broke out. An exchange was opened in Noble's Hotel in Market Square. The people from the town and country were assembled there and bought and sold property at fabulous prices. Farms were knocked off at more than $300 an acre, and town lots in the suburbs at $2,000. The same farms were sold subsequently at $60 to $75 an acre, and the lots at $10. It carried many of the dealers into bankruptcy and ruin."[20]

James Anderson IV's failure in Marietta was a personal embarrassment, and following the sale of his twenty acres along the river and the accompanying ferry right, he moved to York a financially ruined man. Falling sick, he penned his will on May 18 and died shortly thereafter on June 7, 1815. Mary inherited all of her husband's personal effects, their brick house along with three-and-a-half lots of ground, and his "negro girl during the time she has to serve."[21]

Following Anderson's death, his widow Mary moved on with settling her husband's affairs. Their financial assets were complicated and included many unpaid notes for properties that had been hastily sold before they moved from Lancaster County in 1813. Among them was the outstanding bond for $50,000 from Henry Share which had come due on May 1, 1815, only a month before Anderson passed away. Total outstanding principal and interest due to Mary from Share and others totaled in excess of $100,000.[22]

Since Share and his partners had not yet been able to sell the lots in Marietta because releases had not been provided for the outstanding liens of the other Anderson heirs, there was no money available for him to pay off his bond. Share turned to his partners and the Susquehanna and Marietta Trading Company in an effort to raise the capital to pay Mary the outstanding promissory note.

As real estate values had already begun their decline in Marietta, Share's partners provided no help in paying the note, despite their agreement to "share and share alike" in the profits and losses of their joint venture. Share initiated a series of law suits against his partners for non-payment, and only nominal amounts were collected.

The Common Pleas Dockets of York County during the period 1816-1825 show judgments in favor of Henry Share against John Hane (Hoan), John Pedan, Mathias Rank, and the Marietta and Susquehanna Trading Company. These judgments were not able to be satisfied and went through several revivals in an attempt to settle the outstanding debts owed by the partners. At each revival of the judgments, other properties and lots belonging to the defendants were sold, resulting in only token payments to Share.

Henry Share eventually gave Mary Anderson an additional $1,300 towards the outstanding $50,000 bond, but refused to pay the balance. She finally initiated a civil suit in the Court of Common Pleas of Lancaster County in 1821 against Share to recover the remainder of the note. Share alone was personally liable for the entire bond, as he had been the one to sign the original agreement with Anderson. Even though he had signed a subsequent agreement to divide the liability amongst his five partners, they were not named in the suit by Anderson's executrix.

In his defense, Share pleaded payment, contending he had already paid an adequate amount and should not be held liable for the balance. His primary argument centered around the fact that he was not able to resell town lots in Marietta immediately after he purchased the property, an intention he had made Anderson well aware of before agreeing on the sale price and signing the agreement.

At the time of the purchase, land values were high and still rising, but Share had been confident he could still turn a profit despite paying more than the property was actually worth. Since his ability to sell any lots had been delayed or prevented due to the outstanding encumbrances, land values had time to drop significantly and the property was eventually worth much less than he had paid. Share asserted that the amount he had already given Anderson more than covered the current fair market value and felt justified in refusing the payment of the remainder.

Claiming he had been defrauded by Anderson, Share supported his defense with a long list of mitigating circumstances, including the fact that the property title was faulty at the time of the sale. When Share had brought it to Anderson's attention, he had been promised that the releases would be obtained immediately. Based on these promises, the agreement had been signed.

In addition, Share said he told Anderson that he was going to lay out town plots and that "a complete title was expected and indispensible, and that such a one was promised, and indemnity against loss for want of it stipulated."[23] On the faith of Anderson's promises, many lots were surveyed and sold at auction for a large profit, but the sales were never finalized, nor payments made, due to Share's inability to produce a clear title. The "purchase, which otherwise would have been profitable, was rendered ruinously injurious."[24]

Compared to Share's complex defense, Mary Anderson's case against him was straightforward. Three basic facts were presented to show that Share had no legitimate reason for not satisfying the outstanding note per the sales agreement he had signed. First, she established a clear chain of title to the property. Her deceased husband's father, James Anderson, Jr., had purchased it from his father James Anderson, Sr., who had inherited it from his father Reverend

James Anderson, who had obtained a patent for it directly from the Penn family.

Next, she presented evidence that her father-in-law James Anderson, Jr. had died intestate, with the Orphan's Court ordering his real estate holdings to be appraised and passed to her husband James Anderson IV, for whom she was acting as executrix. The stipulations in the order requiring Anderson IV to pay, or secure notes to pay, equal and proportionate shares to the other heir's of his father were also entered into evidence.

Finally, and perhaps to Share's surprise, she offered the signed releases of all the other heirs and proof the notes for their shares of the property had been satisfied. These releases, which her late husband had promised to produce when he originally sold the land to Share in 1813, removed all the outstanding liens on the property and undermined the basis of Share's entire defense. Even though they were obtained after Anderson's death in 1815, and well after Share was to have received them, they were obtained before she brought suit.

In the trial, the jury found in favor of the plaintiff Mary Anderson, and ordered a judgment against Henry Share for the balance of the original note. Share appealed the verdict to the Supreme Court of Pennsylvania, submitting seven exceptions, or errors of the Court. Chief Justice John Bannister Gibson delivered the opinion of the Court, upholding the verdict in favor of Mary Anderson.

Following the Supreme Court's decision, Share renewed his legal efforts against his former partners so he could recover some of his losses and attempt to satisfy the judgment against him. These efforts resulted in verdicts in his favor, but since his partners were suffering from the same financial difficulties due to the economic crash in Marietta, Share had difficulty actually collecting any money.

After the Court of Common Pleas in York County revived the judgments several times as required by law, a Writ of *Venditioni*

Exponas[†] was finally issued for the York County properties to force the satisfaction of the judgments against Hoan, Pedan, Mehaffey and the Marietta and Susquehanna Trading Company. The sheriff was bound to sell the property to the highest bidder and could not return to the Court again with it remaining unsold.

Beginning in October of 1824, the sheriff of York County began auctioning the shares of the eighty-seven-acre property, including the "large two story stone Tavern House, Stables and sheds thereon erected and to which is attached a Shad Fishery and the Ferry Right of the River Susquehanna at Marietta."[25]

The first shares of the property to be sold belonged to the Marietta and Susquehanna Trading Company. On October 23, 1824, they were "sold and struck off to the said Jacob Glatz for the sum of Six Hundred Dollars, he being the highest and best bidder for the same."[26] Presumably this included the shares of James Duffy, Sr., James Mehaffey and Henry Share, three of the original partners who had turned over their interest in the property to the Marietta and Susquehanna Trading Company.

The following November, the sheriff seized the "one equal individual sixth part"[27] of Mathias Rank and auctioned it for $200, and one year later, in November, 1826, the share owned by John Hoan was sold for $50. The final share of the property belonging to John Pedan was auctioned in August, 1827, for another $50. In all four sales, the high bidder was Dr. Jacob Glatz from Marietta.

For a total of $900 dollars paid at the series of auctions over a period of four years, Jacob Glatz now owned the eighty-seven acres along the river in York County, including the ferry right, fishery, stone inn, outbuildings, and other improvements made by James Anderson and tenants Jacob Strickler, Christian Grove and Christian Keesey.

[†] *A Writ of Venditioni Exponas is the last legal step in the process taken by the Court to sell lands seized by the sheriff to settle outstanding debts, and is issued only after several unsuccessful attempts to sell the property have already been made.*

In its first twenty years of existence, Marietta endured a dramatic land boom and collapse. It was estimated that by 1822, "every man in Marietta except four was insolvent" and "houses were sold for the value of their mortar, and farms brought less than their fences had cost."[28] Foreclosures were commonplace, and the sheriff was kept busy disposing of property taken over by creditors. In addition to wild real estate speculation, the volatile banking landscape also had a profound effect on the economy of Marietta.

Immediately following the War of 1812, enormous national debt had driven inflation high and created shortages of circulating bank notes. In order to increase the supply, Pennsylvania enacted the Bank Act of 1814, creating thirty-seven new banks between 1814 and 1817. The Marietta and Susquehanna Trading Company was formed during this turbulent time, and immediately began issuing notes of their own.

Private notes were backed by specie (gold or silver), and banks like the Marietta and Susquehanna Trading Company rarely kept a sufficient amount on hand to redeem all their outstanding notes. Bank notes were used in business transactions like modern-day checks, but could be passed from person-to-person before being redeemed. The guarantee of a bank note's value was the value of the issuing bank's assets, and under normal circumstances, notes could be exchanged for specie at the issuing bank at a zero discount – one dollar of notes for one dollar of specie.

It was common for merchants to accept private notes of a nearby bank, but when they were redeemed far from the issuing bank, there was risk, and therefore hesitancy, in accepting them. Rather than trading at par (face) value, the notes would be accepted at a discount. For example, if Marietta and Susquehanna Trading Company notes were being quoted in Philadelphia at a 5% discount, a merchant exchanging $100 of notes in that city would only receive $95 in specie. The 5% represented the risk in accepting a distant bank's paper, and a discount of about 6% was considered excessive. Notes of less familiar banks represented larger risks and carried higher discounts."[29]

Discount values usually reflected only the transportation costs and interest foregone due to the delay in returning notes to the original issuing banks. But, notes accepted from failing banks meant additional risk due to longer delays in redemption. Excessive discounts ultimately reflected the increased probability of a bank to actually fail.

Pennsylvania experienced a widespread bank panic in 1818-1819, which was generally attributed to "excessive issues of the banks, during the suspension of specie payments" and "chiefly in the abuses of the banking system, which abuses consist first in the excessive number of banks, and secondly in their universal bad administration."[30]

The issue was complicated due to the huge variety of different notes in circulation and the proliferation of counterfeits. Detailed vignettes showing decorative designs helped to curb counterfeits, and the notes of the Marietta and Susquehanna Trading Company featured riverfront scenes of the ferry landing with flatboats in the foreground and warehouses and farmland in the background.

Bank note vignettes from Henry Cassel's Bank and
Marietta and Susquehanna Trading Company
Collection of Author

This general panic, combined with the sudden crash in real estate values in Marietta during the same period, spelled the beginning of the end for the Marietta and Susquehanna Trading Company. Nowhere is this more evident than in an analysis of the discount rates of their notes during the period. Philadelphia regularly published the rates of country banks, and the values fluctuated weekly in proportion to the confidence of the respective private institutions. As published on June 5, 1818, the discount rate for Marietta and Susquehanna Trading Company notes was 5%. Less than a year later on March 30, 1819, the rate was 30%. On June 1 it rose to 35% and on September 10 it reached 50%. By the end of October 1819, the discount rate on their notes was 60%.[31] Clearly the bank was in trouble.

When banks issued notes, they were required to provide a security deposit with the state banking authority. However, this deposit could be held in real estate or mortgages which were prone to inflated appraisals. Compounding the problem was rapidly depreciating real estate values, which did not return the expected value when sold to gain the funds needed to pay outstanding notes.

The Marietta and Susquehanna Trading Company invested extensively in Marietta real estate and a large proportion of their assets were held in mortgages. Many homeowners defaulted on their agreements and did not make the required payment after the agreed upon one-year term. With local property values rapidly declining, only pennies on the dollar were collected when the properties were sold by the sheriff to satisfy the judgments.

Problems for the Marietta and Susquehanna Trading Company escalated when local merchants began to view their bank notes as worthless. Editorials and opinions were widely published in many area papers, and one expressed surprise that another publication's editor could in good conscience "tell the Public that the Notes of a Bank are good, when he would not take one of its ten-dollar Notes for a year's subscription, and when he knows that a Barber, not ten miles from the Bank, would refuse to shave your face for one of its five dollar bills."[32]

Bank Note from the Marietta and Susquehanna Trading Company 1818,
Collection of Author

In nearby Columbia, resolutions were adopted which declared that notes of the Marietta and Susquehanna Trading Company would only be accepted for produce at the Philadelphia discount rate. Similar measures were adopted in Elizabethtown and other nearby towns. An act to revoke the charter of the bank was passed in 1819 by the Senate of Pennsylvania, but the bill never became law and no further official steps were taken.

Investors of the bank finally took matters into their own hands. On May 25, 1821, a group of stockholders met in Lancaster and unanimously approved the following resolution:

"Whereas it is the opinion of the Members of this Meeting, that, whenever a Banking Institution becomes unable to redeem its Paper and keep the Notes issued by it at par, it becomes the duty of the Members of that Institution to close its concerns as soon as possible. That the first duty of such an Institution to the Public, is to pay and redeem those Notes which are now in circulation and pay those debts which have necessarily contracted; and next, to repay the Stockholders the sums which they have paid. And, whereas, the Marietta and Susquehanna Trading-company, for more than 3 years past, has been unable to maintain that Credit which a Banking Institution ought to sustain, and redeem its Paper when offered, keep its Notes at par or pay its honest Creditors, justice to the Public therefore, requires that something effectual should be done."[33]

Basically, the stockholders were demanding the bank close its doors after redeeming all outstanding notes, paying all debts to their creditors, and repaying all monies invested by the stockholders. To do this would require a strict examination of the bank's books, and a committee of seven was appointed to "investigate the concerns of the said Institution, to ascertain the amount of debts due to individuals from said Bank, and also the amount due to said Bank ... and that the said Committee shall have full power to inspect all books, papers, vouchers, and other documents, which belong to the said Bank."[34]

The committee gave notice that they would be visiting the bank on July 5. They were met by the cashier William Childs when they arrived, who informed them he had prepared a complete statement of the finances of the bank, but the Directors had "strictly enjoined him not to expose to the view of the committee the statement which he had made, or suffer them to inspect any of the books, papers, or vouchers of the institution."[35]

Not willing to give up easily, the committee asked when they could meet with the Board of Directors in person, and were told that regular meetings were held the last Thursday of every month. On July 26, they anxiously arrived, expecting a confrontation with the Board, but none of the Directors attended. They demanded the books and financial statements again, and were told once more by William Childs that he had been directed not to provide them the information.

In an attempt to provide stockholders some information about the state of the bank, the committee made informed estimates based on the records they could obtain from other sources. Their report demonstrated their frustration with the bank's lack of aggressive pursuit of money owed to them. "... it does not appear that any measures have been adopted, for the last two years, either to collect the money due to the Bank, to redeem their notes, or pay their debts: nor does it appear that any advantages whatever have resulted to the bank from this delay. Property of all kinds has depreciated within that time, and there have been very few instances indeed, where those who were insolvent in 1819, have since become able to pay their debts: but it is a lamentable truth, than many, very many, who at the time were considered solvent, and whose property would actually then have paid their debts, have since become unable to pay 50 cents on the dollar – Nor is there now any prospect that a further delay will be attended with any advantages to the institution, and why collections have been and still are delayed, it is out of the power of the Committee to say."[36]

Considering the total collapse of real estate values, and the fact a large percentage of the bank's notes were backed by speculative mortgages, it was obvious to the committee that the bank was hopelessly insolvent. The Directors also recognized the severity of the problem, but realized that the liquidation of the bank would most likely bankrupt the entire town. By the end of 1821, the bank charter was declared forfeited, and all that remained was the liquidation of the bank's assets to pay the debt owed their creditors.

On March 19, 1822, five trustees were appointed by the Directors and stockholders to attend to the liquidation of the bank. One of the trustees was the former cashier William Childs, and another was Jacob Grosh. Grosh, a farmer, tavern keeper, legislator, merchant, soldier, real estate speculator, and lay judge, was one of several others who purchased land around Marietta earlier in the decade. Obtaining forty-eight acres at thirteen dollars an acre from Henry Cassel in 1814, he had sub-divided it into building lots and sold them all of them for $500 each. He then repurchased some of them at $600 or more and was heavily indebted to the bank.

Jacob Grosh was an odd choice as a trustee for the liquidation of the bank's assets, as he most likely owed them a great deal of money. Despite the obvious conflict of interest, he and the other trustees spent the better part of the next year sifting through the bank's assets. Either by coincidence or design, the bank never had to deal with the settling of their debts or the collection of money owed to them.

Late on the night of August, 29, 1823, an alleged robbery at the bank insured that records showing to whom they owed (creditors) and those who owed them money (debtors) would be lost forever. A startling announcement appeared in the Lancaster Weekly Journal the following day.[37]

$1000 Reward

A most daring robbery was perpetrated last night on the Marietta and Susquehanna Trading Company, by three villains who seized the Cashier, on the back porch of the banking house and presented three pistols to his breast to enforce silence, dragged him into the bank and compelled him to unlock the vault, from which they took out and carried away all the books and promissory notes and other valuable papers belonging to the bank, and a large quantity of bank paper; one of the villains held the Cashier with a pistol to his breast, until his two comrades had sufficient time to escape with their plunder, and then made his escape. The villains were well disguised and masked, and spoke only in the German Language.

We, the trustees of the Institution, offer the above reward of $1000 for the apprehension and conviction of the villains and the restoration of the books and papers carried off by them, or $500 for the restoration of the books and papers aforesaid.

Notice is hereby given,

That in consequence of the above robbery, and the debtors to the institution are hereby notified to attend at the bank on the 22d day of September next, in order to ascertain the exact amount due by each person. In case of neglect or refusal, measures must and will be adopted by the Trustees to compel their attendance at some other time and place, to ascertain that fact.

> Jacob Gisch,
> Jacob Grosh,
> Jacob Mishy,
> James Patterson, jr.
> William Child.

Marietta, August 30, 1823   10-3nq

Obviously, the trustees of the Marietta and Susquehanna Trading Company were more concerned about determining who owed them money than who their creditors were, since they only called a meeting of the debtors of the bank. However, it is apparent that the stockholders and other interested parties became immediately suspicious of the robbery, as another advertisement in the same issue announced a meeting of the creditors to determine to whom the bank owed money.

"The creditors of the Marietta Bank are requested to meet at the house of Mr. William Cooper, innkeeper, in the city of Lancaster, on Saturday, the 6th inst. At three o'clock P.M. to take such measures as [may] be deemed necessary, relative to the late apparent robbery of the Bank house, in the Borough of Marietta ..."[38]

At the meeting of the creditors, a committee was formed to make an inquiry into the robbery, but they were unable to determine anything from the trustees about the matter. They shifted their efforts to the Pennsylvania House of Representatives and presented an appeal from "... holders of bank notes, certificates of debt, and owners of stock, in the Marietta Bank, praying for an investigation into the conduct of the trustees, and the robbery of the bank ..."[39]

The House of Representatives appointed a committee to investigate, and on March 16, 1824, they made their report, succinctly stating the position of both sides. "... all the books, notes and every scrap of paper which it could be ascertained who were indebted to the Bank, were taken out of the banking house, in Marietta. The trustees allege this was done by robbers who broke into the bank by night. The complainants and agents of the creditors of the bank, allege that no such robbery was ever committed."[40]

The House Committee recommended that the dispute be settled by the court and a jury, but no efforts were made until the following June, 1826, when twelve lawsuits were filed by creditors against the trustees of the bank to recover losses suffered. Since no one was ever tried or even arrested for the robbery, civil action was the only recourse available. Nearly ten years later, a judgment against the bank was reached in each of the cases and it was ordered that real estate owned by the Marietta and Susquehanna Trading Company was to be sold to satisfy the judgments. By that time, the bank had been sold to the Bank of the United States, and there is no record of whether the plaintiffs actually received any damages.

The only tangible asset the robbers, or whoever removed the notes and records, could not steal, was the real estate owned by the bank or the mortgages recorded in the bank's name at the Court House. In lieu of any other financial assets, the only way that anything could be recovered was to have the bank's documented properties sold by the Sheriff. Notices of public sales for buildings and lots "seized and taken in execution as the property of the Marietta and Susquehanna Trading Company"[41] were commonplace in the local papers.

Jacob Grosh is either "the hero or the villain of this story"[42], but many of his contemporaries "certainly believed him to have been responsible and believed further under all the circumstances his conduct was justified."[43] If nothing else, the loss of the bank records saved many people in Marietta from further insolvency by erasing any record of debt they owed the bank. Almost 100 years later, Jacob Grosh was still regarded as somewhat of a Robin Hood figure to the people of Marietta. In one of the addresses delivered at the Marietta Centennial on September 5, 1812, W.U. Hensel remarked about Grosh: "When, to save their townspeople from utter ruin and their town from desolation, worthy burghers conspired to rob to Marietta bank of all its evidences of local indebtedness ..."[44]

The local financial crisis in Marietta mirrored what was occurring across the country. Between the years 1816-1819, the national financial landscape changed drastically. Despite the closure of the First Bank of the United States in 1811, rampant inflation, and record national debt, the nation experienced an economic boom, fueled primarily by an increase in bank note circulation and real estate speculation. The Second Bank of the United States was chartered in 1816 and the New York Stock Exchange was formed the following year in 1817. Excessive lending followed, and once banking institutions recognized the impending crisis, many loans began to be recalled.

Almost immediately, land sales slowed and real estate values fell. "Many banks exercised little caution in the volume of their note issue"[45], and this, coupled with the fraud and poor management of private banks, caused widespread panic across the country. This crash was especially severe in Marietta where growth had been so quick. "So sudden was the collapse that many who could count their prospective wealth by the tens of thousands on Monday morning, before the close of the week were overtaken with comparative poverty, and many of them left the town never to return."[46]

As quickly as Marietta was transformed from James Anderson's fertile farmland into the thriving Borough of Marietta, it collapsed just as rapidly. Marietta did not begin to prosper again until the Eastern Division of the Pennsylvania Canal opened in 1833, which ran along the Susquehanna River from the mouth of the Juniata River to Columbia. This, coupled with building of the Pennsylvania Railroad's rail lines in the 1850s, brought new industry, commerce and prosperity to the area and began another era of expansion.

By 1833, optimism began to return to Marietta. According to a summary of development in the borough, "Prosperity has been, for some time, gradually and steadily rising in value, business flourishes with its usual activity, and every thing wears the appearance of a decent prosperity. In times that are past, a spirit of extravagant speculation prevailed in Marietta, but the evil was one that destroyed itself. With the downfall of private fortunes, also fell the improvements and success of the place. But those days are gone by, and the many projects of a permanent and useful character, denote the healthy tone of feeling, and the spirit of public enterprise which now pervade the community."[47]

Chapter 9

Accomac
1825-1862

"Everything has its limit – iron ore cannot be educated into gold"
                                                    ... Mark Twain

Henry Share and his associates never assumed an active role running the ferry during their ownership. Instead, they leased it from the time it was purchased in 1813 until it was finally sold to Jacob Glatz in a series of sheriff's sales in 1824-1827. First leased to Christian Grove until 1819, it was subsequently taken over by Christian Keesey, an innkeeper from Marietta. Many of the historically significant events that took place at the crossing occurred while it was leased to others, and Keesey's tenancy was no exception.

Keesey had been operating the ferry for about six years, when on a raw day in mid-November of 1825 a strange procession slowly made its way down the muddy road leading to the river's edge. It was led by a team of lathered horses pulling an eight-wheeled wagon carrying a sixty-foot-long, nine-foot-high sheet iron boat weighing in excess of 6,000 pounds. Following the boat was a parade of smaller wagons and carriages containing the curious from York and the surrounding area, bundled in coats and blankets in an attempt to ward off the cold and dreary weather.

The steamboat Codorus was about to make her maiden voyage and a crowd had gathered to watch her slip into the water. Designed by John Elgar, it had been constructed in York at the machine shop of Davis & Gardner on the northwest corner of West King Street and South Newberry Street. The Codorus was the first steamboat in the United States with a hull built completely of iron, and Elgar planned to captain the boat on her initial run up the river in order to prove the usability such a craft on the Susquehanna.

Although many thought upriver navigation of the Susquehanna was impractical due to rapids and low water conditions, Elgar's design drew only about six inches of water completely unloaded, with another inch for every ton of freight or passengers. It had a two-and-a-half-foot-deep hold for cargo and could accommodate seventy people on board. Since there was no cargo scheduled for the maiden voyage, about 100 people were crowded on board when it was launched.

The six-foot-high cylindrical boiler on the Codorus was designed to burn anthracite coal, generating 100 pounds of steam pressure to drive the ten horsepower engine. The unique design surrounded the entire firebox with water, producing the maximum amount of steam possible while at the same time protecting the iron from the excessive heat generated by the coal. Two side-mounted paddle wheels were capable of powering the Codorus "against the current and a strong wind, about five miles per hour."[1]

Elgar was a "self-taught American farm-boy-turned-engineer,"[2] born in York County and raised by his aunt in Maryland. Acting on behalf of a York and Baltimore firm, he designed the innovative Codorus, which was his one and only nautical project. Needing a location to construct the ship, he formed an association with Phineas Davis, co-owner of the Davis & Gardner Foundry, a machine shop located along the banks of the Codorus creek in York City.

In early 1825, the firm of Davis & Gardner began the construction of the Codorus. At a cost of approximately $3,000, the ship was ready for launching by late fall. As reported on November 15, the ship was loaded on a low eight-wheeled wagon and "was drawn through our streets yesterday morning, on her way to the Susquehanna. She is placed on eight wheels, and such was the interest felt on the occasion, that notwithstanding being in weight more than six thousand pounds, the weather being rainy and disagreeable, the citizens attached a long rope to her, and about sixty or seventy taking hold, drew her from the west side of the bridge to the upper end of Main street, amidst the shouts and huzzas of a multitude, such as used to dangle at the heels of Lafayette."[3]

Upon crossing the Codorus Creek, the heavily laden wagon slowly made its way east through the center of town and out the straight and fairly level road which led to the river. Once the confines of the city were behind them, the procession continued through the lush valley farmland of Hellam Township over the next several days, pausing at several of the many inns along the way. Each time it stopped, crowds gathered to admire the boat and discuss its merits with Elgar, who had become something of a local celebrity.

After passing through Hellam and picking up additional followers, the wagon turned left on the road leading directly to the ferry. Recent rains had turned the rough path muddy, and progress was sluggish as the horses plodded over the rolling hills and approached the river. Although it would have been more straightforward to continue directly to Wrightsville, Elgar chose to veer north over the more difficult route and launch the Codorus at Keesey's Ferry.

The Susquehanna north of Keesey's was unobstructed, whereas the low water in late November would have exposed the rocks between Wrightsville and Keesey's. This would have been a significant obstacle for the Codorus had it been launched in Wrightsville, so Keesey's Ferry seemed the more logical choice. Since the road leading from Hellam to the ferry had been rerouted in 1800, the heavy wagon did not have to negotiate the steep hill which dropped sharply to the river at the end of the old road, but the narrow turns as they neared Keesey's made the driver of the wagon slow to a crawl nonetheless.

After reaching the ferry landing, the horses were backed down the dirt ramp and into the water, and once the wagon was submerged, the steamboat floated free of its carriage. Amid the cheers of the gathered crowd, the ship was made afloat and prepared for a series of trials. After the boiler was thoroughly tested, the passengers boarded the ship, and with Captain John Elgar at the helm, the Codorus began the trip up the river to Harrisburg.

The Steamboat Codorus, with Keesey's Ferry in background [4]

The long row of spectators lining the front porch railing of the inn at Keesey's Ferry waved handkerchiefs and hats as the Codorus made its way upriver, and watched until it passed the first curve in the river and out of sight. Among the audience may have been the Keesey's three-year old son Vincent, who was born at the ferry in 1822.

After several successful twelve-mile trips between York Haven and Harrisburg, the Codorus was ready for a longer voyage. Elgar intended to prove that it was practical and commercially profitable to navigate the Susquehanna in a steamboat. Leaving York Haven in the spring of 1826, Elgar steamed up the river passing by Harrisburg and continuing north. At Sunbury he turned onto the east branch of the river, reaching Bloomsburg in early April. All along the trip, he was "cheered at every point by crowds of people who rushed to the shores to see the strange monster that traveled upstream without poles, oars, or sails."[5]

By April 12, the Codorus docked in Wilkes-Barre in northern Pennsylvania amid "the discharge of cannon and hearty cheers of the people, mingling with martial music, and the peals of several bells."[6] With occasional stops in the river towns that he passed, Elgar eventually completed the three month voyage by crossing into New York and reaching Binghamton in late June. Most who witnessed the passage of the Codorus considered the trip a success, but Captain Elgar felt differently about the achievements of his ship.

Even with the low draft of the Codorus, the water of the Susquehanna proved too shallow during certain seasons. The rocky bottom and sand bars created constant challenges for Elgar and the crew, and at one point he was forced to sit idle and wait for the river level to rise before proceeding. Frustrated with the difficulties of the trip, he eventually categorized the venture a failure. For the next year, the Codorus made several other uneventful and unprofitable trips on the river, but Elgar "decided against any further attempts to navigate the river by steam," believing "it to be impractical to do so profitably or with any certain success."[7]

With the experiment of using iron steamboats to profitably navigate the river a failure, the demand for new and improved canals increased. By 1833, the Pennsylvania Canal had opened as far south as Marietta, and the subsequent expansion of railroad lines along the river made year-round commercial transportation practical. The steamship never proved to be a viable solution for navigating the length of the Susquehanna, but eventually found use as ferry transportation.

Over the course of the next several years following the launch of the Codorus, Jacob Glatz finished acquiring the remaining shares of the ferry property. By 1827, he had purchased the last share and obtained sole title to eighty-seven acres along the river, including the two story stone inn and tavern, barn, stables, fishery and ferry right.

Christian Keesey and his wife Amelia continued to live in the inn and operate the ferry and fishery for some time after the ownership transferred to Jacob Glatz. It was prosaically described in an 1827 editorial as "The Ferry house, kept by Col. Keesey, together with the adjoining buildings with their white fronts, contrast beautifully with the appearance of the surrounding hills, presenting that due mixture of art and nature on which the eye of taste so gladly lingers."[8]

The relationship between tenant Christian Keesey and landlord Jacob Glatz was personal as well as business. Jacob's father George died in 1806 at age thirty-two when Jacob was only three years old, and his mother Amelia married Christian Keesey. The Keesey's moved across the river to run the ferry for Henry Share in 1819, and in 1822 their son Vincent was born. Therefore, when Jacob Glatz purchased the ferry, his mother, step-father and half-brother were already living in the stone house in York County and continued to do so until Christian Keesey's death.

Jacob Glatz was born in 1803 into a well-known Lancaster County family. At the time he purchased the ferry, Glatz had recently graduated from the University of Pennsylvania in 1826 with a medical degree. He soon opened a drug store in Marietta off Centre Square, half a block east on the north side of West Market Street. He was appointed Postmaster in Marietta sometime prior to 1833 and held the position until his death in 1845, most likely establishing the Post Office in his drug store. In 1833, Jacob and his step-father Christian Keesey formed a partnership to construct a three-story hotel and boarding house at the upper end of Front Street in Marietta calling it the Canal and Ferry House Hotel.

Jacob and his wife, Susanna Heistand Glatz, had five children while living in Marietta. Their first, Christian Keesey Glatz, was named after Jacob's step-father. Another son, Abraham Heistand, became prominent in his own right. In 1854, A. Heistand graduated from Princeton and was elected to the Pennsylvania House of Representatives (1858-1859), and served two terms in the Pennsylvania Senate (1862-1864 and 1866-1868). In addition to his public duties, he worked a large farm in Hellam Township, York County.

Despite his standing in the community as a doctor, merchant, and land-owner, Jacob Glatz was apparently not a model citizen. In the April 1828 Session of Lancaster County Court, he was found guilty of Fornication and Bastardy. The court determined that Dr. Glatz "on the fourth day of June in the year of our Lord, one thousand eight hundred and twenty seven at the County aforesaid, did commit fornication with a certain Juliana Ely and then and there did beget a female Bastard child, on the body of the said Juliana Ely."[9]

As brothels were prolific in Marietta, Juliana was most likely a prostitute who filed the charges against Dr. Glatz in order to receive financial support for their illegitimate child. This was not the only brush Glatz had with the law. In January 1842, a charge of Assault and Battery with Intent to Ravish (rape) was leveled by Mary Imhoff.

Imhoff alleged that on Christmas Day 1841, Jacob Glatz "did make an assault ... and did beat, wound, and ill treat with an intent, her the said Mary Imhoff, against her will, then and there feloniously to ravish and carnally know, and other wrongs to her did, to her great damage."[10] Perhaps Mary was another prostitute he had treated poorly, or maybe improper advances were made at a Christmas celebration. Regardless of the circumstances, the Grand Inquest determined that the allegations were false and malicious and dropped the charges, and ordered Imhoff to pay the costs of prosecution.

Christian Keesey continued leasing the ferry until he passed away in 1842. Jacob Glatz, with his business and personal interests in Marietta, needed to find someone else to operate the ferry and tavern across the river. Shortly after Keesey's death, Jacob's younger brother John Glatz moved in and took over the operation. John married Mary Strohman a few years later and the couple had five children in five years, all of them dying soon after birth. With one Glatz owning the ferry, and another living in the stone house in York County, the crossing soon became known as Glatz Ferry.

Apparently the thought that gold, copper and other valuable metals existed on the ferry property persisted well into the nineteenth century. It was one of the reasons Philip Syng, Governor Keith, and the Pennsylvania Proprietors had been interested in surveying the property in 1722. Although not without geological basis, no deposits have ever been mined from the area. Gold has been found in streams in York County, but not in bedrock.

The Pigeon Hills near Spring Grove and the Hellam Hills along the river are the two locations in York County containing volcanic rocks composed of basalt and rhyolite. The presence of these rocks is one indicator that gold, copper and other metals may be present. At the ferry, the rocks exposed on the hillside behind the inn and along Accomac Road leading to the river were composed of this ancient sea-floor volcanic lava.

Based on the potential for profitable mining, Jacob and John Glatz entered into a twenty-five-year mineral lease with Lemuel P. Jenks in August 1842. Jenks was a patent attorney from Boston who assisted others with documenting and filing patents. Traveling to Baltimore and Washington for his patent work, he may have crossed the river on the Glatz Ferry and become acquainted with Jacob and John Glatz.

An avid inventor himself, Jenk's personal patents included a "new and Improved Combination of Machinery for the Purpose of Drilling Rocks"[11] and "a new and useful Improvement in Machinery for Separating Ores and other Heavy substances from sand, Rocks, Gravel and other impurities."[12] His interest in mining was evidenced by his ventures in the United States, Canada and Cuba.

Jenk's lease with Jacob and John Glatz included rights to "all mines, pits, and veins of iron ore, lead, copper ore, gold ore, and all other ores, metals and minerals now open or that may be found out by the digging, delving, mining and sinking."[13] The lease pertained to the two tracts of land along the river that Jacob and John Glatz owned in Hellam Township, including the ferry property. The agreement detailed the terms and conditions in respect to expenses, the division of profit from any mines, and any land use restrictions.

Jenks was to "bear and pay all expenses for mining or digging any ore or ores, metals and minerals that may be found."[14] The terms for dividing the gold profits were different than for the less valuable metals. "The Gold ore so mined is to be divided at the mouth of the mine as follows, two thirds of said Gold ore to the said Lemuel P. Jenks ... and the other third to the said Jacob Glatz and John Glatz."[15] Less precious metals such as copper were to be divided five-sixths to Jenks and one sixth to the Glatz brothers.

Additional clauses protected Glatz's property from damage. "One hundred dollars in damages for every acre of land under cultivation which shall be rendered unfit for cultivation by mining and at the rate of fifty dollars for every acre of land now in woodlands spoiled by mining."[16] Jenks was required to dispose of any rubbish and was prohibited from carrying on any mining operations "within one hundred and fifty yards of any building or buildings now erected except the house commonly called the Fish House and red house."[17]

The twenty-five year lease was to become null and void if Jenks did not invest at least one $1,000 a year in mining or the mines did not produce at least $10,000 annually. No extensive mining operations were ever carried out and no significant deposits found, and at some point the agreement must have been voided, as it is not referenced in any further deed to the property. Jacob Glatz died four months after signing the agreement and any proceeds from the lease would have gone to his brother John.

Dr. Jacob Glatz died in his early forties in 1845, leaving his personal effects and his house with two adjoining lots in Marietta to his wife Susanna. His wife served as executrix and his half-brother Vincent Keesey was named an executor. The rest of Jacob's estate was divided amongst his four surviving children; Christian, A. Heistand, Thomas and Ann Margaret. "If they cannot divide it amongst themselves amicably, I do hereby authorize and empower my Executrix and Executor ... to sell and dispose of my property ... The proceeds to be divided equally ..."[18]

The Inventory and Appraisment of the Goods and Chattels completed by Vincent Keesey and Susanna Glatz on December 2, 1845, itemized Jacob's personal effects as well as the contents of his Drug Store. Persons who had accounts at the store whose amounts could not be determined were also listed, with a footnote reflecting the economic state of Marietta at the time - "others, many insolvent."[19]

Susanna Glatz sold Jacob's drug business the following year to John Jay Libhart, a locally renowned figure in Marietta. In addition to being a prolific painter and naturalist, Libhart at various times held the offices of school director, councilman, and lay judge of the Court of Common Pleas in Lancaster. By 1846, he was appointed to Jacob Glatz's former position as the Postmaster in Marietta. Following Libhart's death in 1883, Libhart's Drug Company continued operating in Marietta for many years, well into the twentieth century.

Jacob's widow Susanna retained ownership of the ferry and tavern, remaining in Marietta until sometime after 1850. By 1860, she had moved from Marietta to York County and lived with her son A. Heistand Glatz on his farm in Hellam Township, located just southeast of the ferry. John Glatz continued to operate the ferry for his sister-in-law Susanna until his death on January 27, 1851.

A public auction of John Glatz's personal estate was held on April 21 and was well attended. The boats and many other items belonging to the ferry operation were not included in the sale, and were retained by Susanna Glatz. Since everything else inside the house, barn, and saw mill was sold, it appears the ferry would have temporarily ceased to be a working operation. Buyers included Vincent Keesey, the son of former ferry operator Christian Keesey, and half-brother of Jacob and John Glatz. Born and raised at the ferry, he bid on many of the things he had grown up around. The required sale bill filed with the Probate Court itemized Keesey's purchases, including a stove, dough tray, copper kettle, chairs, lamps, books, and other furniture and household goods.

Following the death of John Glatz in 1851, his widow Mary married George Gohn from Lancaster. Whether the couple lived at the ferry and continued to operate the business, or whether it sat idle in the years after the death of John Glatz, is unknown. Sometime between John Glatz's death and 1859, Susanna began leasing the ferry to John Noel. Repairs were made to the property and it was "prepared to ferry, feed, and drink the travelling public."[20] Weekly advertisements were placed in the local Marietta papers which emphasized Noel's ability to entertain guests and provide first-rate ferry transportation.

THE GLATZ FERRY,
Formerly Keesey's.

The undersigned having leased the above named old established Ferry and Hotel, in Hellam Township, York county, opposite the borough of Marietta, where he is prepared to entertain the public at his bar and table with the best the market affords. He would very respectfully inform the traveling public that having obtained

First Class Ferry Boats,

and efficient ferrymen, and is now fully prepared to accommodate persons wishing to cross the Susquehanna with vehicles or otherwise without delay or detention. **JOHN NOEL.**

The Mariettian, October 8, 1859

Within a few years of leasing the ferry, Noel sought new ways to make the most of the property and began making significant changes. As the volume of lumber coming down the river each year declined, operating the saw mill became unprofitable and it soon ceased operation. It was torn down and replaced with a pavilion which could be rented out for picnics and gatherings, and the ferry and inn became more of a "resort" destination. This trend continued well into the twentieth century, and events such as the following became commonplace.

"Quite a large and pleasant pic nic came off near the 'Glatz Ferry' on Tuesday last. The Marietta String Band furnished the music for the occasion and after spending the day on the hill side, they repaired to Noel's Ferry House, where they danced and amused themselves until ten o'clock, when they embarked on board of one of the ferry flats and slowly, but pleasantly, amid the sweetest strains of music, were soon 'Homeward bound.' This place, near the spring, is now one of the most delightful places for summer parties we know of, and Noel is always in readiness to furnish accommodations for any wishing, at short notice."[21]

Ferry traffic continued to slowly decline due to the increased use of the bridge in Columbia, and during the winter months was almost non-existent. In order to encourage Marietta residents to walk across the frozen river to the tavern, efforts were made to make it as easy as possible. Noel, "of the Glatz Ferry House, ventured to cross the Susquehanna over the ice on Wednesday morning last, and succeeded in placing a row of dead tree limbs – thus forming a guide for others passing over – the entire width of the river."[22]

In early 1863, Susanna Glatz finally decided to sell the ferry she and Jacob owned for almost forty years. The thirty-nine acres in York County and the ferry right was sold on behalf of the estate to Israel Goodman from Marietta. She must have publically acknowledged the intent to sell the property to Goodman early in January, as it was announced on January 10: "We learn that the old Keesey Ferry and Fishery property opposite this place has changed hands. Mr. Israel Goodman, former publisher of the Mariettian, having becoming the purchaser."[23] However, the indenture between Susanna Glatz and Israel Goodman was not recorded until August 19, 1863.

When Jacob Glatz originally purchased the ferry at auction throughout the early 1820's, it consisted of eighty-seven acres. However, his widow Susanna sub-divided the property and sold Israel Goodman only thirty-nine acres, including the river frontage and ferry right. By that time, the fishery had closed due to the construction of the Columbia dam and the saw mill had been shut down, and neither was mentioned in the deed.

Goodman, publisher of *The Mariettian,* must have made the purchase strictly as a business investment. Having no experience running an inn, tavern, or ferry, he continued leasing the day-to-day operations to John Noel. Based on Goodman's reputation as an architect, hopes were high that he would continue developing the ferry property as more of a summer destination. "Mr. G. will put that old favorite resort in 'good trim' in a short time. His well-known architectural skill will have ample scope to make something very pretty for a summer resort at the spring and the grounds adjacent."[24]

In May of 1863, a mysterious notice appeared in *The Mariettian,* replacing John Noel's regular weekly ferry advertisement. On May 18, it was announced that the "Old Keesey-Glatz Ferry has passed into new hands. The present proprietor, Mr. _____ is busy as a nailor these times, ferrying."[25]   The unpublished lessee was John Eckert, and as the new operator of the ferry, he immediately was thrown into one of the most significant historical events ever to take place at the ferry.

"Cor. Accomac Pavilion & River Road,' Accomac, Pa"
Collection of Author

Chapter 10

Accomac
1863-1881

"The hardest thing to learn in life is which bridge to cross
and which to burn"
        ... David Russell

In June, 1863, General Robert E. Lee moved forward with his plans to invade the Union and began shifting his troops northward from the Shenandoah Valley. Once the amassed Confederate army entered Maryland, Lee issued the directive "If Harrisburg comes within your means, capture it."[1] As the Army of Northern Virginia, led by General Richard Ewell, moved into Pennsylvania in mid-June and moved east, rumors of their position and strength reached the counties along the Susquehanna.

Horses and livestock which could be used by the rebels streamed across the river crossings for safety, followed by "men, women and children, the defenseless inhabitants of the Cumberland valley."[2] This was not the first time, nor would it be the last, that refugees would flood the bridges and ferries attempting to escape to the east bank of the Susquehanna.

The prior year, in September of 1862, a similar panic had resulted when the Confederate Army began marching northward across Maryland. After crossing South Mountain, their advance was halted near Sharpsburg, Maryland on September 17. The Battle of Antietam outside Sharpsburg was "the bloodiest single day of any in the annals of the Civil War"[3] and the following day Lee retreated with his battered troops across the Potomac River and back into Virginia.

However, the threat to Pennsylvania soil seemed so genuine that many merchants in York moved their valuable goods across the

Susquehanna, using both the Glatz Ferry and the bridge and ferry at Wrightsville. Now, less than a year later, with the rebels actually in Pennsylvania, refugees once again began to flee across the river.

Lee's original order to General Ewell was to capture Harrisburg, the capital city of Pennsylvania. Ewell split his troops and accompanied several of his divisions as they moved directly northeast towards Carlisle and the capital. Another division of four brigades under General Jubal Early was ordered to march east through Gettysburg and York to the Susquehanna. Early's orders upon reaching the river were to burn the mile-long bridge, then rejoin Ewell in Carlisle.

In response to the Confederate threat, Pennsylvania Governor Andrew Curtain issued a proclamation calling for 60,000 volunteers to defend the state and placed Union General Darius Couch in charge of the defense of Harrisburg. Couch in turn authorized Captain C. C. Haldeman of Columbia to "raise troops and assume command of the same, for the defense of Columbia, Pa., the Bridges, Dams, and Fords in the Susquehanna River in the vicinity."[4]

Community involvement was stressed in communications from General Couch. "Citizens should be turned out en masse to go right across the river to throw up rifle pits or breastworks – not interfering with travel until the last moment, as large quantities of stock will be crossing." Most importantly, he ordered "In no event must the enemy cross these bridges. You will therefore make preparation accordingly."[5]

Preparations to defend the bridge began immediately. Captain Haldeman proceeded to Wrightsville and staked out lines for trenches on the west side of town to serve as the primary line of defense. Volunteers, including a party of over 100 Negros worked in shifts night and day to complete the fortifications. As noted in the Columbia Spy, "They have done excellent service, and the cheerfulness with which they shouldered the pick and shovel is in contrast with the reluctance displayed by many of our whiter citizens to shoulder the musket."[6]

In addition, breastworks were constructed in Columbia to protect the low-head dam. Although the river was running extremely high, making it impossible for anyone to cross on the top of the dam, the gun emplacements gave the citizens of Columbia some additional sense of security. As a final measure, fortifications were constructed on the Hellam Heights in York County, a ridge north of the bridge just below the Glatz Ferry. Artillery placed on this high point above Wrightsville would be used against the advancing Confederates or aimed at the bridge in order to stop them from crossing.

Major Haller, in charge of Union forces in York, inspected the defensive positions and pronounced them "well-planned and properly constructed."[7] Haller sent scouts under Captain M.M. Strickler to watch the Glatz Ferry crossing at Marietta in case the Confederates attempted to ford at that point, and also planned to use the ferry as a crossing point to bring additional troops from Lancaster County if necessary. Although the ferry was unlikely to be used by either side due to the high water levels, Haller was taking no chances.

In Marietta, a local militia unit called the Thomas Rifles was busy recruiting two companies to be used where needed. On Tuesday, June 16, the Rifles, under Captain William H. Eagle, reported to Columbia to assist in defending the bridge. They returned home the next day as there was no immediate threat from the Confederates. On Wednesday evening, orders were given "... to take position at the Glatz Ferry, on the York County side."[8] They remained there for the night, once again returning to Marietta the next morning.

Reflecting the general sense of chaos, local papers took the opportunity to chastise their readers. "Whilst we are glad to record the untiring energy of many of our citizens during the existing crisis, and thank them in the name of the community for their devotion to the good cause, we regret the necessity of complaint that Columbians as a body have scarcely done their whole duty. There has not been want of willingness to act, but rather a disinclination to organize."[9]

Another paper put it more bluntly. "The invaders are near us, only separated by the Susquehanna river. It is impossible to tell what hour they will be upon our soil. What are you doing to repel the enemy? The apathy which exists in our midst must be shaken off at once, or all will be lost. Let every man do his duty in the present terrible crisis, if we would save ourselves from the disgrace and ruin which threaten us."[10]

Meanwhile, the militia and local citizen volunteers manning the fortifications on both sides of the river passed the time "fishing, card playing, and foraging in town for pies, cream, and delicacies. Companies formed glee clubs and music abounded."[11] However casually the threat was regarded, an air of suspicion prevailed as conflicting news of the Confederate advance filtered through.

Strangers approaching the bridge and ferry from the direction of Maryland were given additional scrutiny. On Sunday, June 21, three men were arrested at the bridge after giving contradictory explanations of their identities. They turned out to be Union deserters and were sent to Harrisburg. A few days later, another man was detained near the canal lock in Wrightsville and admitted to being a rebel deserter. Ironically, instead of being arrested like the Union deserters, he took the Oath of Allegiance and was mustered into service in one of the companies of the 27th Pennsylvania Regiment.

With all their defensive preparations in place, the citizens of Columbia and Wrightsville awaited the advance of the Confederate Army. "We have made a fair beginning, and if the Rebels do not come in overwhelming numbers, are even now ready to give them a wrestle for the bridge. We will fight for it before we will burn it."[12]

General Ewell was well equipped to lead the Confederate advance into Pennsylvania, especially the movement of troops across Adams and York Counties. In addition to possessing a detailed map of southern Pennsylvania including the bridges and nearby ferry crossings, Ewell had intimate first-hand knowledge of the area, "having been engaged as a civil engineer on the Wrightsville, York and Gettysburg railroad. He is familiar with every foot of ground in that section of country, and is consequently the most dangerous officer the rebels could have placed in command of a rebel force for the invasion of that section of Pennsylvania."[13]

Ewell ordered General Early to cross South Mountain east of Chambersburg, pass through Gettysburg and proceed to York, where he was to cut the Northern Central Railroad connecting Baltimore to Harrisburg. From there he was to move through York, burn the bridge at Wrightsville, and rejoin General Ewell in Carlisle. If Ewell was to be successful in occupying Harrisburg, the destruction of the railroad bridge was critical. If left intact, the Union Army would use it to bring troops across the river into York County, cut Ewell's supply lines, and attack the Confederates from both the front and rear of Harrisburg.

Early sent Brigadier General John Gordon ahead of his main column, directly towards York and Wrightsville. Just thirty-one at the time, Gordon was already a seasoned veteran. Known as an aggressive commander, he was injured the previous year at Antietam, where he was hit twice in the same leg, once in the arm, and a fourth time in the shoulder. He continued to lead his men until he was hit again in the face, with the shot passing through his left cheek and out his jaw. Only nine months later he was back on duty, leading his brigade of Georgians across Pennsylvania, and would eventually reach the farthest east of any organized Confederate troops upon reaching Wrightsville.

News of the advancing rebel infantry and artillery quickly reached York and Wrightsville via telegraph and first-hand accounts. Money was removed from the banks and sent east to Philadelphia, and the flow of horses, livestock, and other goods across the river at Wrightsville and at Glatz Ferry reached a fever pitch. Drovers passed along news about Early's unhindered march through Gettysburg, motivating more people towards the river. Merchants moved or hid valuable goods, and planned on closing until the rebel threat passed.

Granville Haller, the head of the small contingent of troops charged with protecting York, was not popular, and many felt his presence was not strong enough to deter any serious rebel advance. As General Gordon and his brigade neared York, Haller was persuaded to remove all his troops from York and move them to Wrightsville in order to prevent damage to the town. Haller sent a telegram to General Couch in Harrisburg informing him of the recent developments in York. "Off toward Wrightsville and Columbia. The army approach with the Gettysburg force about 4,000. Will respect private property if not resisted, and borough authorities wish no resistance."[14] Couch immediately wired militia leader Colonel Jacob Frick in Wrightsville that Haller was on his way. "York has surrendered. Our troops will fall back from there to Wrightsville tonight."[15]

When Haller reached Wrightsville early Saturday evening, he found the town disorganized and unprepared. Rolling stock from the western portions of the county was lined up on the rails waiting to cross the bridge, and horses and livestock jammed the streets. Merchants, attempting to save their valuable merchandise, piled crates of all sizes on every available wagon they could find.

As the Confederates advanced across York County, they attempted to purchase the supplies they needed with basically worthless Confederate currency. Since a large portion of local goods had already crossed the river, the scarcity of available supplies and horses did not go unnoticed, as Confederate General George Pickett remarked "The Yanks have taken into the mountains and across the Susquehanna all the supplies they could."[16]

Since locomotives were not allowed on the bridge, railcars needed to wait for horses to tow them across. Adding to the delay was the toll collector, who was doing a brisk business during the crisis. To avoid the lines, some of those waiting diverted their wagons and livestock north to cross at Glatz Ferry or to the nearby Wrights Ferry.

Haller immediately took control of the situation, convincing the bridge company to suspend tolls and commandeering local farm teams, pressing them into service towing the waiting wagons and rolling stock across the bridge. By working throughout the night, the backlog was eventually cleared from Wrightsville, only to cause similar problems in Columbia.

While Haller worked to make the final preparations at the river, General Gordon continued his march east, stopping about ten miles west of York at Farmers.[*] Through a deal brokered with A.B. Farquhar, a local businessman from York, Gordon had agreed to not destroy any private property in the city. In return, he was to be allowed to enter York unopposed and receive the provisions he requested. Although the word "surrender" was not spoken, it was implied by the actions of the citizens of York, and the town became the largest to be occupied by the Confederate Army during the Civil War.

Even though Ewell had ordered the burning of the bridge at Wrightsville, the lack of any real resistance encountered by Early and Gordon as they moved closer to the river shed new light on the situation and presented them with another option. If Gordon's brigade could advance and capture the bridge instead of burning it, Early could move his entire division across the river, cut the line of the Pennsylvania Railroad in Columbia, and advance further east to place Lancaster under contribution for much needed supplies. If Lancaster surrendered as York had done, Gordon could fill his train of empty supply wagons, and have ample provisions to support the Confederate's goal of capturing Harrisburg.

The bridge at Wrightsville was the only one between Harrisburg and Conowingo, Maryland, and capturing it would present the Confederates an opportunity to attack Harrisburg from two sides. Early's division could approach the capital city from Lancaster County to the east while the remainder of Ewell's Second Corps, now in Carlisle, would mount an assault from the west. Early and Gordon agreed on the new plan of attack and changed their objective from destroying the bridge to capturing it. Ironically, the Union troops in Wrightsville were preparing plans to destroy it instead of protecting it.

On Sunday, June 28, Gordon began marching his troops, numbered at approximately 1,500, towards the Susquehanna. On his way out of York, a young girl approached the general and handed him

---

[*] *The village of Farmers is located along Route 30 just west of the York Airport near Thomasville. Gordon encamped near the site of the Paradise Elementary School.*

a large bunch of red roses, with a note in the center describing in detail the number and position of Union forces he would encounter in Wrightsville. According to Gordon, he "read and reread this strange note. It bore no signature, and contained no assurance of sympathy for the Southern cause, but it was so terse and explicit in its terms as to compel my confidence."[17] Pocketing the note, he continued moving out of the city, stopping to rest just east of York[†] before moving on.

As Sunday evening approached in Wrightsville, approximately 1,400 soldiers finished their digging, picked up their rifles, and manned the defensive breastworks laid out in a horseshoe just to the west of the town. As a secondary line of defense, Colonel Frick ordered a group of carpenters to prepare a section of the bridge eight-hundred feet from the Wrightsville side to be blown. In the event they could not hold back the Confederate advance, the troops would retreat across the bridge, igniting the charges behind them. Of the twenty- eight spans on the bridge, the forth span from the west was chosen because it would leave more sections standing for the retreating troops.

The workers sawed through the roof rafters, weakened the side supports, and planted powder and fuses in holes drilled in the arches supporting the roof. Once the charges were ignited, the plan was for the two-hundred-foot span to simply fall into the water and prevent the enemy from crossing. The three Union cannon in Columbia would be used to discourage the enemy from repairing the damage.

As a final precaution, large barrels of kerosene and coal oil had been rolled from Columbia to a section closer to the middle of the bridge. If it became necessary, the barrels would be broken open and spilled over the bridge floor and ignited. It was hoped that any fire would not spread to Wrightsville or Columbia, but Frick was determined to heed General Couch's order to prevent the bridge from being crossed by the Confederates at all costs.

[†] *Gordon's troops stopped to rest at the old York Valley inn, built in the mid-1700s . The stone inn, now the site of a Wal-Mart, was dismantled and rebuilt at Susquehanna Memorial Gardens near Dallastown in 1962.*

At the Glatz Ferry, boats that had been pressed into almost continual service the previous week were removed to Marietta on the far side of the river to prevent them from being used by the advancing rebels. Around noon, people crossing at Glatz had reported that the road from York was swarming with Confederates, and later rumors of rebels crossing just north of the ferry proved false.

Businesses closed in Marietta, and the streets were filled with horses and cattle moving north and east away from the river. All afternoon, the streets were crowded with "excited men and weeping women, all fearing the town would be shelled, and possibly burned to ashes the next day."[18]

At about 5:30 p.m. the vanguard of the Confederate advance was spotted. By 6 o'clock, Gordon reached the next to last rise before Wrightsville and paused to survey the Union positions. It was just as the strange note he had received in York had indicated, with a long line of soldiers stretched across the road at the next ridge, no artillery, and a creek bed extending off to the right leading towards the river.

The Confederates slowly advanced towards the Union defenses, firing on the trenches and opening up their artillery on the town. One of the Negro volunteers was decapitated by a shell, and several other shells found their mark on some of the buildings in town, including the large brick Wright's Ferry House.

As the shelling progressed, Gordon moved some of his troops to the right of the Union line, following Kreutz Creek as the mysterious message had suggested. As Gordon noted in his memoirs, "I did not hesitate, therefore, to adopt its suggestion of moving down the gorge in order to throw my command on the flank, or possibly in the rear, of the Union troops and force them to a rapid retreat or surrender."[19]

Frick had received reports grossly overstating Gordon's strength, with one local newspaper reporting his force to be 35,000 strong. Knowing that his meager defenses could only hold them off so long without artillery support, he did not wait too long before ordering a general retreat.

In meetings earlier that afternoon with Major Haller, the option of destroying the bridge before the Confederates arrived, and using Glatz's Ferry as a crossing in case a retreat was necessary, had been discussed. The boats that had been previously moved across the river to Marietta would have to be brought back, and once the militia crossed to Lancaster County, they would march to Columbia.

However, believing that they would not be hard pressed by the rebels and could instead use the bridge to reach Columbia, they had opted to leave it standing. Once the order to retreat was given, the militia marched down the main street of Wrightsville, through the narrow opening in the barrier of ore cars placed at the entrance, and began crossing the bridge.

At 7:30, with the enemy approaching down the hill towards the bridge, Frick confirmed the order to blow the span which had been rigged earlier in the day. As the Confederates began charging onto the bridge, the fuses were lit and the ensuing explosion shook the structure but did not cause the span to drop into the river as planned.

Frick, at the rear of the Union retreat, saw that the rebels were continuing past the span they attempted to destroy and gave the order to fire the bridge. Torches were thrown on the piles of oil-soaked wood shavings and the oak floorboards of the bridge quickly caught fire. Spurned by the wind from an approaching storm, the fire began to spread in both directions, stopping the Confederate advance.

Once across the river, the Union soldiers, along with residents of Columbia, were able to keep the flames from entering the town. Wrightsville on the west side was not as fortunate. The wind pushed the fire towards the town, igniting the lumberyards and saw mills which lined the shore on both sides of the bridge entrance.

Gordon's troops fought to save the bridge, but residents were not forthcoming with buckets to help them form a bucket brigade. Despite the light rain, the fire spread from the lumber yards and began endangering houses and businesses in town. Citizens were now eager to help the Confederates battle the blaze and more than enough buckets and pails appeared.

The roof and sides of the bridge burned rapidly, and the skeleton of framing timbers continued burning for hours. One by one the spans collapsed and floated downstream hissing and steaming. Each of the twenty-eight spans took about twenty minutes to burn and fall into the river, and by early the next morning, the bridge was gone.

The glow of the blaze was visible for at least thirty miles, from Harrisburg to Hanover, and many thought that the city of York was on fire. The light from the raging flames reflected off the sheer rock wall of Chiques Rock, and illuminated Glatz Ferry with an orange blush of light. The dense smoke was clearly visible in Marietta, rising high above the wall of flames.

"Occupation of Wrightsville, Pa. by Lee's Army, and Destruction of the Columbia Railroad Bridge by the Federal Force, June 26th 1863"[20]

Gordon's troops worked feverishly alongside the citizens of Wrightsville in order to save the town from burning. They were operating under orders from Lee not to destroy private property in the North, and did not want the destruction of Wrightsville placed on their shoulders. However, Northern newspapers were not so kind in their subsequent judgment of General Gordon's actions in Wrightsville. The situation was mentioned in the official military reports of Gordon, Early, and Ewell, and the Confederate generals took offense at the way their actions were misrepresented.

"It may not be improper in this connection, as evidence of the base ingratitude of our enemies, to state that the Yankee press has attributed to my brigade the burning of the town of Wrightsville. In his retreat across the bridge, the enemy fired it about midway with the most inflammable materials. Every effort was made to extinguish this fire and save the bridge, but it was impossible. From this the town was fired, and, notwithstanding the excessive fatigue of the men from the march of 20 miles and the skirmish with the enemy, I formed my brigade in line around the burning buildings, and resisted the progress of the flames until they were checked."[21]

The next time the Confederate Army entered Pennsylvania, they would not be so kind. However, General Gordon and his men gave as much assistance as they could, fighting the fires in town most of the night. In particular, they saved the house of James F. Magee, a wagon maker and the mayor of Wrightsville.[‡]

Magee invited the general to use his house as headquarters for the night and Gordon accepted, promising there would be no additional damage done to the town. The following morning, Magee's daughter Mary Jane Magee Rewalt served the Confederate officers breakfast and vocally expressed her allegiance to the Union cause. General Early soon arrived from York and met with General Gordon. Realizing that their only way to cross the river now lay in flames, Early ordered Gordon to return to York as soon as possible. Reverting back to General Ewell's original orders, Early and Gordon planned to march to Carlisle to rejoin with the rest of the division for a combined assault on Harrisburg.

[‡] *The Magee house stands at 247 Hellam Street in Wrightsville.*

Although Gordon reported only one wounded among his troops, a Confederate soldier buried in June of 1863 along the river shore a few miles north of Glatz Ferry may have been from his command. There are many theories, but very little factual information, about the identity of the unknown soldier and how he died. Presumably drowned, he was found on the riverbank with the gear near his body suggesting he was part of a cavalry unit.

If he was a cavalryman, he may have been part of Colonel William French's 17th Virginia Cavalry unit, which had been attached to Gordon's brigade during their march through Gettysburg and York. French's Wildcats, detached from Gordon's command before they left York for Wrightsville, were ordered to destroy the railroad bridges at the mouth of the Conewago Creek in York Haven, about eight miles north of Glatz Ferry.

The 20th Pennsylvania militia was guarding the bridge in York Haven, but retreated when the Confederates advanced and burned the bridge. Pursued by French's cavalry, the militia withdrew south along the river and crossed to Bainbridge in Lancaster County on rowboats. Although French's unit suffered no documented fatalities during their movements in York County, several men were reported missing in action. The unknown dead soldier may have been one of these missing men, perhaps drowning when attempting to pursue the fleeing Pennsylvania militia across the river.

Another account suggests that after reaching Wrightsville, General Gordon sent a small party of scouts from Colonel Elijah White's Virginia Cavalry unit to look for a place to cross the brigade in case the bridge was destroyed. Passing by Glatz Ferry and finding all the boats moved across the river to Marietta for safekeeping, they continued north along the river shore, eventually building a raft to cross the river and test the water depth. The river was swollen and moving fast due to the recent rains and the raft quickly floundered, throwing one of the soldiers into the swift current. Not being able to swim, he drowned and was reportedly buried along the shoreline.

A third theory was that several confederate scouts or deserters made it across the river near Marietta. According to a local report, "Two spies came over the river at Marietta. They tried to escape, but one was killed and the other captured."[22] Discovered hiding in the bushes along the river by Union cavalry patrolling the area, and perhaps attempting to escape back across the river, they may have been pursued and one of them killed or drowned and buried where he fell.

Another account suggests that the unknown cavalryman was part of General Ewell's command approaching Harrisburg from Carlisle. As the Confederate division got closer to the capital, scouts may have been sent south along the river to look for possible fords to be used for a flanking movement on the city. One may have fallen sick and was buried by his friends.

Regardless of his identity, or the circumstances surrounding his death, the grave of the unknown rebel soldier is the farthest east of any Confederate dead interred during the Gettysburg campaign, with the exception of those who died in captivity or in army hospitals. Located along River Road about two miles north of Accomac, it is marked by a contemporary headstone erected in 1998, replacing a marker washed away during the flood caused by Hurricane Agnes in 1972.

On Monday, June 29, Gordon and his Georgia Brigade returned to York to join General Early for the march towards Harrisburg to connect with Ewell and the rest of the Second Corps. On his way, he received an important dispatch from General Ewell, reporting that the Union Army under George Meade had crossed the Potomac River and was marching across northern Maryland in pursuit of the Confederate forces. Lee realized that if he continued moving his entire force north towards Harrisburg, Meade would sever his supply lines and communication from the South.

Lee ordered Ewell's divisions to retrace their steps back to the west side of South Mountain, where he was to concentrate his forces with those of General Longstreet and General A.P Hill, and prepare for a confrontation with Meade. As Lee explained his decision to his staff, "Tomorrow, gentleman, we will not move to Harrisburg as we expected, but will go over to Gettysburg and see what General Meade is after."[23]

Early's command, including General Gordon, proceeded to Gettysburg and reached the battlefield at approximately 3 o'clock the evening of July 1. They formed the leftmost flank of the Confederate line, immediately encountering Union forces and pushing them back through town. Over the next two days, they engaged the enemy at Cemetery Hill and Culp's Hill, suffering 30% casualties.

Sounds of the battle could be heard in Marietta and "all along the river bank the dull sound of cannonading could be heard, and by laying on the ground the sound became more distinct of the more than a hundred cannon that were raining death-wounds upon thousands of struggling foes."[24]

On Thursday, July 2, with the Battle of Gettysburg in its second day, the Susquehanna River had dropped far enough to allow it to be crossed safely. A contingent of the First City Troop, a militia unit from Philadelphia, crossed at Glatz Ferry that day on a scouting mission looking for Confederates still in York County.

Following the three day Battle of Gettysburg and Lee's subsequent retreat over the Potomac River at the end of the week, the Confederate threat to York and Wrightsville was over. Over the next several weeks, livestock and horses were moved back across the river and merchants retrieved the goods they had taken across the Susquehanna for safekeeping.

Along with the waiting lines of homeward bound refugees and animals, relief workers from Philadelphia and Delaware attempting to reach Gettysburg to provide medical support waited their turn to cross the river. A group of Lancaster County women volunteers, calling themselves the Patriot Daughters, gathered supplies and procured wagons and teamsters to transport them to the battlefield, but encountered problems crossing the river.

Upon arriving in Columbia in the late afternoon, they were assured by the ferry captain that they would be crossed as soon as possible. However, when the boat returned to the shore, others who had been waiting since morning pushed ahead and would not give up their spots for the relief workers.

They "were not alone in this severe trial of patience, for the wharf was crowded with a motley mass of men, wagons and horses, forcibly reminding one of scenes in California, when the golden attractions of that famous land drew so many to its shores."[25] Traffic jams, waiting lines, and impatient crowds were a common site in both Columbia and Marietta. Many westbound travelers used Glatz Ferry at Marietta instead of Wright's, and Front Street was lined with wagons and livestock waiting their turn to cross.

With the Wrightsville Bridge gone, the only way to cross the Susquehanna was to utilize local ferry services or travel to the nearest bridges in Harrisburg or Maryland. Both Wright's and Glatz's Ferry did a brisk business in the months following the Confederate occupation of York County, and this prosperity continued for the next five years until a new bridge was completed in 1868.

The burning of the bridge, although tactically necessary, severely impacted the ability to move goods across the river. It was a critical wagon and railway link between Lancaster and York Counties, and its destruction created a transportation void that only ferries could fill. In the years leading up to the Civil War, the volume of ferry traffic had been in steady decline, but as a result of the destruction of the bridge, the economic value of the Glatz Ferry escalated overnight.

Ironically, it was the construction of the original covered bridge that caused financial hardship for James Anderson IV when he owned the ferry in 1813, and now the fact that it was gone provided a financial opportunity for Israel Goodman, the current owner. His timely purchase of the ferry from Susanna Glatz in January of 1863, only five months before the Confederate invasion, allowed him to cash in on the financial potential of the property and its renewed prosperity.

In May, only a month before the burning of the bridge, John Eckert took over the Glatz Ferry lease from John Noel. In his first few months, Eckert was kept busy handling the sudden increase in traffic. After the chaos of the Confederate invasion subsided, the following announcement appeared on July 18, 1863. "Mr. Eckert having leased the old Keesey-Glatz Ferry, opposite this borough, is now prepared with new boats to attend to all calls without delay."[26] Regular weekly advertisements resumed and continued for another year, when the ferry once again changed ownership.

The Glatz Ferry.

Formerly Keesey's,
OPPOSITE MARIETTA.

THIS old Ferry—one of the oldest and most safe crossings on the Susquehanna River—is now in charge of the undersigned, who has refitted the old and built new boats, which will enable him to do ferrying with safety and dispatch. No unnecessary delay need be endured. Sober and experienced Ferrymen always engaged. No imposition in charges as the following list will show :

Farm Wagons, each	$1:00
Horses, per head	:25
Single horse and rider,	:25
Two-horse Carriage and two persons,	1:00
Buggy, horse and two persons,	:50
Foot Passengers, each,	:12

Stock of all kinds at the old charges.
All Luggage over fifty pounds, 25 cents per 100 pounds extra.

JOHN ECKERT.

July 15, 1863.

The Weekly Mariettian, July 15, 1863

The ferry continued to prosper and Eckert enjoyed an excellent reputation, and was mentioned in *The Weekly Mariettian* later that summer: "Mr. Eckert, of the Glatz Ferry, is doing a fine business. We almost hourly hear the horn blowing. He is very attentive and his charges very reasonable."[27] John Eckert continued operating Glatz Ferry for Israel Goodman until the property and ferry right was sold to James Duffy on May 25, 1864. Goodman only held the property about a year before selling it to Duffy, a prominent businessman and landholder in Marietta, for $3,000.

"We understand that Mr. James Duffy has purchased from Mr. Israel Goodman, for three thousand dollars, the old 'Keesey-Glatz' Ferry, immediately opposite this borough. There are divers [diverse] rumors as to what purpose it is intended to be put. Some say it is to be fitted up for a summer watering place – others, a safe harbor for timber, &c. It would, unquestionably, be well calculated for either. Mr. Duffy's well-known liberality and wealth will, no doubt, enable him to make something very fine in shape, out of it."[28]

Apparently the community wondered about his motivation for making the purchase, and was probably even more surprised when he kept it for only a few months before selling it to John Coyle on July 5, 1864. It is unknown why James Duffy retained ownership for such a short time, but when it was conveyed to John Coyle the deed included the following clause: "The said James Duffy and Martha D. his wife, reserve unto themselves and immediate family the right to be conveyed over and across the Ferry free of all expenses to themselves and at such times as they may see fit to use it."[29] Perhaps John Coyle persuaded him to sell the Ferry as long as he promised Duffy an unlimited supply of free trips across the river.

The deed to John Coyle from James Duffy for the thirty-nine acres described an odd-shaped plot of land with about three-quarters of a mile of riverfront. The ferry landing was on a narrow extension of the property east of where the road from Hellam met the river, and the barn, inn and other outbuildings lay to the immediately to the west of the road. The orchards and fields stretched out behind the house on a gently sloped hill.

Although the indenture from James Duffy to John Coyle did not give a detailed description of the property, when it was next sold in 1889, an account of the same acreage included "improvements that are erected which consist of a large two story stone (part roughcoat) dwelling house with cellar underneath, and with a porch the entire length of the front and one end thereof, Frame boarded summer house, with fireplace and chimney therein and with brick and stone bake oven under cover, adjoining said summer house, frame boarded spring house and a pump house, with a well of water with pump therein, frame boarded ice house, part stone and part brick smoke house, frame boarded bank barn, frame boarded hog pen, with granary on top and with a frame boarded wood house attached, a large frame boarded building formerly used as a saw mill, and other out buildings. There is an apple orchard and other fruit trees, grape vines, about 12 acres of cleared land (balance wood or timberland), springs of running water and the 'Coyle's Ferry' landing on this tract and a stream of water and the public road leading from Wild Cat Run to Wrightsville runs through the said above described messuage."[30]

John Coyle lived in Marietta with his wife Mary Ann and their young son, John Jr., before purchasing the ferry from Duffy and moving across the river and into the stone house. The younger Coyle was Mary Ann's illegitimate son and had been raised by the elder Mr. Coyle since he was a small boy, taking the last name of his step-father. They had lived in their new home for less than a month when once again fear of another Confederate invasion gripped the area and Coyle's Ferry was overrun with people fleeing east across the river.

For the second time in less than twelve months, troops under the command of General Early were back north of the Mason-Dixon Line and this time Pennsylvania residents had something to fear. During the early summer of 1864, Lee was stubbornly defending Richmond and the Union army was growing frustrated at their inability to take the Confederate capital. They began vindictive raids in the Shenandoah Valley, looting towns and burning the personal property of Confederate officers and civilians.

The previous year, General Lee had issued Order No. 72 protecting private property during the invasion of Pennsylvania, but since that time things had changed and the Union Army was not affording the South the same respect. Confederate General Jubal Early "came to the conclusion that we had stood this mode of warfare long enough, and that it was time to open the eyes of the people of the North to its enormity, by an example in the way of retaliation."[31] He chose Chambersburg, Pennsylvania, as his target, and ordered General John McCausland to lead the raid.

Rumors of an impending invasion sparked panic along the Susquehanna once again, and merchants packed up their goods and drove their horses and livestock towards the river well before McCausland even reached Pennsylvania. Since the bridge over the Susquehanna in Wrightsville had not yet been rebuilt, the tide of refugees was forced to use the local ferries to carry wagons, cows, and horses across the river to Marietta on flatboats.

According to *The Weekly Mariettian*, "This vicinity is in great tribulation just now. The refugees from Maryland, Cumberland, Adams, Franklin and York counties are crowding the ferries at this point, and at Columbia to get, with their horses and livestock, on this side of the Susquehanna, bringing with them all kinds of tales of the doings and number of the rebels. The 'Glatz Ferry', opposite this place, was worked double-handed during the whole of Thursday night, and drives of horses were hourly seen going through town."[32]

John Coyle purchased the ferry only five days prior to the publication of the news concerning McCausland's raid, and the ferry was still being referred to as Glatz Ferry. Just like new tenant John Eckert was immediately inundated with business after the destruction of the Columbia bridge the year before, Coyle was kept busy round the clock as soon as he took possession of the ferry with the flood of people crossing the river in advance of the supposed rebel invasion.

Around 5:30 in the morning on July 30, General McCausland fired several warning shots over Chambersburg. After ringing the courthouse bell to call the citizens to the town square, McCausland ordered his troops to burn the town. The Confederate soldiers broke into houses, evicted the owners, and set their homes on fire. They looted stores and residences, and devoured any liquor they could find. After the Confederates received money to spare homes and property, some burned them anyway. Leaving as suddenly as they entered, the raiders were gone by early afternoon.

McCausland's raid on Chambersburg was the last time the Confederates would enter Pennsylvania, and shortly afterwards, the refugees who had fled across the Susquehanna returned to their homes and shops. Although no Confederate troops had actually entered York County, "many startling rumors were afloat, calculated to frighten timid men and nervous women."[33]

During his first hectic month of ownership, John Coyle would have profited substantially by McCausland's Chambersburg raid and the ensuing panic of refugees fleeing across the river. This prosperity continued until the new bridge over the Susquehanna was completed four years later in 1868.

Following the burning of the Wrightsville Bridge in June of 1863, The Columbia Bank and Bridge Company sold all interest in the surviving piers to the Pennsylvania Railroad, who rebuilt the covered bridge in 1868 at a cost of $400,000. Completed in less than a year, the span consisted of the rail line, a carriageway, and a pedestrian walkway. Since the PRR now owned the bridge, the towpaths for the canal were not included in the reconstruction and canal boats had to be towed from Columbia to Wrightsville with steam-driven tugboats.

As a safety precaution, the new bridge was not entirely made of wood as the previous structures had been. The first span on each end and two of the spans in the middle of the bridge were made of iron in an effort to keep any fire from destroying the entire bridge or spreading between Columbia and Wrightsville. Lasting only twenty-eight years, it was destroyed by a hurricane on September 30, 1896.

After normal bridge traffic resumed, life at the ferry slowed to its former pace. For the next thirteen years, Coyle's Ferry carried people, livestock, and wagons between Marietta and York County and provided food and lodging for travelers. Workers from the eight anthracite coal-fired iron furnaces which lined the river between Marietta and Columbia used the ferry to frequent the tavern, as did laborers from the numerous ore banks and lime kilns in the area. In addition, the Coyles took passengers up the river to Wild Cat Falls, a picnic area and social gathering place a few miles upstream.

Business was good and the Coyles prospered. When the river was running high from the spring rains, the ferry catered to the seasonal influx of rafters following the flow of lumber down the river. After selling their logs in Marietta or Columbia, the raftsmen would enjoy a drink of whiskey and a hot meal and spend the night in one of the Coyle's shared upstairs boarding rooms before heading back upriver to Williamsport and points north to pick up another load of logs.

In the spring, Mr. Coyle set tobacco and planted corn and potatoes in the rocky fields behind the inn. Summer meant long hot days cultivating the garden and orchards behind the house, tending to the vegetables, fruit, and flowers. Mrs. Coyle grew some of the finest free-stone peaches in the area, and anything she didn't use in the kitchen was sent across the river to sell at the market house or exchanged for other supplies. As fall approached, apples were harvested and stored for the winter or sold.

Apparently the Coyles were able farmers, and they occasionally shared their harvest with their friends at *The Weekly Mariettian*. Notices sporadically appeared in the paper prior, and immediately after, the Coyles purchase of the ferry, including: "We received a basket of very fine peaches a few days since, of Mrs. John Coyle. They were some of the finest we have seen this season," "Our neighbor Coyle, a few days since, sent us a fine turkey. Here is an example worthy of imitation – who will follow suit? – don't all speak at once," and "The largest and finest Tomatoes that we have seen this season, was a basket full sent us by our neighbor, Mrs. John Coyle, a few days since."

A few years before Coyle purchased the ferry, the saw mill had been torn down and replaced with an open pavilion along the creek which led to the river, and the Coyles rented it out for picnics and parties during the warm months. Summer was also the time to make improvements and repairs to the buildings on the property.

Year-round, except when the river was frozen, Mr. Coyle took rowboats and flatboats back and forth across the river. When John Jr. was old enough, he helped with steering the boats and eventually began rowing passengers across alone. However, carrying wagons and livestock on the flatboats was a two-person job, especially when the current was strong or the water high. Low water brought a different set of challenges with rocks and mud, but the water in front of the Coyles was generally deep enough for crossing even in times of drought. Over the years, John Coyle, Sr. established a reputation as a strong ferryman.

The Coyles were occasionally mentioned in local editorials, including one concerning the condition of shad fishing in the river. "When will John Coyle, the present owner of the "old Keesey fishery" (which was at one time one of the most important fisheries on the Susquehanna) – opposite this place, throw in his seine and try to 'fish-out' some of the finny tribe."[34] In another, "A large black snake – over ten-feet long – was killed a few days since, near the garden of the old "Keesey ferry," which was regarded by all who saw it, as a monster. John Coyle, who now owns and keeps the ferry, says the hill is literally alive with nearly all kinds of snakes."[35]

However successful the Coyles were, their family life was a different story. John Jr. was a difficult child, and between his physical ailments and his mental issues, the Coyles had their hands full. Born on March 15, 1855, he was not the biological son of Mr. Coyle. His mother Mary Ann had married her much older husband when John Jr. was very young and her only other son had been killed in the Civil War. John Jr. was nine years old when the Coyles moved across the river to the ferry house in 1864, and the older he grew, the more unmanageable and unpredictable he became.

When he was sixteen, John severely injured his left hand in a duck-hunting accident. He had taken a gun and gone up the river shore by himself, and while crawling under a log it had accidently gone off. It discharged close to his head and the load went through his left hand, taking off the tip of his index finger and leaving two others permanently disfigured. Hearing the muffled shot, his mother immediately went to see what had happened. Mr. Coyle was in Lancaster that day and Mrs. Coyle had to take John across the river alone to her brother William Hinkle to get help. He was taken to the doctor for treatment and spent the next seven weeks at his grandmother's house in Marietta recuperating from the injury.

In August 1872, less than a year after the shooting accident, John contracted a severe case of typhoid fever. Not able to walk until after Christmas, he suffered for many months, spent most days bedridden, and lost a significant amount of weight. From that point forward, he complained of severe headaches and exhibited fits of anger followed by bouts of melancholy.

His parents spent many years and over $1,500 taking him to various doctors attempting to get him help for what they perceived as a disordered mind. On several occasions, Mr. Coyle had gone back to James Duffy to borrow money, perhaps to help pay his enormous doctor bills. At one point, they had tried to put their son in an asylum, but were talked out of it by neighbors who told them it would only aggravate his condition.

None of the medicine seemed to help, and John grew increasingly more violent. He began drinking at an early age, which only served to make him more moody and withdrawn. His erratic behavior and immature actions soon gave him a reputation in Marietta of having an unsound mind. John had attempted suicide several times by shooting himself, poisoning himself with rat poison, and threatening to cut his throat with a razor, but was prevented from following through by his parents or aunts and uncles.

Through his teenage years, his parents continued to try to get help for John. One doctor recommended a change of scenery and his father hired a friend to take John to Havre de Grace, Maryland, on a fishing trip. While there, Coyle witnessed a drunken fight which ended in a shooting. The incident scared him so much that he insisted on coming home immediately.

To make matters worse, John and his step-father did not have a good relationship, and their verbally abusive and physically violent disagreements could frequently be heard across the river in Marietta. On one occasion, John returned home drunk and went to the barn with a loaded duck gun. Thrusting it through the door, he pointed it at his father and began yelling obscenities. Mr. Coyle seized the cocked gun by the barrel, and in the ensuing struggle managed to get his finger on the trigger and discharge the gun into the air. Dropping the gun, John turned and ran away.

Following many of these arguments, John would frequently disappear for several days at a time. After searching the hills trying to find him, his parents would often find him sitting under a tree with his head in his hands. At one point, his depression became so bad that Mr. Coyle hired a neighbor for a whole winter to watch him, sleep in his room, and take care of him.

Despite the success John and Mary Ann Coyle enjoyed with the ferry operation and tavern business, their reputation was eventually defined by the actions of their son. His frequent spells of drunken anger and unpredictable behavior spilled over into his mid-twenties, and began to shape the Coyle's future in ways they could not have imagined. Commonly known as "Crazy John Coyle" in Marietta, the younger Coyle soon earned a reputation as a simple-minded and potentially dangerous individual. On Decoration Day, 1881, things would take a turn for the worse.

Part II

Endings

Chapter 11

Coyle's Ferry
Monday, May 30, 1881

"Murder is born of love, and love attains the greatest
intensity in murder"

                                  ... Octave Mirbeau

Decoration Day began like most other days. Mrs. Coyle woke Emily at 5 o'clock to attend to her chores and returned to her bed. Lately Emily had been doing all of the morning work herself, as Mary Ann's rheumatism often kept her confined to bed. It was barely light when Emily rose, and after slipping on a plain white work dress and splashing some cold water on her face from the washbowl, she brushed her long black hair and fastened it in a pony tail. Easing herself from the room so as not to disturb Mrs. Coyle, she went down the back kitchen stairs in her stocking feet, stopping to sit on the bottom step to lace up her shoes.

She gathered some kindling from the wood box by the back door, filled the stove, and attempted to get the fire burning. There were hardly any embers still glowing from the previous night and she had trouble getting it to relight, so she retrieved the bellows from behind the bar in the tavern room. Returning to the kitchen, she quickly had it burning brightly with little effort, and started a full pot of water heating so it would be ready when the Coyles got up and came downstairs.

After the water began to heat, she picked up her empty milk pail from the bucket bench by the back door and poured in some warm water. Grabbing a clean rag from the rag box, she took the pail and moved quietly through the hallway and went out the front door, closing it carefully behind her.

Emily crossed the length of the front porch and slowly descended the stairs, taking her time to absorb the beauty of the cool and cloudless morning. All was still and silent, except for the muted rush of water flowing over the dam in the creek and the faint sounds of a late migrating flock of geese. They were retracing the route back to their breeding grounds in Canada and their musical honking grew louder as the V-shared formation moved upriver. After crossing the road and opening the barn door, Emily paused for a moment to watch the birds wing their way home.

As if signaled by the whistle blast of an early morning train passing by across the river in Marietta, the pale pink glow of sunrise suddenly erupted into dazzling brilliance as the first rays of the sun peeked over Chiques Rock and shot a long streak of silver up the river towards the inn. The sudden glare stung her eyes and aroused Emily from her daydream, and as the geese and the whistle faded into the distance, she turned to start her day.

Through the open door, the bright sunlight illuminated the inside of the stable, and there was no need to light the lantern hanging inside the door. Leaving the double doors wide open, Emily crossed to the horse stalls, reached into the oat bag with a wooden scoop, and filled each of the feed boxes.

She moved to the next stall and led the cow out, walking her to the stanchion on the outside of the stall and tying the rope off to an iron ring on the wall. After maneuvering the cow's head into the wooden collar to hold it in place, she dipped her rag into the pail of warm water and washed the cow's udders. She threw out the rest of the water, put the empty pail under the cow's swollen teats and sat on the small milking stool with her back to the open barn door.

As Emily began her milking, she suddenly recalled it was Decoration Day, and just as quickly remembered the destruction of her flower crosses on Saturday. Initially saddened by the thought, she smiled to herself as she imagined the fun she was going to have in Wrightsville with her friends, despite John's effort to ruin it for her. She was especially looking forward to seeing Helen Magee in a few hours and talking to her about getting some help in leaving the Coyles.

"Em, I want you to marry me." The voice caught Emily by surprise, and she snapped her head around with a startled look. The unexpected intruder was framed in the glare of the bright sun, and she didn't immediately recognize who was standing in the open door. Recovering from her initial alarm, she realized that it was John and asked, "You scared me John, what are you doing out here at this time of the morning?"

"You heard me; I said I want you to marry me." "Now, that's no way to properly ask a girl something like that!" she nervously teased, eager to take the seriousness out of the moment. She turned her head back to her work and began milking again, hoping that he would go away and leave her alone. She didn't want another argument with John ruining the whole day for her again, especially not today.

"It's not funny, Em, and I'm not askin." Realizing that simply ignoring him wasn't working and he wasn't going to let her alone that easily, she thought it best to answer him directly. "No, John, I won't, it's as simple as that." As if he didn't understand what she was saying, he just continued to stand there, staring at her with his blank look.

Emily stood up, put down the half full pail of milk and turned to face him in the doorway. Placing her hands on her hips, she mustered the most serious tone she could. "Just like I've told you before, the answer is still no."

"But I love you and I know you love me too!" Taking her time to think of an appropriate response, she finally replied "I know you do, John, at least you think you do. But I don't. It's in that head of yours that I do, but I never have. I won't be your wife or any other man's."

"Then by god, I'll shoot you, I swear it, cause if I can't have you no one else will either." She was frightened by the tone of his voice and could sense his anger rising. His hands were still down at his sides, and as he slowly lifted his right hand, she could see he was holding a pistol. "Put that gun away right now, John! If your father sees you with that you're going to be in for it!"

"I don't care about the old man. He doesn't run my life and the son-of-a-bitch can go to hell." She laughed at his comment, more an anxious reaction to her mounting panic than anything. Instead of taking the edge off the situation, John lifted the Smith & Wesson .22 caliber seven-shooter the rest of the way and pointed it directly at her.

"I told you the other day that I was only gonna ask you once more - so either you say you will or ..."

She was starting to get angry and interrupted him in a sarcastic tone, "Or what John? You're really going to shoot me? You're too much of a coward to shoot a girl!" Throwing her chest out, stamping her foot angrily, and pointing at her breast, Emily spoke her last words, "Then kill me quick, do it right here!"[1]

In an instant, Emily realized her mistake, and also realized it was too late to take it back. If there was one thing that sent John over the edge, it was when he felt he was being mocked. For a moment, there was complete silence.

The shot was deafening in the confines of the small barn, and it echoed off the hillside and across the river.

The ball struck Emily in the center of her chest, passing through her heart and exiting her body on the lower back, just to the right of her spine. Emily did not speak, but stared at John for a few seconds as the life drained from her. She quivered and fell to the dirt floor, instantly dead.

John walked over to her body and gazed down at her lifeless form. After a moment, he slowly turned the gun to his head and fired. The shot grazed the scalp behind his right ear and glanced off the side of his skull. Stunned, yet determined, he held the gun against his chest and fired again. Once more the ball deflected and caused only a painful flesh wound. The force of the shot caused him to lose his balance, and he dropped his gun and fell across Emily's body.

After realizing he was not seriously hurt, John stood and fled from the barn, leaving Emily where she fell. Going back into the house through the rear door, he headed straight for the tavern room and sat at one of the long tables, holding his hand against the wound on the side of his head. He tried to pretend that nothing had happened, and that his pain was caused by just another one of his excruciating headaches. He closed his eyes and willed for the image of her lying dead in the dirt to go away, but all he could see was her looking at him with her large dark eyes after he had pulled the trigger.

Mrs. Coyle, awake but still lying upstairs in bed, heard the three muffled pistol shots. Thinking it was the blows of an axe, she was not initially concerned. She soon realized that John would not be up and about yet, especially not working, and Emily wouldn't be splitting firewood. A sense of dread came over her, and not wanting to take the time to dress, she threw on a housecoat and struggled painfully down the stairs.

Coming out on the front porch through the entry door furthest from the barn, she noticed the stable doors were hanging wide open and assumed Emily was still inside doing her morning work. Calling "Emma" and receiving no answer, she tried several more times with the same result. In a moment, the upper front door opened and John stepped out, startling his mother with his ghastly appearance. Blood was running down behind his ear and seeping from the front of his shirt, and his eyes were wild looking and glaring like fire.

Slowly approaching to within a few feet of his mother, he muttered, "Mother, there is no use to call Emma, for I've killed her and shot myself. She's lying dead in the stable."[2]

Mary Ann cried out in shock and went back into the house as fast as she was able, screaming for her husband. Throwing on only a pair of pants, John Sr. rushed down the back stairs a moment later and met his wife in the kitchen, where she recounted what had just happened. Still only partially dressed, he left the house by the back door and hurried to the barn.

Meanwhile, Mrs. Coyle returned to the front porch to see if John was seriously hurt, asking him why he had done such a thing. In an excited voice, he whined "She set me crazy. Ruined me. I went out to the barn to see if she was as good as her word promising to marry me. She said she wouldn't, and dared me to shoot her."

When Mr. Coyle neared the barn, he began calling Emily's name, but all was silent. Upon reaching the open doors, he found her lying where she had fallen, on her right side with her back to the door. Hurrying over, he called softly to her, lifting her left arm to see if she was still alive. When he released it, it fell heavily and lifelessly to the ground, and he knew it was too late to do anything for her.

As he strode out of the barn and approached the front porch, John noticed him coming and quickly backed himself towards the door. Mr. Coyle rejoined his wife, and John retreated into the house and started up the stairs, calling for his father to come inside. "Pap, I want to talk to you."

Not wanting to leave Mary Ann, who was frantic with grief and sobbing uncontrollably, Mr. Coyle replied "John, you have done a horrid deed. I think your brain is not right and you're dangerous, you might shoot me."

John assured him he would not and returned to the porch to confront his father. He was haggard and pale, and Mr. Coyle thought to himself that he looked like a man right after death. After retelling his version of the events in the barn, and scared about what would happen to him, he begged his father not to let the law take him away. Grasping his fate after he was told the law must take its course, John told his parents there was still one load in the gun and pleaded with them to kill him. Upon hearing this, Mrs. Coyle broke down in tears again and John left them, going into the house and up to his room.

Mr. Coyle followed, and after making sure John was in his room, finished dressing and hurried back downstairs. Telling his wife to watch John to make sure he didn't leave the house, he quickly saddled one of the horses and left to alert the neighbors and get some help. He needed to fetch Justice Magee and a doctor, but he didn't want to leave Mary Ann at home with John alone any longer than he had to. Deciding to go to his nearest neighbor, Henry Mathews, he headed up along the creek on the road towards York. Mathews lived about a quarter of a mile from the river on a small farm at the intersection of the first road towards Wrightsville.

It was still early, about 6:00 a.m., when Mr. Coyle neared Mathew's house and found Henry in his barn getting ready to let his cows out for the day. He hurriedly explained what had happened and asked Mathews to go for Frank Magee, while he would go find someone else who could ride in the opposite direction to Wrightsville for a doctor. Mathews told Coyle to go back home to his wife and he would personally take care of going to Wrightsville to get Justice Magee and find medical help.

Magee lived on a farm a few miles north of the ferry on the road leading to the ore bank at Codorus Furnace, but Matthews knew that he was not at his farm. Henry told Mr. Coyle that while in Wrightsville the previous day, he had talked to Frank and knew he was staying at his sister's house in town in preparation for the Decoration Day ceremonies. Frank's sister Mary Jane still lived in the same house on Hellam and Third Streets where General John Gordon had been entertained at breakfast during the Civil War when the Confederates had saved their house from burning.

Mr. Coyle quickly returned to the house and tried to calm his wife until help arrived. John was still up in his room, and for a few minutes things were calm and quiet. Over the next hour, a number of persons gathered at the ferry from the surrounding area, alerted during Mathew's ride into town. All were shocked at what had happened, but most were not surprised that John had eventually gone too far and gotten himself into serious trouble.

A little before 8 o'clock, Justice Magee, Constable John Shenberger and Dr. George Rebman arrived from Wrightsville and took possession of the premises. Insisting that the curious onlookers keep their distance, they met Mr. Coyle on the front porch and were told the details of the shooting.

As Magee walked towards the barn, he wondered how he was going to tell his daughter about Emily's murder. Helen had approached him on several previous occasions to ask for his help in finding Emily find a way to leave the Coyles and assist her in obtaining another job. All he could think about now was that he should have paid more attention to his daughter. He felt guilty about not doing something sooner, and not doing something that could perhaps have prevented her murder. Unable to help Emily any longer, he was determined to do all he could to bring Coyle to justice and make him pay for his actions.

Magee and Rebman proceeded to the barn, where they found Emily's body outside one of the cow stalls. The cow was still tied to the stall door, and a half-empty pail of milk sat a few feet away. The revolver was found lying about two feet from her head, with one ball still left in the cylinder. By that time, Dr. John Thompson and his brothers William and Alex had arrived from Wrightsville and helped carry Emily's body into the western end of the house.

Dr. Thompson and Dr. Rebman removed Emily's clothing and performed a cursory exam, probing the wound and looking for other injuries. There was a minimal amount of blood, with only a few drops around the entrance and exit wounds on her chest and back. Although an obviously serious injury, they could not definitively determine if it was the cause of her death.

Meanwhile, Justice Magee and Constable Shenberger went upstairs to John's room, where they found him lying on his bed. Magee spoke first, saying "You've done a bad morning's work John." Coyle replied that he was sorry he had not finished himself off. Although dejected, John did not look seriously injured and Magee placed him in the custody of the Constable, who promptly arrested him.

Across the River   *Page 205*

Going back downstairs, Magee found that Dr. Alexander had arrived and was examining Emily's body with Dr. Thompson and Dr. Rebman. He asked them to go up and talk to John, make an assessment of his injuries, and determine whether he was able to be safely removed to York. William Thompson and his brother Alex, Mr. Coyle, and neighbors William Sweeny and Daniel Moore went upstairs with the three doctors and crowded into John's small room.

Mr. Coyle was the first in the room. He leaned over his son and whispered "Johnny, this is bad work, and I would sooner see you in your grave." "It's too late now, I've shot her and she's dead," John replied, and Mr. Coyle stepped away. Upon seeing Dr. Alexander in the room, John turned his back and exclaimed "Doc, for god's sake give me a revolver so I can I shoot myself." Dr. Alexander told him there was no need for that and to remain calm.

Questions were being fired at John from all directions. William Thompson asked how he felt and John told him he had pain in his breast. Asked why he did it, John replied that he shot at Emily Saturday, but this time had done it right. William Sweeney wondered if he had held the pistol close when he shot himself, but John didn't know. The situation was getting out of control with everyone talking at once, and Dr. Thompson abruptly ended the questioning and asked for the room to be cleared so they could complete their examination.

After everyone left except the three doctors and Constable Shenberger, Dr. Thompson told John to get out of bed so they could take a look at him. Getting no response, Thompson asked again, "Can't you get up?" and John muttered "I can't." Dr. Rebman took his pulse, and finding it nearly normal and his breathing free and easy, commented "You ain't going to die yet." Dr. Thompson was getting impatient and said "Well, I think you can," and pulled John up by the collar to a sitting position on the edge of his bed.

After a moment, Thompson grabbed John's arm, pulled him the rest of the way to his feet, and walked him around the room several times. Sitting him back down, the doctors once again took his pulse and looked at his wounds. They probed for balls and found none, and determined that his injuries were only surface wounds. There was very little blood except for what had dried on his clothes and skin, and there was no evidence of any other internal injuries.

The doctors returned downstairs to report their findings, followed by Coyle and Constable Shenberger. After Dr. Alexander told Justice Magee that there was no injury that would prevent Coyle's removal, he was promptly turned over to Officer Edwin Dietz from Hellam Township, who had been deputized to take the prisoner to York. There was no formal arrest warrant, and Magee told them he would prepare the paperwork and send it the following day. As the crime had been committed in Hellam Township and not Wrightsville Borough, Magee told them to have Justice of the Peace William Houck from Hellam accompany Officer Deitz and Coyle to the jail.

As the officers led John off the porch, Mrs. Coyle broke down, frantic with grief, and had to be taken back into the house. John pleaded with Justice Magee to allow his father to accompany him to jail, but having no sympathy for the murderer, the request was denied. Mr. Coyle had little compassion for the adopted son who had caused him so much trouble, and was more visibly upset about Emily's death than about John being taken to jail.

As John was being put in the wagon which had been brought from Wrightsville by Officer Dietz, the crowd that had gathered at the ferry became increasingly agitated, crying for John to be lynched on the spot. The murder created intense excitement in only a few hours, and the news spread to Marietta across the river, "... and hundreds of persons crossed to the other side for the purpose of learning the particulars of the sad affair. It was almost impossible, however, to learn much, as everybody was in a high state of excitement and unable to provide anything but the most vague accounts of the shooting."[3]

Shortly after 9 o'clock, the wagon with Coyle, Officer Dietz and Constable Shenberger pulled away from the ferry. John glanced over his shoulder, taking in the wide river, the stone inn, and the white barn where his life had changed forever. Uncertain of his fate, he didn't realize he was looking at the scene for the last time.

After arriving in Hellam, Justice Houck exchanged places with Constable Shenberger. On the way to York, Coyle spoke to Dietz and Houck, complaining he had been taken away from home without being given a chance to change his clothes. He asked for a handkerchief to wipe his head wound, and began to lament about the constant hardships he had endured throughout his life.

The conversation soon turned to the murder, and Officer Dietz asked if he shot Emily and why. Coyle responded that love was the cause and Emily said she would not marry him or anyone else. He explained that after threatening to shoot Emily, she stood up and dared him to do it. John confessed to the officers "Emily's trouble is over, but mine is about to begin,"[4] and realized that his actions would probably kill his mother too. After commenting that his parents often said he would end his life on the gallows and it certainly looked that way now, he grew silent and sullen for the rest of the trip to York.

Meanwhile, at the ferry, acting coroner Frank Magee convened the official inquest to determine the time, manner and cause of death. This process required the empanelling of six jurors and the presentation of evidence from witnesses to the incident. In this case, although the facts seemed readily apparent and obvious, Magee followed procedure and after the examination of Emily's body was completed, began the inquest in the tavern room.

The jurors included Alex Thompson, D.H. Moore, William Thompson, W.S. Sweeney, Dr. John Thompson, and Dr. George Rebman, who was appointed foreman. After the doctors described Emily's injuries, Mr. and Mrs. Coyle were called as the only witnesses. They described as best they could the events of this morning, periodically interrupted by Mary Ann's uncontrollable sobbing. The sole evidence presented was the revolver found in the barn, which Magee had in his possession. The jury deliberated only a few minutes, and returned the verdict of deliberate murder, finding that Emily came to her death by a pistol shot wound, inflicted by John Coyle, Jr. Although it had no civil or criminal trial significance, the verdict was recorded in case it was needed for court proceedings.

By noon, Coyle arrived at the York County Prison near the railroad tracks on Chestnut Street in downtown York. The front of the imposing brown sandstone jail, built in 1853, resembled a castle with two tall square towers flanking an even taller round central tower. The rear building was a two-story brick prison block with a long open center corridor with a row of cells on each side. As he passed under the front archway and through the massive oak doors, he suddenly realized he would not be going home again.

The York County Prison, built 1853
Courtesy of the Police Heritage Museum, Inc. York Pa.

Although John said there was no need to lock him up and that he would do whatever was needed if they treated him right, he was nonetheless heavily ironed and led to Cell 18 by the jailor, Sheriff Samuel Altland. Coyle's fifteen-by-eight-foot cell was on the first floor of the forty-cell prison and was the first on the right, next to the bath cell and nearest to Altland's quarters where he lived with his family.

Sheriff Altland was a farmer and brick-maker by trade. After serving four years as a constable in Carroll Township, he was elected sheriff in 1880 and moved to the York County Prison with his family to take over his duties as resident jailor. His son Philip acted as deputy sheriff and his other son Henry served as a prison guard. Mrs. Altland, the prison matron, cooked meals and did laundry for her family as well as the inmates.

John complained to Altland of his wounds, and Dr. S. J. Rouse was immediately summoned to conduct a thorough exam. After probing both wounds, he proclaimed John's injuries as non-serious. Coyle told Rouse that he had a history of being weak in the head and wanted to be sent to the hospital. The jail was part of a complex of public buildings, including the hospital and the York County Poorhouse, but Dr. Rouse felt it was not necessary. His initial observation was that John did not seem to understand the seriousness of his crime, but he saw no signs of insanity.

By the time John arrived at the jail, the press had already been notified of the crime. Rushing to get information about the murder in time for the evening editions, reporters went to both the jail and the ferry. Accounts appeared the same day of the murder in the *York Dispatch*, the *Lancaster Daily Intelligencer*, and the *Lancaster New Era*. Facts of the crime were telegraphed across the country, and accounts were published the following day in the *New York Sun*.

Visiting John in jail shortly after he arrived, reporters were given an opportunity to interview the prisoner. He told them it would have been better had he killed himself and confessed to the crime, but expressed remorse only in the fact that he had not shared the same fate as his victim. Coyle spoke freely of the crime, and although appearing somewhat incoherent, provided some details of the shooting. After answering a few initial questions, he declined to talk any further, and the reporters left with little new information.

Local headlines on the day of the murder, such as "Murder & Suicide," "A Double Tragedy," and "Horrible Murder," quickly spread the basic facts. Much of the information printed immediately after the crime was conflicting and eventually proven to be erroneous, and editorials left no room for doubt of Coyle's guilt. Most reports implied that Coyle's suicide attempts were shams and portrayed him as a drunken, violent murderer. Through these initial accounts, the public got their first impressions of John Coyle, Jr.

As John settled into jail that afternoon, the scene back at the river was one of mass confusion and intense excitement. According to local accounts, several hundred people had visited the house from both York and Lancaster counties trying to get details of the murder. Sympathy for Emily and Mr. and Mrs. Coyle contrasted with the anger towards John, and talk of his mental instability and irrational behavior over the years flowed freely.

Emily's sister Annie, who lived in Harrisburg and worked as a clerk in a dry goods store, was notified of the morning's events via telegraph. Upon receiving the news of the murder, she immediately left on the first train for Marietta. Arriving in the early afternoon, she first went to see her grand-uncle Simon Myers who lived on Gay Street. Together they crossed the river to see Emily's body and learn the details of what had happened.

John Bastian, a cabinet-maker and the local undertaker, accompanied Simon and Annie Myers across the river. Bastian lived in a log house half a block from the square on the south side of Main Street in Marietta and had his wood shop in a building at the rear of his lot. Besides furniture, he also made wooden coffins and prepared bodies for burial. Simon had asked Bastian to come along to take care of Emily's body and directed Bastian to put the corpse on ice as soon as possible.[*]

---

[*] *Ice was commonly used to keep a corpse cool until it could be buried. The body was put in a specially designed ice box or on a cooling board, a flat board with holes, and placed on top of ice blocks. Embalming was not widely used in 1881, but became more popular after the Civil War when it was necessary to allow the bodies of soldiers to be preserved until shipped to their hometowns.*

After arriving at the ferry, Bastian fashioned a crude cooling table in a shed at the western end of the house by laying out long boards on several large blocks of ice dug out from a layer of sawdust in the ice house. Leaving a gap between the boards to allow the ice to cool her body, he laid a clean sheet over the table, followed by Emily's corpse and another clean sheet, covering her to the neck.

After Bastian finished, Annie went to view the body and spent some time alone weeping over her dead sister. Mary Ann Coyle retrieved some of Emily's personal effects to give to Annie, including the pale blue dress from her clothes chest for the undertaker to use for her burial. Taking the dress, Bastian promised to return the next morning and carry Emily across the river to prepare her for internment in Marietta.

Other relatives, including Mary Ann's sister, Kate Hinkle, came to the ferry during the afternoon. She spent the day trying to console Mrs. Coyle, who was still extremely broken up from the morning's events. Emily's grandfather Samuel Myers, with whom she had lived in Chambersburg, was notified but did not make the trip to York County. Coincidentally, an unnamed suitor from Chambersburg had arrived in Marietta that morning and was planning to come across the river to visit Emily, but learning of the murder he left on the first train home, not wanting to see her body.

By the time a *York Dispatch* reporter arrived at Coyle's Ferry in the early evening, "the excitement had died out, and unusual quiet reigned."[5] Riding up to the inn, he found Mr. and Mrs. Coyle sitting on the front porch. When he approached, John's parents talked freely and "appeared willing to impart all they knew of the sad affair,"[6] despite the number of times they had been asked the same questions all day.

Perhaps hoping to temper the brutality of the murder, the article which appeared the following day in the *York Dispatch* began with an account of the ferry and surrounding area. "The view from the porch is one of exceeding beauty ... on both banks of the river the scenery is wild and romantic ... a river road, a beautiful drive, though wild and rough, leads from the ferry house to Wrightsville ... on pleasant evenings the river is dotted with skiffs and row boats containing pleasure parties ... Coyle's ferry was a favorite resort for pleasure parties of various kinds, and many have been the exciting scenes enacted in the neighborhood."[7]

Mr. Coyle began by giving some personal information about Emily, including where she had been born and subsequently lived, along with a detailed physical description. He complimented Emily, calling her "very handsome, short in stature, but well proportioned, with fine complexion, black hair and large grey eyes ... industrious and willing to work ... kind and attentive," but perhaps for not taking John threats seriously enough, he added "quite ignorant."[8]

He placed some of the blame for the shooting on Emily, explaining that John was "fascinated by her appearance and manner" and "she tantalized him beyond all endurance with her coquettish ways ... she had promised to marry him, but afterwards changed her mind, and declared she cared nothing for him."[9] Admitting that John openly threatened to kill Emily several times, he said he had previously warned her that his son was dangerous, but she was not afraid and had dared John to harm her, not thinking that he would.

Mr. Coyle expressed that he had always considered John to be of unsound mind, and thought his troubles were aggravated by hard drinking. Describing attempts to get help for his son's disordered mind, he claimed the doctors told him nothing could be done. Perhaps attempting to plant the idea of John's mental instability, he recounted several attempts where John had physically attacked and threatened him. The interview concluded with a detailed description of the morning's events.

Decoration Day, which had begun on such a promising note, finally came to a close, with Emily lying dead at the ferry and John locked in a jail cell in York. The Coyles tried to find sleep, but it was to elude them that night, and for many nights to come. Thinking back over the years of trouble and heartache that John had caused, they knew the next few months would bring them even more pain.

Chapter 12

York County Prison
Tuesday, May 31, 1881

"Imprisonment is as irrevocable as death"
... George Bernard Shaw

Except for the short visit by the reporter from *The Dispatch*, John had been left alone for the remainder of his first evening. The gas lights in the prison were turned out promptly at 9 o'clock and John spent an uncomfortable night listening to the trains which ran constantly on the tracks on each side of the prison. He tried to close his eyes and sleep, but every time he heard the rail cars and the whistle of the engine, he thought of his home and the sounds of the train across the river in Marietta.

After a sleepless and painful first night in jail, John sat on the edge of his bed and watched the narrow rectangle of light cast by the rising sun move slowly down the door of his cell. It entered the room through a three-foot-six-inch by five-inch slit in the large cast-iron window set high off the floor. Even standing on his toes, all John could see was the bright blue early morning sky.

The cell was fifteen-foot long, eight-foot wide, and ten-foot high. The two-foot-thick interior walls were made of plastered brick, and the exterior end wall with the window was two-and-a-half-foot-thick sandstone. On the wall opposite the window were two doors, the inner one made of cast iron lattice and the outer of thick oak with a screen peephole and food wicket. As the weather had been hot the previous week, the outer door was propped about a third of the way open, but not far enough so that John could see into any of the other cells.

The sparse furnishings consisted of a pine bedstead with a straw mattress and pillow, a stool, and a table which folded down against the wall when not in use. A small cabinet contained two blankets, two sheets, a bible, a small mirror, a towel, soap, a tin pan for washing, and a small comb. Utensils, salt and pepper, a bottle of vinegar, and a two quart can of molasses were provided for meals. Fresh water was provided by turning an iron key on a small spigot which emptied into a wooden bucket on the floor.

A toilet pipe was located in one of the corners, connected to an eight inch water main which ran at a slight angle along the length of the outside wall. On one end was a closed valve and on the other a water tank. Every morning, the lower valve was opened and the pipe purged with water from the reservoir, flushing the contents into the sewer. The valve was then closed and the pipe was filled with a few inches of water.

Shortly after Coyle woke, Sheriff Altland explained the prison rules. A pull string, connected to a bell in the hallway, was to be used to call if needed. John would be allowed outside in the yard for one hour each day and could use the bath cell, with hot and cold water, once a week if desired. Every other week he would be given a tablespoon of lime, to be mixed with water and poured into the privy pipe.

Three meals of bread and water would be provided each day with an occasional boiled egg. Meat and soup were served on Wednesdays and Saturdays, and friends were allowed to bring food to his cell. Tobacco was permitted, but not provided by the county. The molasses supply was to last thirty days and John would be allowed one candle per week. A physician would visit twice a week, paid by the county, and could be called if necessary.

The York County Prison, completed in 1854, was designed to accommodate the implementation of the Pennsylvania System of discipline. The System had been widely used in Pennsylvania for a little over fifty years by the time John Coyle spent his first night in prison. However, its origins dated back to William Penn and the beginnings of Pennsylvania itself.

The Pennsylvania System advocated solitary confinement, complete silence, and private labor, as well as instruction in morals and religion. Occupations included weaving, shoe making, and the production of nails and brooms. Following the implementation of the System in state penitentiaries, prison reformers turned their attention to county prisons. These facilities were generally used for holding prisoners "some of whom are charged with no offense, but are held to secure their appearance as witnesses – others of whom are charged with offenses of various grades, but some of these are innocent and will so appear on trial; some are guilty and will be punished – others of whom are already convicted of trivial offenses, and are subjected to only a few weeks or months of detention."[1]

Since more prisoners were incarcerated at the county level, advocates of the Pennsylvania System were convinced it could be applied at that level and reach a larger inmate population. Following debates in the legislature, the search began for an architect who could oversee the construction of new county facilities and design them for the implementation of the more strict approach to imprisonment.

Edward Haviland, the architect of the York County Prison where John Coyle was incarcerated, was the preeminent designer of prisons, schools, churches and other public buildings in Pennsylvania. His father, John Haviland, was well known for designing the Eastern State Penitentiary in Philadelphia, the first penal institution planned specifically to accommodate the principles of the Pennsylvania System.

Using the architectural concepts developed by his father, Edward was contracted to design a series of Pennsylvania county prisons during his career, including York County (York, 1854), Cumberland County (Carlisle, 1854), Lycoming County (Williamsport, 1868), Northampton (Easton, 1869), Blair County (Hollidaysburg, 1870), Carbon County (Jim Thorpe, 1871), and Cambria County (Ebensburg, 1872). All were styled with similar castle-like facades and incorporated design features conducive to the Pennsylvania System.

Acknowledging the influence his father had on his own work, Edward Haviland described the design of the York County prison in an issue of The Pennsylvania Journal of Prison Discipline. "While carrying out the principles of prison-construction which were laid down by my father in fundamental, I have endeavored to keep pace with the progress of the age, by introducing several improvements which have been suggested by additional experience in relation to detail."[2]

The new prison replaced the dilapidated former jail on the corner of South George and King Streets and was built on the northeastern outskirts of the city, just outside the borough limits at the end of Chestnut Street. Constructed on the sprawling grounds of the York County Poorhouse and Hospital, the jail was bounded in the rear by the Northern Central railroad leading east to the river and in front by a spur of the Pennsylvania and Maryland Railroad leading south.

The prison consisted of a castellated façade housing offices and living quarters, a rear building containing a two-story cell block, and a yard enclosed by a high stone wall. Two square towers were connected by a curtain wall overhanging the steps leading to the massive oak entrance. Above the arched doorway hung a large marble tablet with the names of the architect and builders.

Rising behind the curtain wall was a central polygonal tower, which contained the main ventilation shaft and an observatory. From the front, the brown sandstone and blue limestone prison resembled a fortress, characterizing the strength of the structure and the grim nature of its purpose. All of the stone used to construct the prison was obtained from local York County quarries.

The prison office and meeting rooms were located on the first floor of the front building, along with the apartment for the sheriff and his family. The living quarters contained a parlor, a dining-room, a kitchen with a range, large oven and pantry, and a laundry with cast-iron boilers and wash tubs. Bedrooms were located on the second floor, as well as the stairway to the central tower and observatory. Only one doorway connected the front building and the cell block, secured by a grated wrought-iron door and a second of oak.

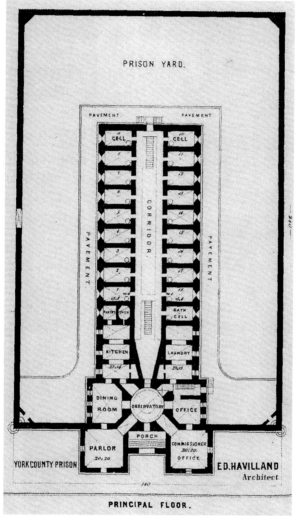

Architect's ground floor plan of 1853 York County Prison [3]

The rear cell block contained cells on both floors, arranged on each side of a fifteen-foot-wide corridor with a vaulted brick ceiling and brown sandstone tiled floor. The open corridor was lit from above with ten skylights located in the sides of the arched roof and a large semi-circular window provided additional light. A cast iron stairway at each end of the corridor provided access to the second floor, which contained a narrow balcony in front of each row of cells.

In addition to cells, a bath and shower was located on the first floor, with hot and cold water. The large eight-bed infirmary on the second floor was well-ventilated and lit by three large windows secured with wrought-iron grating, and faced east to obtain the perceived health benefit of the morning sun. The York County prison was the first in the state to include an infirmary as part of the original design.

A twenty-foot-high stone wall surrounded the yard, capped with iron and sunk four feet in the ground. The yard was accessed via the sheriff's quarters or through a door at the end of the corridor in the cell-block. Apparently the sheriff and his family were not provided with the same conveniences as the prisoners, for in each of the front corners of the prison wall were the toilet facilities for their use.

Although the York County prison was designed for the implementation of the Pennsylvania System, it was rarely enforced. As was the case in most counties, local sheriffs served as the jail keepers and were responsible for making sure that the penal recommendations of the state were followed. However, other duties outside the jail often precluded them from instituting cellular labor or keeping prisoners from associating with each other.

This was most certainly the case in York County, where Samuel Altland, in addition to his frequent duties escorting prisoners to and from the Court House and attending court proceedings, had other business interests which demanded his attention. During his tenure as sheriff, he continued to maintain his brickyard in Dillsburg and a seventeen-acre woodlot in Warrington Township.

Even though reforms were constantly proposed, local sheriffs remained the keepers of county prisons in Pennsylvania. Plagued with continual over-crowding and the election of a new administrator every three years, county jails in Pennsylvania were rarely administered according to the Pennsylvania System. This situation was documented each year in the Annual Report of the Board of Commissioners of Public Charities, which included the results of yearly inspection visits and the conditions of each county jail.

The first of these reports in 1870 included a detailed description of the York County prison, and described some minor changes made to the facility following its opening fifteen year earlier in 1855. Three cells on each side of the first floor corridor had been joined together forming two larger rooms, one for the congregation of the prisoners, and the other for religious services which were held every Sunday. Although it was "regarded as one of the best prisons in the state,"[4] the inspectors noted that the frequent change in management at every election caused difficulties in administering the prison as consistently as it should be.

Documenting a situation which would become a theme in future annual reviews, they stated "Although the prison is well adapted to the separate system of discipline with labor, the prisoners are allowed to congregate during the day, apparently without any restraint as to the character of their crimes, their vicious propensities, sex or other condition; all mingle together. This state of things ought not to exist in any prison ..."[5]

The inspectors felt that running a prison required experience, which "... could not be expected from those whose duties and habits of life have always been in other directions. It is no disparagement to the intelligent and excellent gentleman who officiates as sheriff of York County at present ... his principal duties lie in a different direction, and perhaps there is no one more competent to perform them; but the keeper of a prison should be a person who can devote all his time to the management of those under his care; and when he has shown himself to be well qualified for the duties for which he was selected, he should not be subject to removal merely because of the expiration of his term."[6]

Conditions had not improved by 1879, and the report for the year contained many of the same comments, including "The practice of strict separation ... is not deemed to be very important," "during all hours of the day they occupy the lower corridor and the cells communicating," "little or nothing is done to counteract the baneful effects of uninterrupted idleness," and "employment is not provided."[7]

The report also noted that since the separate system had not been implemented in York County, its construction in such a manner had been a waste. "It seems to be worse than folly if our county penal institutions are to be conducted in this careless manner, to incur the heavy expense for putting up buildings of that kind. A building with a single apartment, with enclosures sufficiently strong to prevent escapes, would answer the purpose, wherever that way of conducting them prevails. But as public sentiment becomes enlightened upon the improved systems of dealing with the criminal class, the necessity will occur for a more rigid compliance with the requirements of law – the separate confinement, at hard labor, of persons found guilty of crime."[8]

By the time John Coyle entered the jail in York County, the prisoner count was down to thirty-five, including a youth under the age of fourteen guilty of larceny, three vagrants and three females housed in the upper tier. The annual inspection on July 30, 1881, conducted two months after his arrest, noted his presence, "One charged for homicide is held for trial."[9] The situation at the jail was much the same as it had been for the previous ten years, with the report once more stressing the importance of separating the prisoners from one another, "The extent to which indiscriminate association is practiced in this prison is a wrong which should be corrected."[10]

The Pennsylvania System, although never extensively implemented in the United States, was widely copied throughout the world. "It was not until 1913 that the system was definitely and legally abandoned, although it was in practice on the wane only a short time after it was initiated."[11] As was the case in York County, overcrowding due to an ever-increasing prison population forced administrators to place two or more inmates in a single cell, thereby negating the primary principle of the System. This, along with the cost of building prisons large enough to house each prisoner individually and the ineffectiveness of inmate labor, eventually doomed it to obsolescence.

The York County Prison soon outgrew its capacity and the front castle façade was torn down in 1906 and replaced with a larger brick addition containing eighty-four cells. The rear cell block where John Coyle was imprisoned was eventually torn down, and the entire prison was abandoned in the late 1970's when a new county facility was built in Springettsbury Township in East York.

The deteriorating prison on Chestnut Street remains vacant, waiting to be torn down or developed for another use. The poorhouse and hospital have long since been demolished and the Alexander D. Goode Elementary School stands in their place. Portions of the original cell block where John Coyle was housed, including one of the massive cast iron window frames and iron lattice cell doors, are on display in the Police Heritage Museum in downtown York.

As John sat in Cell 18 the morning after the murder, John Bastian returned to Coyle's Ferry to carry Emily's remains back across the river to Marietta. With the help of Mr. Coyle, they moved her corpse from the shed next to the house to an ice box that Bastian had brought with him. After loading it into the back of the undertaker's wagon, Mr. Coyle ferried Bastian back to Marietta and immediately returned home to his still grieving wife Mary Ann.

Emily's body was taken to the undertaker's shop at the rear of Bastian's house on Main Street and prepared for burial. There had been little bleeding, but as Bastian and his assistant Mrs. Kaufman began handling Emily's body, blood began to ooze freely from her chest wound and mouth. They carefully washed her, brushed her hair, and dressed her in the pale blue dress that Mrs. Coyle had given Bastian the previous day.

They placed Emily in a loose shroud, pulled up to her waist, and placed her in a simple wooden coffin. She was then taken to the house of her grand-uncle Simon Myers on Gay Street, where the funeral was to be held the following day. Emily was laid out for viewing in the front parlor, where all the furniture had been removed to accommodate visitors and flowers. There were already some arrangements in the room, and Bastian made sure that he placed a black floral wreath on the front porch to signify a house of mourning.

Emily was to be buried in the Marietta Cemetery on Wednesday, and Bastian sent John Deppeler to dig her grave. The exact location is unknown, since some accounts reported her being buried in the Marietta Cemetery and others the Samaritan Cemetery. The Marietta Cemetery on Fairview Avenue does not contain a headstone for Emily, and the Samaritan Cemetery no longer exists. Old property maps of Marietta locate a small cemetery on the corner of Gay Street and West Prospect Avenue which may have been the Samaritan Cemetery, but any remains would have been moved when the lot was developed. If Emily was relocated to the Marietta Cemetery, she now lies in an unmarked grave. It is possible she is buried in the Marietta Cemetery in the plot owned by her grand-uncle Simon, which is marked with a single headstone for his wife Sarah Myers

The process of prosecuting John Coyle began immediately. The proceedings of the Coroner's inquest held the previous day at the scene of the crime were delivered to Edward D. Ziegler, the District Attorney in York. The findings read "That the said John Coyle, Jr. did violently, feloniously and of his malice aforethought, fire the said pistol, the ball therefrom penetrating the heart of aforesaid Emily Myers, and giving to the said Emily Myers a mortal wound, of which said mortal wound the aforesaid Emily Myers then and there instantly died: so the said John Coyle, Jr., then and there feloniously killed and murdered the said Emily Myers, against the peace and dignity of the Commonwealth of Pennsylvania."[12] Ziegler scheduled the presentation of the findings to the court for the following Thursday, June 9, and immediately began preparing his case against Coyle.

Ziegler, an 1865 graduate of Pennsylvania College in Gettysburg, taught at the York Academy* for three years. While

---

* *The York County Academy, incorporated in 1787, was located on North Beaver Street in York. In 1929, it co-located with the York Collegiate Institute on the corner of South Duke Street and College Avenue. After merging in 1934, the school moved for the final time in 1965 to the current location on Country Club Road.*

teaching, he studied law and was admitted to the York County Bar in 1868. After serving as the Clerk of the County Commissioners for several terms, he was elected as District Attorney in York County at age thirty-seven, a post he held from 1881 to 1883. The prosecution of John Coyle would have been one of the first cases he tried as the new D.A., and was probably Ziegler's first capital case. He went on to serve in the U.S. House of Representatives in the Fifty-Sixth Congress from 1899-1901, then returned to York to resume his legal practice.

A few of Coyle's friends, including several young ladies, visited him on his first full day in prison. Since he did not generally associate with people his own age, most likely these visitors were curiosity seekers attempting to find information about the murder. The prison rules were not strictly followed, and visits in his cell during the time he was in York were not unusual.

As John was being led to jail at the ferry the previous day, his father had promised he would come to visit as soon as possible, but had not arrived by late afternoon. Although John was more attached to his mother, and would have liked her to come to the jail, he knew she was not able to easily leave the house and travel due to her rheumatism. As the day wore on, John became worried about not seeing his father and began to get anxious concerning his fate.

In the middle of the afternoon, a reporter visited with John and was granted an interview. Coyle spoke freely of the murder and told the reporter he was sorry he had killed Emily and that he loved her, but stressed the fact that she promised to marry him and had gone back on her word and dared him to kill her. He told the reporter he went to the barn with the intention of getting Emily to agree to marry him, and when she refused, he was so exasperated and maddened with rage that he didn't know what he was doing when he shot her.

After answering a few initial questions, John refused to talk any further and the reporter was left to draw his own conclusions from their brief conversation. Although the resulting article speculated Coyle would probably plead insanity due to his reputation for erratic behavior, and reported his parents had apparently spent large sums of money treating him, the paper was not hesitant to pass judgment on his sanity. "His conversation, behavior, and appearance are those of a perfectly sane man."[13] The correspondent felt that John did not seem to comprehend the enormity of his actions, but "evidently thinks it justifiable, from the girl's treatment to his advances."[14]

John was described as haggard, restless, and nervous, and his lone condition was pitied by the other inmates. His poor physical appearance was attributed to the fact that he was a prolific drinker and "was recovering from the effects of a prolonged debauch, which are yet visible upon his face."[15] He told the reporter he no longer wanted to end his life, but was anxious to be relieved of the pain caused by his wounds. During the interview, he constantly bathed his head and chest with cool water from his cell, and he was of the opinion that the doctors weren't taking his injuries seriously enough.

Hurrying from the prison with his interview, the reporter filed a hastily prepared article in time for typesetting and publication in Tuesday's edition of several newspapers in both York and Lancaster County. Reports of the murder were published only one day after it occurred as far as New York City, where headlines announced "A Rejected Suitor's Crime – Shooting a Girl Dead who Refused to Marry Him, then Attempting Suicide."[16]

After the reporter left, John had no more visitors until Sheriff Altland's son Phillip brought his evening bread. He eventually tried to get some sleep, but his head wound was painful, and the one on his breast prevented him from finding a comfortable position. As Emily lay peacefully at rest in Simon Myer's parlor in Marietta, John spent another sleepless and fitful night listening to the noisy and unfamiliar sounds of the city and the trains heading towards his home.

Chapter 13

Marietta, Pa
Wednesday, June 1, 1881

"An indictment is not a conviction"

... Howard Coble

Wednesday morning dawned clear and bright in Marietta, the early sun filtering through the honey locust trees which circled the silent graveyard. The trees were planted around the outside of the low iron fence and formed a perimeter around the orderly rows of graves. They were in full bloom, and the combination of the morning light and the copious yellow flowers resulted in a golden glow which saturated everything within.

A slight breeze swayed the branches gently back and forth, circulating the sweet fragrance throughout the cemetery and making the air pregnant with their heavy scent. The green grass and white headstones exuded an air of permanent peacefulness, interrupted only by the large mound of newly excavated earth. As if the grave was impatiently awaiting its occupant, a shovel was stuck expectantly in the pile of fresh dirt.

All morning, beautiful floral arrangements were delivered to the home of Simon Myers on Gay Street, just down the street from the Marietta Cemetery. Smaller sprays were arranged inside the casket and larger bouquets covered the floor, filling the parlor with their intense colors. Meanwhile, people began filling the house to get a last glimpse of Emily.

Emily was not well-known personally in Marietta, and had only visited her grand-uncle Simon on a few occasions. However, her brutal murder was headline news and attracted both friends and relatives of her grand-uncle, as well as the morbidly curious.

The town was full of people from both York and Lancaster Counties, but conspicuously absent were any members of the Coyle family. However, John Coyle, Sr. had spoken to Simon Myers privately earlier that morning, telling him he wanted none of the friends or relatives of the deceased visiting them across the river. Mr. Coyle was confronted by several people when he left, who blamed him for the trouble caused by his son. Attempting to defend himself, he told them he had taken the gun from John the previous Saturday when he had fired at Emily, and did not know where he had gotten another.

The funeral service for Emily began promptly at 3 o'clock at Simon Myers' house, officiated by Reverend Bauman of the Reformed Church and Reverend Shannon of the United Brethren in Christ Church. Only a small number of friends and relatives remained at the house, as the majority of people had already gone directly to the cemetery to await the burial. By the time the funeral procession made its way to the grave, the cemetery was full, and the internment was "one of the largest ever witnessed in Marietta."[1]

John Bastian, Simon Myers, and several neighbors carried Emily's coffin from the parlor to the waiting wagon of the undertaker. After the floral arrangements were heaped around her casket, the cortege moved slowly up Gay Street and through the cemetery gates. When it arrived, the crowd parted and allowed the hearse to pass.

After the wagon made its way to Emily's final resting place, the pall bearers lifted her coffin from the wagon and placed it on the ground at the head of the open grave. Following a short prayer, it was slowly lowered into the ground and John Deppeler closed the grave and covered it with the floral arrangements from the wagon. Leaving Emily alone with the trees and the breeze and the sweet smell of flowers, the crowd solemnly filed out of the cemetery.

After leaving Marietta the morning of Emily's funeral, Mr. Coyle spent the better part of the afternoon in York arranging for a lawyer. He visited his son in jail to discuss plans for his upcoming defense, but John wanted only to complain about the pain in his head. After a brief emotional visit, Mr. Coyle left the prison and retained the services of Henry L. Fisher, Esq. as John's legal counsel.

Henry Lee Fisher was one of the most prominent lawyers of his time in York County, and his legal services did not come cheap. Admitted to the York Bar in 1853, Fisher practiced for over fifty years in York until his death in 1909. Although Mr. Coyle was reputed to be quite wealthy, most of his savings had been spent on John's medical treatments over the years, and whatever was left over had been put back into the ferry and tavern business. In fact, only two months earlier, he had gone back to James Duffy for financial help. Coyle had purchased the ferry from Duffy in 1864, and he knew the wealthy landowner would have the money he desperately needed.

Even though the Coyles had a somewhat tarnished reputation, Duffy lent $1,000 to Mr. Coyle in April, just a month before the murder. Assuming that the money had not already been spent, Coyle was most likely using it to fund the legal fees for his son's defense. As was typical, fifty percent was required to secure the loan, and according to the judgment filed with the court, the note was due in one year "for the payment of Five Hundred dollars ($500.00) with interest at the rate of 6 percent per annum for the same lawful money aforesaid on the first day of April, 1882."[2]

Marietta, Pa
Saturday, June 4, 1881

Once the case was turned over to the District Attorney, the evidence against John Coyle began to be assembled. Although it seemed like a straightforward case, Edward Ziegler had to start from the beginning and gather information from those that had been present immediately after the shooting. He wanted no loopholes or opportunities for Coyle to challenge the basic facts. One of the early questions that puzzled the prosecutor was the fact that Emily had died instantly with one shot, while two subsequent shots fired point-blank by John in an attempt to commit suicide seemingly had little effect.

This apparently was a key point for Ziegler to resolve and he ordered an autopsy to be scheduled on Emily's body as soon as possible. He contacted York County Coroner John Ahl to coordinate the exhumation of the body and gave him instructions to determine why the single shot had been instantly fatal. Dr. Ahl and Dr. M.J. McKinnon, a physician at the newly founded York Hospital, made plans to conduct the autopsy on Saturday, June 4.

Dr. Ahl wired Dr. John A. Thompson of Wrightsville, one of the physicians who had been at the scene of the murder and had participated in the initial coroner's inquest, asking him to accompany them. In addition, he sent a telegram to John Deppeler, the grave digger in Marietta, requesting to have Emily's remains disinterred for the post-mortem examination.

Dr. John Ahl was just beginning his second two-term stint as York County Coroner, first elected in 1849 and recently re-elected in 1878. Ahl, a York native, was born in 1822 and educated at the York County Academy, earning his medical degree at Washington University in Maryland in 1845. Shortly after the Civil War, Dr. Ahl served as the acting physician at the York County almshouse and prison. At the time of his death in 1902, the eighty-year-old Dr. Ahl was the oldest practicing physician in York.

Saturday morning dawned gloomy and wet, and Drs. Ahl and McKinnon boarded the first train east at the passenger station on the corner of North Duke Street and North Street in York in a light rain. Immediately after pulling out from the platform, they passed by the rear of the York County Prison, where John Coyle was just being served his morning bread. The thirteen-mile trip took almost ninety minutes, roughly as long as it would have taken by horse and carriage. The train stopped every few miles, and finally arrived in Wrightsville at the terminus of the York and Wrightsville Railroad at the foot of the covered bridge crossing the Susquehanna.

Dr. Thompson and his son John, a twenty-two year old medical student, were waiting for them at the station when they arrived. After brief introductions, Dr. Thompson told the doctors from York that his son was interested in observing the forensic process and asked if they had any objections to him accompanying them. Dr. Ahl and Dr. McKinnon agreed it would be a valuable experience for the young medical student, and after loading their bags containing their tools and specimen jars into Dr. Thompson's carriage, they immediately set off across the river to Columbia.

After crossing Chiques Ridge, they reached the cemetery in Marietta around 10 o'clock as the slight drizzle was just ending. Arriving much earlier, John Deppeler had just finished exposing the top of Emily's coffin when the carriage arrived. While the sexton finished his exhumation, the three doctors and the soon-to-be doctor chatted about the case and the procedures they planned to use. Drs. McKinnon and Thompson would perform the internal exam with John Thompson assisting, and Dr. Ahl would record the official notes.

When Deppeler was finished, they helped him heave the casket out of the ground, placing it at the head of the open grave just as it had been three days previous. This time however, the five of them were alone in the graveyard with Emily. Several curious onlookers gathered nearby, but were asked to stay outside the fence while the doctors conducted their ghoulish work. They donned full-length white aprons, asked Deppeler to retrieve a bucket of water from one of the nearby houses, and turned to their work.

Emily's body was left in the coffin during the autopsy, and after removing the shroud from her lower body, Dr. Thompson fashioned it into a small pillow. They rolled Emily over, unbuttoned the back of her pale blue dress, and folded it down past her waist and over her legs. While she was still on her stomach, they examined the exit wound, determining that the bullet had passed between her eighth and ninth rib, five inches from her spinal column. When Emily was turned back over, the makeshift pillow was placed under the small of her back to push her chest upward to facilitate the exam.

Dr. McKinnon opened his leather roll of surgical instruments and placed them across Emily's thighs. He made a single cut in her chest with a scalpel, starting in the middle of the neck, passing through the entrance wound in the center of her chest and ending at the top of her pubic bone. Since the bullet had struck her five inches directly below the top of the sternum, it should have missed her vital organs. Like the D.A., they were also puzzled why she had died instantly.

After opening her chest, Dr. McKinnon searched the abdominal cavity with his hands looking for the ball, but found none. His first observation was that the heart was in malposition, lying directly below the sternum instead of inclining to the right. The bullet had passed through both lower chambers of her heart and Dr. Thompson noted "the hole in one of the ventricles is large enough to admit my little finger, the other not quite so large."[3] After passing through the heart, the bullet went through the lower right lobe of her lung, and splintered the lower edge of her eighth rib before exiting.

Positional anomalies of the human heart are rare, and Emily probably experienced symptoms such as an elevated heart rate or shortness of breath all her life. The graveside diagnosis answered the question of her immediate death and according to the doctors, "If the heart had occupied its normal position, the ball would have passed to the right of the heart, and while the wound might have caused death, it could not have been instantaneous as in this case."[4]

After no other internal injuries or abnormalities were found, Dr. McKinnon removed the heart from her body and put it in glass jar of alcohol, placing it in the possession of Dr. Ahl. Although not necessary since the funeral had already taken place, and no one else would be viewing the body, they crudely sewed her chest back together and redressed Emily. After washing their hands and removing their bloody aprons, they closed the coffin and packed their instruments. The sexton had returned to the cemetery shortly before the autopsy was finished, and with the doctors' help, returned Emily's coffin to the ground. The doctors soon left, and Deppeler and his son began refilling the grave with dirt, covering Emily once again.

On Monday, June 6, exactly one week after the murder of
Emily Myers, the results of the coroner's inquest held at Coyle's Ferry
were filed with the York County Court. A hearing was scheduled for
Thursday, June 9, to present the findings to the presiding judge. When
the proceedings came to order, Judge Wickes of the Court of Oyer &
Terminer read the petition prepared by District Attorney Ziegler.

"In the Court of Oyer and Terminer, of York County, Penna.
To the honorable Pere L. Wickes, Judge of said court, the undersigned
District Attorney, of said county, respectfully informs the Court, that an
inquisition was indented and taken at Coyle's Ferry, in the county of
York, on the thirtieth day of May, A.D. 1881, before Frank J. Magee,
one of the justices of the peace, in and for said county, upon the view
of the body of Emily Myers, then and there lying dead, upon the
solemn affirmation of Dr. G.A Rebman, Alexander R. Thompson,
William S. Sweeney, William A. Thompson, Daniel H. Moore and
John A. Thompson; That said inquisition was filed in your Honorable
Court, on the sixth day of June, A.D., 1881. That the finding of the
inquisition is, that John Coyle, Jr., in and upon the aforesaid, Emily
Myers, feloniously, violently, and of his malice aforethought, made an
assault, and that the said John Coyle, Jr., did violently, feloniously, and
of his malice aforethought, kill and murder the said Emily Myers. That
no information in the usual form, under the oath of any person, has
come to the knowledge of the District Attorney against the said John
Coyle, Jr., for the crime charged and found, by the said inquisition.
That the said John Coyle, Jr., has been arrested and is now in the
custody of the Sheriff, of said county, for the crime of murder. The
undersigned District Attorney, therefore, respectfully submits to the
Court, what action, if any, should be taken by him, under the above
facts, in prosecution of the said John Coyle, Jr., for the felony found
and charged as aforesaid.

Edward D. Ziegler
District Attorney"[5]

The Court of Oyer & Terminer[*] had its origins in England, where judges were commissioned to rule on cases of treason, felonies and misdemeanors. In the United States, it referred to criminal court sessions in Pennsylvania and some other states. Judge Pere L. Wickes was in his sixth year as an elected law judge in York County by the time the Coyle case came before him, and the District Attorney's petition was handled expeditiously, as were most of his cases.

Wickes had a strong family tradition of legal service in Maryland, his father being a prominent lawyer and his brother a judge. Educated at Princeton, he moved to York in 1866 and served as an attorney for the Northern Central and Pennsylvania Railroad until his election as judge. Following the Coyle case in 1882, he succeeded Robert J. Fisher as president judge of the York Judicial District. After three years, he moved back to his home state of Maryland in 1885, where he was appointed a judge in Baltimore.

In terms of his reputation on the bench, Wickes was known as a no-nonsense judge with a "quick, active, comprehensive intellect, and unimpeachable integrity, great administrative abilities. Consequently, his courts are characterized by a speedy dispatch of business, perfect decorum, and an economical administration of the law."[6] Although it would not be the case in the Coyle trial, Judge Wickes "suffered few reversals by the supreme court of the State, which is evidence not only of his success on the bench, but also of his fairness as a judge."[7]

After considering the District Attorney's petition, Judge Wickes directed an indictment to be prepared and presented to a Grand Jury the following day. According to the official ruling, "On presentation of this paper, the Court orders the District Attorney, to prepare and send to the Grand Jury an indictment, charging such offense as the finding of the inquest dictates, and as such will meet the demands of justice."[8]

---

[*] *a term of French origin meaning to "hear and determine"*

The following morning, on Friday, June 10, John Coyle left the prison for the first time since his arrest. Sheriff Altland shackled his wrists with iron cuffs and escorted him to the York County Courthouse to be present for the Grand Jury proceedings. The jury consisted of twenty-three local citizens, randomly selected from the juror's wheel and appointed for a term of about a month. Their job was to hear and rule on potential cases presented by the District Attorney's office.

Unlike a "petit" jury of twelve who decide if a defendant is guilty of criminal charges, a "grand" jury determines only whether there is enough evidence of a crime to warrant a trial. If, after hearing the facts and examining evidence, the Grand Jury decides not to allow the District Attorney to prosecute, the case is dismissed and a verdict of "no true bill" is returned. However, if enough evidence exists to justify a trial, a verdict of "true bill" is returned and the charges which the District Attorney is allowed to file are written on the indictment.

For John Coyle, the Grand Jury was the first stop in his long legal journey and the first of many court appearances. Chances of a true bill being returned were a foregone conclusion, especially since he freely admitted to committing the murder. Prosecutors were almost always given permission to proceed with criminal cases as it was not necessary to prove guilt, and all the District Attorney had to do was convince the jury that Coyle *may* have committed the crime.

In the indictment against John Coyle, the Grand Jury immediately returned a true bill, finding enough probable cause to send the case to trial. They had listened intently as District Attorney Ziegler read the bill of indictment and a prepared statement containing the essential facts of the case. After retiring to the Grand Jury Room, they deliberated only a few minutes before reaching their decision.

Following the reading of the verdict, Coyle was brought before Judge Wickes for arraignment, and the case was assigned No. 58 in the June Quarter Session 1881 of the Court and Oyer and Terminer of York County. Before Wickes had a chance to read the indictment, Henry Fisher interrupted to ask permission to consult with his client in private for a few moments. The request was granted and the judge indicated they could use the petit jury room. Sheriff Altland escorted Fisher and Coyle from the courtroom, and once in the jury room, Fisher asked Altland to leave so he could speak to his client privately.

Altland hesitantly left them alone and closed the door, only to return a few minutes later indicating the Court preferred that he remain with them. Fisher agreed, stipulating the sheriff be there only to retain custody of Coyle and was not to speak of their conversation with anyone. After Altland nodded his head in assent, Fisher discussed with Coyle what would happen in the courtroom and how he should plead to the charges when asked. Although he vehemently denied doing so at the ensuing trial, Fisher presumably was setting the stage for a defense of insanity and coached Coyle to answer in such a way that would give the appearance that he was of unsound mind.

After returning from the jury room, the indictment was read before the court, formally charging Coyle with the first degree murder of Emily Myers. According to an Act of the General Assembly dated the March 31, 1860, "All murder which shall be perpetrated by means of poison, or by lying in wait, or by any other kind of willful, deliberate or premeditated killing, or which shall be committed in the perpetration of, or attempt to perpetrate arson, rape, burglary, shall be deemed murder of the first degree."[9] As the indictment declared that Coyle had murdered Emily "feloniously, willfully, and of his malice aforethought," it was clear the District Attorney would be pursuing a first degree charge.

Judge Wickes asked Coyle if he was guilty of the felony of which he stood accused and how he wished to plead. Coyle immediately responded "I don't know anything about it." Wickes explained the charges on the indictment again, indicating he was asking the prisoner to plead guilty or not guilty. Coyle responded in the same manner, and after the judge repeated the question a final time, the identical answer was given. Judge Wickes then directed a plea of "not guilty" to be entered on the bill of indictment, along with Coyle's peculiar response of "I don't know anything about it."[10]

Since the defense was unprepared for the trial to begin immediately, the Court ordered the case to be deferred until the October Term. District Attorney Ziegler gave his consent to hold the case over and Judge Wickes banged his gavel to end the proceedings.

Sheriff Altland led Coyle from the courtroom and down the front steps of the courthouse, where a small group gathered waiting to get a glimpse of the murderer before he returned to jail. Amid the questions and shouts of the angry crowd, Coyle turned his head away and climbed on to the jailer's wagon without saying a word. It was painfully obvious that everyone on the steps had already formed an opinion of Coyle's guilt and the punishment he should receive.

Although the legal proceedings against John Coyle began with the return of a true bill from the Grand Jury, the court of public opinion had already reached its verdict at least a week earlier. On Thursday morning, June 2, only three days after the murder, the morning edition of the *York Daily* published an anonymous editorial, laced with sarcasm and religious fervor. Signed "Justitia[†]," the editorial dismissed the validity of the insanity defense. Quoting the scriptures, the writer of the piece condemned John Coyle, Jr. to death before he ever appeared in court. The following passionate editorial, along with the many newspaper accounts which detailed the crime, did not allow much chance for an impartial jury in York County.

A CARNIVAL OF BLOOD

EDS. DAILY: Not long since one the Harrisburg papers contained the account of a young man, who some years ago, wantonly, and without provocation, killed his father. He was tried for the offence, and sentenced to a few years

---

[†] *the Latin personification of justice depicted by a blindfolded female goddess holding the scales of truth and carrying a sword*

in the State prison. His father was the son of an eminent and well-known citizen of the State of New York, and himself a resident of that State. After a short confinement he was pardoned on the ground that a longer confinement would seriously affect his mind and make him an idiot. He immediately went away with his mother, and traveled in Europe, where he spent some time, and then returned entirely restored in health, and took up the study of law. A short time after that young man, A MURDERER OF HIS OWN FATHER, passed a successful, and the papers say, "a brilliant examination" and was admitted to the bar in his native town. This is the history of A MURDERER, in this land, in the Christian commonwealth of New York. The "plea of insanity" was set up. And presumably Christian men took the blood of this inhuman wretch upon their heads, and let him live, contrary to the plainly declared will of God. And, more, he has been allowed, with hands bloody with gore of a father slain, to enter a profession that is supposed to be devoted to the administration of exact justice. Where is this to end? And the press is teeming with accounts of horrid murders, committed under most atrocious circumstances, and few are adequately punished, or even punished at all. In Allegheny county, in this State, over twenty murders were committed last year, and none suffered death, and we are informed but one, or two, were convicted. This is enough to startle any man interested in the execution of justice, or the preservation of human life.

We are again furnished with another "horror," and this time nearer home. "The Coyle Ferry Tragedy" has made its little sensation. An unusually attractive young woman has been shot by a miserable and worthless scamp, for the enormous crime of refusing to marry him. She, poor thing, no doubt selected the best of the two alternatives offered her.

But already the heartless murderer knows what will save him probably. He begins to talk about "insanity." He has not read the papers to no purpose. He knows what stuff Governors, Boards of Pardon, and juries are made of in these days, and so, first, the girl was to blame, she would not marry him. And then whiskey is to blame. And lastly, his head is weak. It has been known all these years that he was insane(!!!) $1,500 have been spent in having him examined(!!!) His venerable father thought "his brain was not right," after the shooting. Well, Mr. Editor, are we going to have another farce in the administration of justice! The Scriptures know no such thing as "insanity" in the matter of murder. Why shall the decay of a tissue or the inflammation of a portion of the human system produce a moral, or immoral action? Why don't men become "insane" in matters of benevolence and life saving? Parallel the thousands of murders in this country, with cases in which men give up all they have, and make themselves poor for the good of others. No, the insanity is all on one side. It is to evil. When David wanted to feign insanity before Akish, king of Goth, it did not occur to him to kill somebody. He just "let his spittle run down his beard" and scratched the gate-post. And Akish said: "Lo, ye see the man is mad." "Possession of Devils" is the true explanation of the murderer's condition, as it was of the "demonic" in the tombs who was so "exceedingly fierce that no man dared pass that way."

And God's law, the "the murderer shall be surely put to death," is the only way to make human life safe, as it is the only one to cleanse the land from the blood-guiltiness.

JUSTITIA

Henry Fisher, the defense attorney representing John Coyle, must have been furious upon reading the editorial by Justitia. The trial was not to begin for another four months, and with negative publicity already being published, it would be difficult to select a panel of twelve impartial jurors and expect them to be unbiased. He hurriedly penned the following rebuttal in time for inclusion in the evening edition of the *York Dispatch* and rushed it to the printing office. In his reply, he attempted to mitigate any damage done to his client by attacking Justitia with his own round of sarcasm. He pleaded with the public to ignore the comments of the anonymous writer and allow Coyle to have the opportunity of a fair trial.

THE CRY FOR BLOOD

MR. EDITOR: - Some pious, blood thirsty soul – probably a monomaniac on the subject of "the rope" – has been permitted (very injudiciously, I submit) to indulge in an insane raving for gore, supported by an amount of scripture, over the very inappropriate signature of "Justitia," in the *York Daily* of this morning. What seems to trouble

"Justitia" is the late Coyle "CARNIVAL OF BLOOD," and, moreover, that Coyle, the accused, is actually to have decent chance for his life in a court of justice, and might possibly escape hanging, even on the "plea of insanity," though "the Scriptures know no such thing in the matter of murder." What a pity it is, that such a repository of wisdom as "Justitia" must be, should write over a fictitious signature and deny the world the pleasure and advantage of looking upon and taking knowledge as such a consummate "LL.D. A.SS!"

"Justitia" (I can't use the pronoun because I don't know the sex) thinks "we are going to have another farce in the administration of justice." Coyle is going to set up the (always) false plea of insanity and upon it be acquitted, and turned loose upon the community, with a court's license to kill and murder at his free will and pleasure. But "Justitia" knows all this. Gifted with a supernatural vision, "Justitia" has penetrated the wonderful workings and structure of the human brain and seen for "Justitia's" self that John Coyle, Jr., is and was perfectly sane when he killed Miss Myers, the girl he *so ardently loved* that he desired not to survive her refusal to marry him.

The gross impropriety of thus attempting to forestall public opinion and arouse public hatred and prejudice in the hearts and minds of those whose province it will be to try the prisoner, did not occur to "Justitia." Let me suggest to that sapient individual, who is so exceedingly anxious to have Coyle's case prejudged, to *defer sentence* until after Coyle has been tried. "Justitia" *may* then be in a better condition to know what Coyle was really charged with; what his plea was; what the evidence for and against him was; what the verdict and sentence, and whether or not the trial was a farce.

Respectfully,

H.L. Fisher,
(Attorney for John Coyle, Jr.)
No 7. East Market St, over Weiser's Bank, York, Pa.

<u>Chapter 14</u>

The Insanity Dodge

"One precedent creates another. They soon accumulate and constitute law"

... *Marcus Junius Brutus*

Following his arraignment on June 10, John Coyle returned to cell 18 at the York County Prison to await his trial. His next court appearance was not until October, and while his lawyer began preparing for his defense, John spent the summer nursing his self-inflicted wounds and receiving occasional visitors.

His father came to the jail infrequently and his mother visited even less due to her rheumatism, seeing her son only a few times. Without John to help at the ferry and in the fields, it was hard for them to spare the time to ride into York. Most of his visitors were from Marietta, and even though most of them had avoided John before the murder, his newfound notoriety made him somewhat of a local celebrity and a curiosity.

Although the insanity defense was not completely unknown at the time, it was by and large limited to high profile capital cases. It was regarded as a last ditch effort and "usually resorted to by criminals who have no other hope of escape from punishment than the 'insanity dodge.'"[1] Henry Fisher was taking a risk in attempting to persuade a local jury of Coyle's innocence due to his unsound mind. However, unless Fisher could convince the jury of his client's insanity, Coyle would most certainly be executed for Emily's murder.

The science of understanding the human mind and diagnosing insanity was in its infancy, and using it as a criminal defense strategy was usually met with disbelief and disdain. Medical experts were practically non-existent, at least ones the Coyles could afford to retain, and Fisher would have to rely on the testimony of people who knew John personally to demonstrate his mental imbalance. The opinions of Justitia were shared by many in the community, and Coyle's claim of insanity had already been condemned in the local papers. Fisher would have an uphill battle ahead of him.

A recent trial in New York paralleled the Coyle case in many respects. Jacob Gerhardt, accused of murdering his former sister-in-law Mena Gerhardt, had gone to trial only a month after the murder of Emily Myers. Following Mena's refusal to marry him, Gerhardt allegedly followed her "to the barnyard, and, after knocking her down, pounded her head in a shocking manner."[2] Gerhardt entered a plea of not guilty by reason of insanity.

Fisher was uncertain whether he would have Coyle take the stand on his own behalf, but the strategy had worked for Gerhardt. While testifying, he "became greatly excited, sobbed and groaned,"[3] and apparently convinced the jury he was insane. Gerhardt was found guilty of second-degree murder and sentenced to life in prison and avoided the death sentence.

As this was the first time in his career Fisher was attempting to defend a client on the basis of insanity, he would have researched previous cases where the plea had been used successfully. He most certainly would have referenced the trials of Richard Lawrence (1835), Daniel M'Naghten (1843), and Daniel Sickles (1859), all of which resulted in acquittals.

Washington, DC
January 30, 1835

The funeral of Congressman Warren Davis took place on a damp, dreary day at the U.S. Capital. Following the service, Andrew Jackson was leaving through the rotunda when a well-dressed man in a long black coat and top hat stepped from behind a column and calmly approached. With two shots fired from about thirteen feet, Richard Lawrence became the first person to attempt to assassinate a U.S. president. However, due to the damp weather, both shots misfired.

Lawrence, an unemployed house painter, suffered from delusions of persecution, believing he was King Richard III of England and heir to the British throne. During the trial, Lawrence frequently interrupted the proceedings, asserting his identity as the King of England, and the jury deliberated only five minutes before returning a verdict of not guilty by reason of insanity.

Since the court had the authority to confine an insane person for an indeterminate amount of time, the acquittal was actually a better outcome for the prosecution than it was for the defense. A not guilty verdict by reason of insanity allowed the court to imprison Lawrence for life, whereas a guilty verdict would have limited the court to imposing only a one year sentence for assault. The fact that the victim was the President did not factor into the decision.

District Attorney Francis Scott Key, author of the Star Spangled Banner during the War of 1812, realized that a strong prosecution that resulted in a conviction with minimal jail time was a less desirable option than a weak prosecution that produced lifetime imprisonment. Therefore, he agreed to the broad definition of insanity presented to the jury in order to allow the judge the maximum latitude in sentencing. After spending twenty years in jail alongside convicted criminals, Lawrence was confined to a government mental hospital where he passed away in 1861.

Henry Fisher, preparing John Coyle's insanity defense in 1881, could have drawn several parallels to the Lawrence case. Insanity in criminal trials was generally proved, or disproved, by how the defendant looked, acted, or was regarded by those who were acquainted with the accused. Fisher had spoken to Coyle's family, interviewed those who knew John, and read all the information about the case published in the local newspapers. Immediately after Emily's murder, Mrs. Coyle described her son's eyes as wild looking and glaring like fire. Others indicated he was obsessed with marriage, and John himself attributed his mental state at the time of the murder as being caused by Emily's continual rejection of his proposals.

According to documents about Lawrence written after his trial, "The only thing in his appearance which might be supposed to indicate insanity is a certain wild expression of the eye..." and "his habits, it would seem, were generally speaking, correct; but an aberration of mind on particular subjects had been evinced for some years past."[4] This precedent would have been encouraging to Fisher, as he realized that he may not have to prove Coyle completely insane, but perhaps only in a limited scope in order to gain an acquittal.

Drawing further parallels to the Coyle case, Lawrence "had formed an attachment for a young lady, which was not reciprocal; and from that period he became more than usually melancholy, peevish, and quarrelsome."[5] Like Coyle, who was frequently called "Crazy John Coyle" and taunted in Marietta for his erratic behavior, Lawrence through his ranting had "procured for him among the boys in his neighborhood in which he resided, the title of 'King Dick!' and by which title, they used, in derision, to salute him in the streets."[6]

District Attorney Edward Ziegler and defense attorney Henry Fisher would have to contend with the myriad of conflicting non-expert testimony regarding the mental condition of John Coyle, much as Prosecutor Francis Scott Key and defense attorneys W.L and J.F. Brent had in the Richard Lawrence case. Defense witnesses in the Lawrence trial testified they "have often said he was a crazy man, and have heard others say so," and "it was the general impression of the neighbors that he was insane."[7] However, District Attorney Key produced prosecution witnesses who countered with "have known prisoner fourteen years; he was very steady, and remarkably reserved in his manners" and "was a remarkably fine boy; rather an exception to the general order of boys; reserved in his manners; but industrious and of good moral habits."[8]

As would be the case in the Coyle trial, it was left up to the jurors to form their own opinions regarding whether the defendant was insane or not, without the benefit of hearing qualified medical testimony. Expert psychiatric witnesses were not available to help Henry Fisher prove Coyle's insanity, but previously established guidelines existed which served as tests of insanity for criminal proceedings. These tests were developed following the acquittal of Daniel M'Naghten[*] for the murder of the British Prime Minister's private secretary Edward Drummond in 1843, in an effort to assist jurors in determining a defendant's state of mind at the time a criminal act was committed.

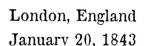

London, England
January 20, 1843

Daniel M'Naghten suffered from paranoid delusions stemming from his belief that he was being persecuted by members of the British Conservative Party, also known as Tories. For years, he complained to the police, his father, and anyone else who would listen that he was being followed by Tory spies due to his radical political views. Instead of providing protection or investigating his claims, M'Naghten was labeled insane.

On the afternoon of January 20, 1843, M'Naghten approached a man walking along Downing Street in London. He believed the man to be Sir Robert Peel, the Conservative Prime Minister of the United Kingdom. From behind, he fired a shot into the back of his victim and was immediately subdued by a constable before he could fire a second round. However, it was not the Prime Minister he shot, but Edward Drummond, his private secretary. Although the wound was initially thought to be minor, Drummond died five days later from complications following leeching treatments.

When brought before the court the following morning, M'Naghten gave vague responses when asked how he wanted to plead, and left it up to the court to record a plea of not guilty for him.

---

[*] Frequently misspelled, M'Naghten was also referred to as M'Naughton, McNaughton or McNaughten in court documents and other published accounts.

Court:	"Will you answer the question? You must say either guilty or not guilty"
M'Naghten:	"*I am guilty of firing*"
Court:	"By that, do you mean to say you are not guilty of the remainder of the charge – that is, intending to murder Mr. Drummond"
M'Naghten:	"*Yes*"
Court:	"That certainly amounts to a plea of "Not guilty;" therefore, such a plea must be recorded"[9]

Fisher, researching the case prior to the arraignment of his own client, realized M'Naghten's ambiguous replies may have helped convince the jury he was mentally unsound. Adopting an identical strategy, he most likely coached John Coyle to respond in a similar way when asked the same questions by Judge Wickes.

Like Coyle, M'Naghten became withdrawn and irrational, having "been shunned and ridiculed ... tortured by headaches" and "his mind made vulnerable by constitution and molded by life circumstances."[10] His lawyers had incorporated those factors into M'Naghten's defense, and Fisher, encouraged by their success, decided to use those same reasons as a basis for Coyle's insanity.

Less than two months after the murder of Drummond, the trial of Daniel M'Naghten took place at the Central Criminal Court in London. Both the prosecution and the defense agreed that M'Naghten suffered from delusions of persecution, but based their cases on their own interpretations of insanity and criminal responsibility. The prosecution argued he was responsible for the act in spite of his condition and was able to distinguish right from wrong, and the defense contended M'Naghten's delusions led to a loss of self-control.

The prosecution relied solely on the testimony of neighbors, teachers and acquaintances, who stated M'Naghten appeared sane and in control of his faculties. They argued that he operated a business, pursued normal interests, taught himself French and studied academically throughout his life. Confident of their case, the prosecution opted not to call any medical experts. However, the defense, in addition to witnesses giving evidence of his odd behavior and constant complaints of persecution, produced medical witnesses to substantiate their position. These witnesses stated, without any doubt, that M'Naghten's delusions "deprived the prisoner of all restraint over his actions."[11]

Without leaving the courtroom, the jury immediately returned a verdict of not guilty by reason of insanity. M'Naghten was transferred from prison to the State Criminal Lunatic Asylum at Bethlem Hospital where he spent the next twenty-one years classified as an imbecile. He moved to the newly completed Broadmoor Asylum in 1864 and died a year later. However, the significance of the M'Naghten case was not found in the crime, the trial, or the outcome, but in the public outcry that followed.

The verdict sparked an immediate protest from the public, the press, and in Parliament. Queen Victoria, concerned about the ease in which an acquittal had been reached, criticized the English legal system for allowing it and wrote to the Prime Minister requesting an inquiry by the House of Lords. A series of questions was posed to fifteen judges of the Court on the subject of criminal responsibility, and the opinions of the judges were delivered in June 1843.

Although the judge's answers would influence the rules of law regarding legal insanity for more than a century, the so-called M'Naghten Rule was not without criticism. The findings were not the result of a court proceeding based on evidence and the judges were under no obligation to provide answers. Although they were merely the views of the panel on hypothetical questions, their opinions became the most significant test of criminal culpability in cases where the state of mind of the accused was in question.

The M'Naghten Rule replaced other guidelines which had been in place for the previous two-hundred years. Initially, an accused could be found guilty and held responsible for their crimes if they had the mental capacity equal to a child of fourteen. Fourteen was chosen because common law at the time presumed a child under that age could not discern right from wrong. Eventually, this test was replaced by the "wild beast" supposition, where insanity could result in a verdict of not guilty only if the accused did not know what they were doing, "no more than a brute or wild beast, or an infant."[12]

Prior to the M'Naghten Rule, acquittals in cases where insanity was used as defense were rare and only reserved for the most severely deranged defendants. The evidence presented in the M'Naghten trial clearly failed to prove his mental capacity indistinguishable from "a wild beast," and the fact the he was acquitted nonetheless prompted the inquiry into the verdict and subsequent redefinition of the guidelines regarding insanity and criminal responsibility.

Simply put, the M'Naghten Rule stated that in order to acquit on the basis on insanity, it must clearly be proved "that at the time of committing of the act the accused was laboring under such a defect of reason, from disease of the mind, as not to know the nature and quality of the act he was doing, or if he did know it, that he did not know he was doing what was wrong."[13] The rule also recommended that juries should be instructed that the accused was to be presumed sane until proven otherwise. It failed, however, to take into consideration that it was possible for someone to understand their actions were wrong, but still be unable to control the urge to act.

As a result of the M'Naghten case and the ensuing guidelines put forth by the panel of judges, the interpretation of criminal liability as it related to mentally disturbed defendants was permanently altered. The M'Naghten Rules became the standard test for determining legal responsibility of the insane in England and the United States, with virtually no modifications, until well into the twentieth century. In 1962, the American Law Institute proposed a modified standard based on the M'Naghten Rules, taking into account the concept of irresistible impulse and evidence presented by psychiatric and medical experts. Today, roughly half the states use the M'Naghten Rules, with the other half adopting the newer ALI Standard. Pennsylvania continues to use M'Naghten as the legal basis for insanity.

Although the Lawrence and M'Naghten trials were helpful to Fisher in preparing his defense of Coyle, he would have wanted to find a case where insanity had been successfully used to defend a crime committed as a result of unrequited love. Integral to his ability to prove Coyle's innocence was establishing the fact that Emily had triggered a violent projection of his chronic insanity by encouraging his affection and then rejecting him. For this, Fisher would have turned to the case of Daniel Sickles and the murder of Phillip Barton Key in 1859.

Washington, DC
Sunday, February 27, 1859

Daniel Sickles, a powerful New York Congressman from Manhattan, was aware of the rumors of an affair between his twenty-two-year-old wife Teresa and forty-one-year-old Philip Barton Key, the son of Star-Spangled Banner author Francis Scott Key. District Attorney Barton Key and Sickles were friends, and Key frequently escorted Teresa to society functions when Dan was too busy with his Congressional duties. The affair was carried on with little discretion, and even the servants at the Sickles' home were aware of their trysts.

Sickles eventually confronted Teresa about her relationship with Key. Initially denying everything, she eventually broke down and confessed the details of her meetings. Sickles made her write an exhaustive confession, presumably to be used in subsequent divorce proceedings. After it was finished, she signed it and Sickles summoned the servants to sign as witnesses.

"I have been in a house on Fifteenth Street, with Mr. Key. How many times, I don't know. I believe the house belongs to a colored man ... Commenced going there the later part of January. Have been alone and with Mr. Key. Usually stayed an hour. There was a bed in the second story. I did what it usual for a wicked woman to do. The intimacy commenced this winter, when I came from New York, in that house – an intimacy of an improper kind. Have met a dozen times or more, at different hours of the day. On Monday of this week, and Wednesday also."[14]

The following morning, Sickles happened to glance out an upstairs window and noticed Barton Key walking back and forth across the street. He was signaling to Teresa by waving a white handkerchief, hoping to catch her attention with their prearranged signal. Enraged, Sickles stormed down the stairs crying "That villain has just passed my house, my God, this is horrible."[15] He left the house and approached Key, who was standing on the corner of Pennsylvania Avenue in front of Lafayette Park, directly across the street from the White House. Had President James Buchanan been looking out the north windows of his office, he would have been a witness to the murder, committed by his good friend Daniel Sickles.

As he neared Key, Sickles called out "Key, you scoundrel, you have dishonored my house – you must die!"[16] Pulling out a small pistol, he fired a shot which grazed Key in the hand. When Sickles raised his arm to fire again, Key grabbed him by the collar of his coat. The two grappled on the street and the derringer fell from his hand and onto the pavement. Struggling away, Sickles pulled out a second pistol and leveled it at Key. Key pleaded "Don't murder me,"[17] and pulled his opera glasses from his pocket and threw them at Sickles. Instead of showing mercy, Sickles fired a second shot, hitting Key two inches from the groin. As Sickles continued to rant about the dishonoring of his marriage bed, Key leaned against a tree and sank to the ground.

Had another shot not been fired, Key's injuries would not have been fatal, as the bullet in the thigh had not severed any arteries. But, when Key tried to attract attention and called for help yelling "Don't shoot me! Murder! Murder!"[18] Sickles fired again. The gun misfired, so he cocked and shot again, this time hitting Key in the chest, missing his heart but puncturing his liver. Sickles placed the gun close to Key's head and pulled the trigger a final time, but Key was spared an immediate death by another misfire.

Sickles calmly walked to the house of Attorney General Jeremiah Black, discussed politics with several visitors in the hallway, and surrendered to Black. Upon being told that Key had died, Sickles muttered "One less wretch in the world."[19] Black summoned the police, who arrested Sickles and escorted him to a damp, insect-ridden cell in the Washington Jail.

The lawyers who defended Sickles were led by the renowned James Brady, who had an excellent record in murder trials and specialized in the use of the insanity plea. Other lawyers included the passionate and forceful Edwin Stanton, who would become the future Secretary of War under Abraham Lincoln, and John Graham, who was famous for his ability to soften the emotions of the jury.

If Sickles were found guilty, he would be sentenced to hang, and if found not guilty by reason of insanity, he would be committed for an indeterminate amount of time. Since Sickles, a well-known public figure, was obviously a sane person, his legal team knew their only hope of a complete acquittal was for him to be found not guilty by reason of *temporary* insanity. Sickles was convinced he was justified in the murder of Key and agreed to the strategy, realizing it was the only way he could walk away a free man.

Since the elected District Attorney, Philip Barton Key, was now dead, the prosecution was handled by a younger, less experienced deputy Robert Ould. Feeling that the meek and inexperienced Ould would not aggressively prosecute Sickles, the Key family appealed to President Buchanan to appoint a special prosecutor, but were denied the request.

The trial began with the reading of the indictment, to which Sickles replied not guilty. The proceedings started off badly for Ould, and the difficulty in finding impartial jurors to hear the case proved to be a bad omen for the prosecution. Seventy-two of the first seventy-five called sympathized with Sickles, and over the course of the three days it took to select a panel, two hundred more were excused for being bias in favor of the defendant.

Ould did his best to portray the murder as premeditated and deliberate, but found that the interest in the case lay more with the adultery of Teresa than the actual slaying of Key. John Graham's opening statement for the defense, interspersed with a liberal dose of biblical quotes, depicted Sickles as a victim and righteous defender of his marital rights. Graham argued that Sickles should not be held responsible for Key's death, since "if he was in a state of white heat, was that too great a state of passion for a man to be in who saw before him the hardened, the unrelenting seducer of his wife?"[20]

The opening statement for the defense lasted three days, after which Ould presented the State's case against Sickles. Although it was clear that the defense strategy was to portray Key as a blatant philanderer who deserved his fate, Ould neglected to expose Sickles' own reputation as a flagrant adulterer. His best effort was to call eyewitnesses to the murder who did nothing but tell the same story over and over again.

On the other hand, the defense team produced many witnesses who gave evidence of Sickles' state of mind when he confronted Key. Former Secretary of the Treasury Robert Walker testified he was in "an agony of despair, the most terrible thing I ever saw in my life ... I feared if it continued he would be become permanently insane."[21] In his closing argument, Graham asked, "Was Mr. Sickles, at the time of the homicide, such a creature of instinct, of impulse, that he could not resist, but was carried forward, like a mere machine, to the consummation of that so-called tragedy?"[22]

Apparently the jury agreed, and at the conclusion of the three week trial, returned a verdict of not guilty after deliberating for a little over an hour. Jurors interviewed after the trial indicated they felt Sickles was justified in the murder and the violation of Teresa had been vindicated. According to the *New York Times*, the jury "gave their verdict on the principle that, in the absence of any adequate punishment by law for adultery, the man who violates the honor and desolates the home of his neighbor, does so at the peril of his life, and if he falls by the outraged husband's hand he deserves his doom."[23]

The hypocrisy of Sickles' philandering and his numerous affairs, many the knowledge of his wife, was ignored.

The verdict sparked celebrations around Washington, and most felt Sickles had acted reasonably given the circumstances. He went on to achieve the rank of Major General in the Union Army and was wounded at the Battle of Gettysburg in 1863 when a twelve pound cannonball shattered his right leg below the knee[†], effectively ending his military career. Following the Civil War, Sickles served as the Military Governor of South Carolina and the Ambassador to Spain, eventually returning to the House of Representatives in 1893 for a two-year term. He died in 1914 and was buried in Arlington Cemetery with full military honors.

Generally accepted as the first use of the temporary insanity defense in America, the trial of Daniel Sickles for the public murder of Phillip Barton Key broke new legal ground in the United States much like the M'Naghten case had in Great Britain. Philip Phillips, one of the lawyers on defense team, was convinced that the success of the temporary insanity plea had changed the legal system, and remarked after the trial "An honest, upright, and intelligent American jury had established a precedent which all civilized nations would henceforth recognize and be guided by."[24]

Although Henry Fisher would have been able to draw few specific parallels between the Sickles case and his defense of John Coyle, he would have been encouraged by the ease in which the jury was convinced of Sickles' insanity. However, unlike the eloquent orator John Graham, he knew he had no chance in portraying John Coyle as a victim and Emily Myers as deserving her fate, or convincing the jury that the homicide was justifiable.

Like District Attorney Ould, Fisher would also struggle with the process of jury selection. In Fisher's case, finding jurors who had not already formed an opinion of Coyle's guilt would prove

---

[†] *The shattered leg bone of General Sickles is on display at the National Museum of Health and Medicine at the Walter Reed Army Medical Center in Washington, D.C.*

challenging. In contrast, empanelling jurors was problematic in the Sickles trial for the opposite reason, as finding jurors unsympathetic to the defendant Daniel Sickles was difficult and time-consuming.

Fisher was optimistic of his success in the Coyle trial due to the apparent ease in which similar cases had been decided in favor of the defendant. However, in the midst of his defense preparations during the summer of 1881, a sensational murder case grabbed the attention of the nation. The assassination attempt of President James Garfield by Charles Guiteau on July 2, 1881, only a month after the murder of Emily Myers, would have adversely affected popular opinion on the legitimacy of the insanity plea.

The American public and press were outraged at the shooting of Garfield, and Fisher realized his chances of an acquittal based on a defense of insanity would now be substantially more difficult. Guiteau became an overnight media sensation with his outrageous behavior and public statements, and any potential juror in the Coyle case would have heard about the case and been leery of acknowledging insanity as a valid excuse for cold-blooded murder.

———— ∿∿∿ ————

Washington, DC
July 2, 1881

Charles Guiteau, an unsuccessful small-claims lawyer and religious lecturer, had a lifelong reputation of shady deals and erratic behavior. Wandering from place to place, the itinerant Guiteau was known as arrogant, egotistical and occasionally violent. Always scheming and rebellious against authority, his father was convinced he was possessed by Satan and once wrote "To my mind he is a fit subject for a lunatic asylum, and if I had the means to keep him would send him to one ..."[25]

After moving to Washington D.C., Guiteau had written a speech for James Garfield to use in a debate and was convinced he played a part in the outcome of the 1880 presidential campaign. Even though it had never been read, Guiteau was certain he was instrumental in Garfield's election. He immediately began lobbying the new administration for a position, demanding to be appointed as the French Ambassador. He wrote countless letters to President Garfield and his Secretary of State James Blaine, but never received any response.

After personally confronting Blaine, Guiteau was told "Never bother me again about the Paris consulship so long as you live."[26] Guiteau became bitter and resentful over the continual rejections and his letter writing became more intense and threatening. He eventually came to the conclusion that the removal of Garfield was the only way to save the Republican Party and purchased a pistol. Guiteau began stalking Garfield, and after passing up several opportunities because the moment did not feel right, on July 2, 1881, he decided to act.

After only four months in office, President Garfield was preparing to depart for a two-week vacation. Arriving at the Baltimore and Potomac Railroad station with no bodyguards or security, Garfield walked into the waiting room for departing trains. He passed a small, shabbily dressed man who turned as Garfield passed, firing a shot which grazed the president's shoulder. Garfield exclaimed "My God, what is this?"[27] and threw up his arms as Guiteau fired again. This time the bullet lodged in the President's lower spine and Garfield crumpled to the ground. Barely conscious, the president was taken to an upstairs room of the train station.

Guiteau was apprehended without a struggle by the quick-thinking policeman Patrick Kearney. Without offering any resistance, he was led out of the building proclaiming "I am a Stalwart[‡] of Stalwarts! I did it. I will go to jail for it; Arthur is President, and I am a Stalwart!"[28] Amidst cries calling for Guiteau's lynching, Kearney and his prisoner safely reached the police station several blocks away. Only then did the officer remember to relieve Guiteau of his gun.

[‡] *The Stalwarts were a Republican splinter group who supported ex-President Grant and vice-president Chester A. Arthur and opposed Garfield's presidential nomination.*

Garfield was taken back to the White House, where a team of doctors offered conflicting opinions on how to save his life. Probing the wound with unsterilized instruments and bare hands, they caused numerous infections and Garfield became increasingly weak during the course of the summer. He suffered immense pain in his feet due to nerve damage in his lower back, and had constant abdominal problems. No surgery was performed because the bullet could not be located, and his treatments included doses of quinine, morphine and brandy. Hoping that fresh sea air would speed his recovery, he was moved to a beach cottage near Long Branch, New Jersey on September 6.

Garfield died two weeks later on September 19 from complications resulting from poor medical treatment, and formal proceedings against Guiteau began in earnest. On October 8, the indictment was filed and his arraignment was held a week later. Guiteau felt confidently qualified to lead his own defense, but reluctantly accepted assistance from his brother-in-law George Scoville. Coverage of the pre-trial events was extensive and was followed closely by the entire nation.

On January 25, 1882, the jury found Guiteau guilty of the murder of President Garfield after deliberating for only an hour. To the end, Guiteau was convinced he would be acquitted. He made plans for an extensive speaking tour after his release and spoke of a presidential bid in 1884. The conviction was appealed, but the verdict was upheld and Guiteau was hanged on June 30, 1882, in Washington, DC. After his death, it was speculated that a defect in his brain had caused his insanity. When it was removed during his autopsy, his brain appeared to be fairly healthy, although slightly asymmetrical.[§]

The timing of the Garfield shooting and ensuing legal proceedings could not have been worse for John Coyle. All summer, the public had been inundated with details of the Garfield shooting, the

---

[§] *Part of Charles Guiteau's preserved brain is on display at the Mutter Museum in Philadelphia, Pa.*

bizarre antics of Guiteau, and the debate over the use of the insanity defense. Coyle's trial began on Wednesday, October 19, less than a week after Guiteau's arraignment, and would been fresh on the minds of any prospective juror. Finding an unbiased jury in York County willing to accept insanity as a valid defense would be a tough obstacle and Fisher's early optimism began to wane.

Most Americans, as well as the medical community, felt that Guiteau's act was caused by a depraved, immoral lifestyle rather than a legitimate illness. John Coyle certainly had a reputation for hard living and heavy drinking, and unless Fisher could convince the jury his actions were the result of a long pattern of insanity founded in disease or injury, chances of an acquittal were slim. He would have to be careful to steer the testimony away from Coyle's alcohol abuse and violent outbursts, as jurors were more likely to blame his actions on his many vices as opposed to any mental illness.

Coyle read the newspapers and followed the Guiteau case closely from his jail cell, becoming more nervous and anxious as his own trial neared. He confided in Sheriff Altland about his worries, wondering what effect Guiteau's crime would have on his chances. Several attempts had been made to kill Guiteau following his arrest, and Coyle asked to be closely guarded on his trips from the jail to court. He feared for his life, claiming at one point that someone had thrown ether[**] into his cell for the purpose of killing him. Although calls for his lynching were made when he was taken from the ferry following his arrest, no actual threats had been made since being jailed.

As the summer neared an end and the October Quarter Session was about to begin, Henry Fisher realized the complexity of the Coyle case and engaged the help of William C. Chapman to assist as defense counsel. Chapman had a reputation as an accomplished criminal lawyer and Fisher hoped to put his renowned oratory skills to good use in the courtroom.

[**] *Fumes from Ether, a liquid compound used in the nineteenth century as an anesthetic and recreational drug, could have caused nasal or eye irritation. In the open space of a prison cell, it would hardly have been life-threatening.*

Chapter 15

York County Courthouse, York, Pa
Wednesday, October 19, 1881

"We have a criminal jury system which is superior to any in the world; and its efficiency is only marred by the difficulty in finding twelve men every day who don't know anything and can't read"
                                ... Mark Twain, 4th of July speech 1873

The trial date of John Coyle, Jr. for the murder of Emily Myers finally arrived, and he rose early for his first court appearance since his arraignment in June. After using the bath cell, he dressed in the new clothes his mother brought to the prison for him. According to observers, Coyle "was very neatly and fashionably dressed in a black suit, cleanly shaven and quite genteel in appearance"[1] when he arrived in court that morning.

The *York Dispatch* had published a summary of the upcoming proceedings the previous evening, and spectators began arriving in York on the early trains all morning. Hoping to avoid a confrontation with their neighbors from Marietta who had been called as witnesses, Mr. and Mrs. Coyle left the ferry early and rode the distance in their wagon instead of picking up the westbound train in Hellam.

Some of those subpoenaed were in town since the previous day, but most of the thirty-five witnesses for the defense and twenty for the prosecution arrived the day of the trial. A notice had been posted in the local Marietta papers the previous Saturday calling all witnesses to be at the Pennsylvania Railroad depot at 8 o'clock on the morning of October 19. Tickets would be furnished to take them to York.

A small crowd gathered outside the courthouse and another at the jail, hoping to get a glimpse of the murderer. The heavily ironed Coyle was led from the jail through to the waiting Sherriff's wagon and he refused to acknowledge them as they called to him. Keeping his head down and staring at the ground, he was described when he arrived at the courthouse as "somewhat careworn and dejected."[2]

The normal procedure for transporting prisoners to court appearances was on foot. Since the crowd outside the jail was getting boisterous and Coyle had expressed fear over being shot, especially after the assassination attempts against Charles Guiteau, Altland decided to take him in the wagon with his son Henry as an additional guard. The prison wagon pulled away from the excited mob, turned first on Chestnut Street, then south on Queen Street. As the wagon neared Market Street, they could see and hear another crowd that had gathered on the front steps of the courthouse. Altland continued through the intersection and turned into the alley which led to the rear of the courthouse.

Altland escorted Coyle through the small entrance door in the high brick wall which surrounded the rear yard, across the yard, and into the rear of the building. Court was not due to begin until 9 o'clock, but since they had arrived about thirty minutes early, Altland and Coyle retired to the Sherriff's office next to the main court room.

Coyle's trial was held in the second York County Courthouse, built in 1841. The original courthouse, located in the town square, had been in use since 1756, and was the site of Continental Congress from September 1777 to June 1778 while York served as the nation's capital.[*] Bricks from the first courthouse were used to construct the walls around the rear yard of the new courthouse, and were all that remained of the colonial building after it was torn down in 1841.

The new courthouse remained the seat of government for York County for the next sixty years. It had been occupied by Confederate General Jubal Early during the Civil War, when he used the sheriff's office to issues his demands for supplies and money. John Coyle now sat in the same room with Sheriff Altland, awaiting the start of his trial.

---

[*] *A replica of the first Colonial Courthouse was built in 1976 at 205 West Market Street in York to commemorate the Bicentennial.*

By 1899, the county had outgrown the courthouse and commissioned York architect J.A. Dempwolf to design a larger facility. Built on the same site as the 1841 courthouse, the new building used some of the design elements as the one it replaced, including the salvaged granite columns and cupola. It was modified and expanded over the years, and remained in use for over one hundred years.[†]

York Co Courthouse, York Pa, ca. 1876 [3]

On Wednesday, October 19, 1881, the trial of John Coyle, Jr. began with the ringing of the courthouse bell. Court convened promptly at 9 o'clock with the Honorable Pere L. Wickes presiding. Before the defendant and his counsel were brought into the courtroom, District Attorney Edward Zeigler made a motion to have George W. McElroy appointed as Special Counsel for the Commonwealth. Since the matter being tried was a capital offense, the motion was granted.

[†] *The courthouse where Coyle was tried now houses county administrative offices.*

George McElroy was a well-known local lawyer and speaker. Following his discharge from the Union Army, he was admitted to the York Bar in 1864. After serving as Special Counsel during the Coyle trial, McElroy was elected District Attorney in 1883, succeeding Edward Zeigler.

It was the District Attorney's sole responsibility to try the case, but because William Chapman had joined the defense team, Zeigler felt out-manned and requested the appointment of a Special Counsel to assist in the prosecution of the case. Since appointees were private citizens and not county employees, they were due no wages for serving as Special Counsel. Apparently this did not sit well with McElroy, who submitted a claim for compensation to the County Commissioners immediately following the Coyle trial.

The opposing legal teams were now ready to begin the tedious process of jury selection. District Attorney Zeigler sat at the head of the prosecution table. On his right was Mrs. Elizabeth Mack, a widowed aunt of Emily Myers, and to her right sat George McElroy. At the adjoining defense table, Henry Fisher and William Chapman were seated with the prisoner and his parents.

The reporters present in the courtroom noted that the elder Mr. Coyle "appears in feeble health and remained in court only a short time. Mrs. Coyle is an old lady, attired in deep mourning and required the use of a crutch." As for the defendant, he was described as "seemingly indifferent to, and uninterested in the proceedings, giving little heed to anything except his aged mother who sits by his side."[4]

In addition to the Stenographer, who sat within the front rail of the bar, Court Crier Captain James Blasser and Clerk of Courts William A. Thompson were present to repeat the names of the jurors called by Sherriff Altland and administer their oaths. The courtroom gallery was packed with spectators and reporters who were eager to witness the proceedings. However, selecting the jury turned out to be a long and monotonous two-day process.

Quarter Sessions of the Court of Oyer and Terminer in York County were held four times a year in January, April, August, and October. The sheriff and the County Commissioners were required to meet prior to the first session to select a sufficient number of "sober, intelligent and judicious persons"[5] from the list of taxable citizens in the county to serve as jurors for the upcoming year. The name, occupation and place of residence for each person selected was written on a small slip of paper and placed in a jury wheel.

The jury wheel was a revolving container used to randomly select jurors for duty. In order to preserve the integrity of the process, specific state laws dictated the procedures to be followed. As soon as the requisite number of slips had been placed in the wheel, it was locked, secured with sealing wax, and impressed with the seals of the sheriff and commissioners. Thirty days prior to each Quarter Session, the wheel was turned and a sufficient number of names drawn for the upcoming court, after which it was locked and resealed.

Both the sheriff and the county commissioners were required to be present for this process, and after the names were drawn, the commissioners took possession of the wheel and the sheriff was given the key. A list was drafted by the Sheriff and delivered to the Prothonotary's office containing the names of those selected. After the cases to be tried in the upcoming court were scheduled, a formal writ was sent back to the sheriff instructing him to issue summons for the prospective jurors at least ten days prior to the start of the session.

In 1881, the jury list for the Coyle trial contained only the names of men, as women were prohibited from serving on juries in Pennsylvania until 1920. Although a woman first served on a jury in 1870 in Wyoming, it was a short-lived experiment. Following the passage of the Nineteenth Amendment in 1920, most states, including Pennsylvania, declared that since women had been guaranteed the right to vote, they were also qualified to serve on juries.

By contrast, blacks had been granted the right to testify in state courts as early as 1866 and guaranteed the right to vote with the ratification of the Fifteenth Amendment in 1870. The Civil Rights Act of 1875 declared "no citizen ... shall be disqualified for service as a grand or petit juror in any court of the United States, or of any State, on account of race, color or previous condition of servitude."[6] Court records for the Coyle trial do not indicate whether any men of color from York County were called to serve as jurors.

The name of each juror summoned by the Sheriff was written on a separate slip of paper by the Clerk of Courts and placed into a box for use during the trial. A venire, or pool of jurors, was then drawn from the box only upon an order of the court. Potential jurors were called before the District Attorney and the defense counsel for pre-trial questioning, and were required to be present until selected for duty or dismissed. They were paid one dollar a day for appearing, plus six-and-a-quarter cents per mile travelled.

By law, either the prosecution or the defense could challenge any prospective juror for cause and have them disqualified if questions were not answered satisfactorily or if any appearance of impartiality was apparent. In addition, both sides had the chance to peremptorily challenge any juror and dismiss them without giving any reason, even before any questions were asked. The Commonwealth was allowed four peremptory challenges and the prisoner was allowed twenty.

At 9:30, Judge Wickes ordered the impaneling of the jury "to consist of twelve good and lawful men of the said York County to try the issue joined."[7] After the court issued an order for the first regular venire of sixty jurors, the names were drawn from the jury box and the selected jurors were moved into the main courtroom. Five of the sixty were absent and the appropriate fines were issued.

After each name was called by Sheriff Altland and repeated by Court Crier James Blasser, the prospective juror stood and approached the bar, or railing, dividing the front of the courtroom from the gallery.

William Thompson, Clerk of the Court, then administered the oath: "You, and each of you, do swear that you will and truly try the issue joined between [the Commonwealth of Pennsylvania], plaintiff, and [John Coyle, Jr.], defendant, and a true verdict give, according to the evidence, unless dismissed by the court or the cause be withdrawn by the parties?"[8]

The prisoner was required to stand and face each juror, and the lawyers for the prosecution and the defense were asked, "challenge or no challenge?" Either could have the juror dismissed with no questions asked, and if neither used one of their allotted peremptory challenges, questioning began. The Clerk asked six questions, after which both sides had a chance to challenge the juror for cause.

"Have you any conscientious scruples against finding a verdict which might or would result in capital punishment?"

"Have you formed or expressed an opinion as to the guilt or innocence of the prisoner?"

"Upon what have you formed this opinion?"

"Is the opinion you formed such a fixed opinion as will prevent you, as a juror, under oath, from finding an impartial verdict in this trial, according to the evidence given, or will it require evidence to remove it?"

"Have you any bias for or prejudice against the prisoner at the bar"

"Are you related in any manner to the prisoner or the deceased?"[9]

The first question was used to determine the prospective juror's opinion of the death penalty. Of the 111 jurors questioned over the course of the next two days, all five who indicated they would not be able to convict if it resulted in Coyle's hanging were challenged for cause by the Commonwealth. Predictably, none were challenged by the defense as a result of their opposition to the death penalty.

Each juror was then asked if they had already formed an opinion in the case. If so, additional questions were posed to see if the opinions were so firm that after hearing the law and evidence, they could not render an unbiased verdict. If the juror answered no, the next three questions were skipped.

The first juror called, Christian Lehman, caused an immediate dispute when he answered that he had already formed an opinion. The defense challenged for cause, claiming that Lehman could not serve as a juror. Judge Wickes ruled that any man who had read a newspaper had probably formed an opinion, and could only be excused if his opinion would prevent him from finding an impartial verdict.

After further questioning, Mr. Lehman responded it would require a lot of evidence to convince him of Coyle's innocence, as opposed to evidence convincing him of his guilt. Since the defendant was supposed to be presumed innocent until proven guilty and not the other way around, Lehman was challenged for cause by the defendant and dismissed.

Fifty-eight jurors were eventually challenged by the defense for already having an opinion - none were challenged by the prosecution for the same reason. The District Attorney realized that any preconceived opinions would be in favor of Coyle's guilt and therefore did not challenge any for being bias against the accused. The defense, however, needed jurors who would be open to the insanity plea and did not want anyone selected who already believed Coyle to be guilty.

Nine of the prospective jurors were excused because they could not understand English well enough, two others due to deafness, and one because of a heart condition. Many were of German descent and could not understand every word, but understood common talk well enough and were accepted. None were related to the Coyle family or Emily Myers. The prosecution used all four of their preemptory challenges and the defense used their allotment of twenty, without providing any reason or cause.

Following the questioning of Henry Neff, the first venire of sixty jurors had been exhausted, with only nine jurors having been accepted. Those sworn were informed they would be sequestered for the duration of the trial and that overnight accommodations had been made for them at the Central Hotel. They were put in charge of tipstaves[‡] David Myers and Alfred Koch and removed from the courtroom. The jurors were told they would not be allowed to separate and should not allow anyone to discuss the case with them. Those challenged or excused were released and allowed to leave.

Since a complete jury of twelve had not been chosen from the first regular venire of sixty, Judge Wickes ordered a special venire of thirty to be returned in the afternoon and adjourned the proceedings at noon. Court reconvened at 3 o'clock and the nine jurors selected during the morning were brought back into court. Coyle then returned, securely manacled, and took his place beside his attorneys.

Sheriff Altland returned the special venire of thirty jurors as requested and filed the names with the court. Two of those called were not present and were each fined ten dollars for their non-appearance. However, both must have arrived shortly thereafter as they were questioned later in the day. At 3:15 p.m., the impaneling of jurors resumed with the questioning of Henry Deitch of York, who was promptly sworn in as the tenth juror. Only one other juror was accepted during the afternoon session bringing the total to eleven, and by 4:30 p.m. the special venire had been exhausted. The court ordered a second special venire of twenty-five jurors to be returnable the following morning at 9 o'clock and court was adjourned for the day.

As Coyle was being led from the courtroom, he seemed unconcerned about the proceedings and commented to a friend that he "did not care which way it went."[10] In interviews with some of Coyle's acquaintances who were in court that day, the general opinion expressed was that Coyle looked much improved since he went to jail and some could hardly recognize him. One witness who was

---

[‡] *A tipstaff served as a guardian and escort. Other duties included ordering meals and relaying important information between the jurors and their families.*

summoned from Marietta remarked that "though he had known him all his life, he never saw him looking so well."[11]

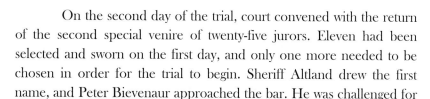

On the second day of the trial, court convened with the return of the second special venire of twenty-five jurors. Eleven had been selected and sworn on the first day, and only one more needed to be chosen in order for the trial to begin. Sheriff Altland drew the first name, and Peter Bievenaur approached the bar. He was challenged for cause by the defense due to a prejudice against the prisoner and his dismissal set the tone for the rest of the morning's session.

George Strayer, the fourteenth juror to be questioned on Thursday, indicated he had formed an opinion in the case but it would not influence his verdict. Since his answers satisfied the lawyers and no challenge for cause was raised, he was promptly chosen as the twelfth juror. However, when the oath was being administered and Strayer was asked to kiss the bible, he hesitated and said there was some misunderstanding about his opinion.

When Strayer had been asked whether he comprehended the English language well enough, he responded he understood some, but not all, and "he could render a verdict that would not affect his opinion."[12] The D.A. was obviously confused with his backwards answer and realized that Strayer's knowledge of English would be a problem. Zeigler challenged him for cause, and the defense objected, as they felt it would be in Coyle's best interest to have jurors who may not be able to completely understand the fine points of the law. The objection was overruled and Strayer was dismissed.

Dr. Kehm, a physician from Dover, asked to be excused because his medical practice was busy and he could not afford to be away from his office. Judge Wickes informed the doctor that the court did not exempt physicians and the request was denied. Since the defense did not want anyone with medical knowledge, and perhaps strong opinions on insanity, serving on the jury, they used one of their peremptory challenges to dismiss Dr. Kehm.

Finally, at 10:30 a.m., Sheriff Altland informed the court the second special venire had been exhausted. Of the first 110 jurors questioned, nine were selected from the first venire of fifty-five, two from the second panel of thirty and none from the third venire of twenty-five. The Commonwealth had one peremptory challenge left and the defense none. According to accounts, it was "probably the first time in the history of criminal practice in this county that a third special venire has been rendered necessary."[13]

Judge Wickes ordered a third special venire of twenty additional names and adjourned for the morning. After lunch, court reassembled, the first name drawn by the Sheriff was John Mayer, a cigar maker from York. When questioned, he responded he had formed an opinion from what he had read in the newspapers, and although it would take strong evidence to overcome his opinion, his verdict would not be influenced by his feelings.

Mayer's answer was similar to many others over the previous two days, and the defense predictably challenged for cause. They claimed that since his opinions would take strong evidence to change, he was not capable to act as a juror. However, Judge Wickes was growing tired of the same challenges and was eager to begin the trial. He ruled that since Mayer had indicated his opinion would not influence his verdict, he would make a competent juror. The challenge was overruled and Mayer became the final juror in the Coyle trial.

The "Twelve fair honest and lawful men of the County of York who were severally sworn or affirmed according to law to well and truly try and true deliverance make between the Commonwealth of Pennsylvania and John Coyle, Jr. the prisoner at the bar"[14] consisted of the following men; William H. Neff, W.J. McClellan, Peter Heiges, John Krafft, John Shellenberger, William A. Mitzel, John Fulton, Frederick Greiman, William P. Mundis, Henry J. Deitch, Thomas Ramsey, and John Mayer.

Chapter 16

York County Courthouse, York, Pa
Thursday, October 20, 1881

"If you violate Nature's laws you are your own prosecuting attorney, judge, jury, and hangman"

... *Luther Burbank*

After the last juror was sworn in, Judge Wickes wasted no time in starting the Coyle trial and immediately called for the District Attorney to make his opening statement to the jury. Edward Zeigler began his address at 2 o'clock, and over the next thirty minutes clearly explained the Commonwealth's case and the evidence to be presented.

"If the Court please, Gentleman of the Jury:

The bill of indictment in this case charges that John Coyle, Jr., the prisoner at the Bar, on the 30th day of May, A.D. 1881 in this county, and within the jurisdiction of the court, with force and arms, etc., in and upon the body of one Emily Myers, in the peace of God and the said Commonwealth, then and there being feloniously, willfully, and in his malice aforethought, did make an assault, on her the said Emily Myers then and there feloniously, willfully, and of his malice aforethought, did kill and murder, contrary to the form of the Act of the General Assembly in such case made and provided and against the peace and dignity of the Commonwealth of Pennsylvania.

The Act of the General Assembly of the 31st of March AD 1860, declares that: 'All murder which shall be perpetrated by means of poison, or by lying in wait, or by any other kind of willful, deliberate and premeditated killing, or which shall be committed in the perpetration of, or attempt to perpetrate arson, rape, burglary, shall be deemed murder of the first degree, and all other kinds of murder shall be deemed murder of the second degree.'

The indictment contains only one count, and charges a willful, deliberate and premeditated murder. To constitute murder of the first degree there must not only be malice, but there must also be an intent to take life, and the killing must be the willful, deliberate and premeditated act of the prisoner. If there be an entire absence of malice, and if there was on the part of the prisoner no intent to take life, and if the act was not 'willful, deliberate and premeditated', the offence is not murder of the first degree.

An important inquiry, therefore addresses itself to our minds at the very beginning of this case. It is this: Did John Coyle, Jr. intend to take the life of Emily Myers and was his act 'willful, deliberate and premeditated'. If so he is guilty in manner and form as he stands indicted.

To sustain a conviction under this indictment, Gentleman of the Jury, the Commonwealth ought to be able to show, and I promise you that it will be able to show, that Emily Myers, on the 30th of May last, was the victim of criminal violence, that she is in fact dead, that the violence inflicted upon her person was done maliciously, with a design to take her life, and that is was inflicted willfully, deliberately and premeditated, and that it was done by the prisoner.

The Commonwealth will prove three things: First, Emily Myers is in point of fact dead. Second, that she died a violent death, and the manner of her death. Third, that the prisoner at the bar destroyed her life as charged in the bill of indictment.

Applying, therefore, the facts of this case in the possession of the Commonwealth, to these three points, we will show first that Emily Myers is dead, that on the morning of the 30th of May last she was awakened from her slumber by Mrs. Coyle, who called her and directed her to go out to the barn and milk the cows. Emily Myers and Mrs. Coyle slept in the same room. In response to the call and direction given by Mrs. Coyle, Emily Myers arose, dressed herself and left the room in possession of perfect health. This was the last time that Emily Myers was seen alive. When she was next seen she was lying inside the south end of the Coyle barn near the door dead. Thus a beautiful, young lady about 16 years of age, just blooming from the spring time of her life into the still more beautiful and charming summer of her existence, leaves the house in full possession of all her mental faculties and constitutional vigor, and soon thereafter is found 'sleeping the sleep that knows no waking.'

People gather around the lifeless form, and as they gaze upon the dead body, they say – what cruel and inhuman wretch, what monster of iniquity could thus hurry into an untimely grave one so young, so beautiful, so innocent.

The evidence on the part of the Commonwealth that Emily Myers died a violent death is overwhelming, and the manner of her death will be proven.

The examining physicians found a penetrating wound through the sternum, and another wound about midway between the sternum and spine on the right side between the 8th and 9th ribs. The wound through the sternum was the place of entrance of the fatal bullet, and the lacerated wound on the right side of the victim was the place where the bullet left the body. After the burial of the body in Marietta, a post mortem examination was made by distinguished physicians who discovered that the seat of life, the heart, was pierced through and through by the fatal ball. We will produce the heart and show you, gentleman of the jury, this fact and you will have no difficulty, after hearing the testimony in concluding that the death of Emily Myers, was a violent one, that it was done by the steady arm of someone who fired from a revolver the shot that killed her. There were no other marks of violence on the person of the deceased, and the revolver which was used by the inhuman monster, lay not far from the victim.

And now, Gentleman of the jury, I will state to you in what manner the Commonwealth will connect the prisoner at the bar with the awful crime. We will prove by four or five witnesses that the prisoner at the bar made a free and full confession of the crime. The witnesses will detail to you these confessions. To one witness the prisoner said 'You need not call her – she is in the stable dead'. He said further 'I shot her and shot myself, and I am going to die'.

He said further in answer to a question by a witness for the Commonwealth, John I want to know why you did this horrible deed! The prisoner answered 'She ruined me, and set me crazy – she promised three times to be my wife, and went back on me'. He said 'I went out to the stable to see whether she would be as good as her word, that he had asked her to marry him and she said no she wouldn't.' The prisoner then said 'Then I'll shoot you, for no other man shall have you'. The prisoner further stated that 'she stamped her foot and dared him,' that she threw herself back and placing her hand on her breast said 'do it quick.' The witness then asked him if she spoke or did anything, and he answered 'No she just stared at him and quivered and fell over.'

To three witnesses for the Commonwealth the prisoner, in answer to the question, John - did you shoot Emily Myers? answered 'Yes, I did'. In response to the question why? The prisoner answered 'Love was the cause of it. I wanted her to marry me, and she said she wouldn't be my wife or any other man's wife, and then I shot her. He said 'I shot her in the end of the barn towards the house'. To another witness the prisoner said 'I have finished her, I have done the work right this time.'

These confessions, gentleman of the jury, will be proven to have been made by the prisoner, without any threat or promise having been previously made. These confessions connect the prisoner with the crime, and conclusively show that the prisoner destroyed the life of Emily Myers. The remaining fact which the Commonwealth must prove to make out the case against the prisoner is to show that his act was willful, deliberate and premeditated. As evidence establishing this fact the Commonwealth will prove by several witnesses that within a few days previous to the crime he threatened to take the life of the victim.

On the 27th of May – three days before the crime was committed, the prisoner said as he was ferrying the witness across the Susquehanna River, 'John, I have trouble. In answer to the question what is your trouble, the prisoner answered 'I will tell you but you might blow on me'. The witness then answered 'No, I won't'. The prisoner then said 'I would like to get married, but I haven't the means'. The witness then asked him how he ever expected to get the means carrying on the way he did, and the witness further asked 'who would have you?' The prisoner then answered 'the maid, but mother is opposed to it. I asked her twice to marry me and she refused, and I intend to ask her again, and then by God before anybody else shall have her, I'll shoot her'. At this moment some persons were observed on the river's bank, and the prisoner cautioned the witness not to talk so loud, as 'the Marietta folks might hear us.'

To another witness who was at Coyles ploughing, as this witness rested from his work, the prisoner approached him and said 'I have trouble, if I can't marry the girl, I'll shoot her or get her out of the road some way or other'. To another witness the prisoner said on the 22nd of May last – eight days before the crime, 'I'll shoot her, if she won't hold connection with me'. The witness had spent the better part of the day at Coyles, and on leaving the prisoner accompanied him a short distance from the house, and while sitting on a rock and conversing with the witness made the threat to take the life of the victim as I have stated to you.

Gentleman, I have in this brief way submitted to you the case of the Commonwealth against the prisoner at the bar.

I have stated the logical order of our proof, and we will endeavor to confine ourselves to it, acting impartially as we have done from the beginning to the end of the case – having a care that the interests of the people are protected and a violated law vindicated on the one side, and at the same time expressing an earnest desire that the prisoner may have – and as I know he will receive at the hands of this court, counsel and jury a perfectly fair and impartial trial.

I do not regard as inappropriate, gentleman, in the opening address, to refer to the fact that as the prosecuting officer of the county, I have associated with me in the trial of this case an assistant counsel. It is a case of utmost importance as well to the people as to the prisoner. I have thought much about this case. I have considered the possibility of unforeseen events happening which might prevent me from carrying this trial to its end, for it may be a lengthy one. I have considered in such an event the heavy burden to the taxpayers of the county. I have considered that alone in the trial of a case of the gravity of this one, it might be said justice was not done the people. And when I reflected upon the fact that the prisoner was to be, as he is now, defended by two gentleman of eminent legal attainments, - men who stand in the first rank of criminal lawyers, then it was upon my own motion, by the grace of this court, that Geo. W. McElroy, Esq., a gentleman of legal attainments equal to those of the prisoners counsel, became associated with me in this trial. When this trial is ended with such aid as I have, and the prisoner defended as he is, with the verdict whatever it may be, - let all the people be content.

I am glad we have upon this jury, old men and men comparatively young. Some of you are fathers and are advanced in years, so that having these classes represented upon this jury, I feel that in the hands of such men justice will be done between the people and the prisoner.

It is needless to ask you to give patient attention to this case. This I know you will do. Under the solemn sanction of your oaths as Jurors, so act throughout the trial, and so form your verdict upon all the evidence and the law of the case, that you may be enabled as honest conscientious jurors, when the trial is ended, to say I have done my job fearlessly and conscientiously."[1]

In his opening address, Zeigler clearly outlined the prosecution's strategy. He explained the indictment of murder in the first degree and the criteria of law that needed to be met to sustain it. Next, he identified the three essential facts the Commonwealth would establish in order to substantiate the charge. He would prove that Emily was dead, killed violently by John Coyle, and that the murder was premeditated. To the D.A. it was an open and shut case.

The burden of proof would not be hard for Zeigler and McElroy to prove. Emily was pronounced dead by the coroner and her heart would be produced in court to drive home the point. John had confessed to several people immediately after the shooting, and made statements in the weeks prior threatening to shoot Emily. Since the defendant was presumed by law to be sane, Zeigler was not planning to produce witnesses to testify concerning Coyle's mental condition, but would re-direct any witness who, under cross-examination by the defense, tried to imply he was unsound.

Of the forty-seven witnesses subpoenaed by the Zeigler, only twenty-seven were called to testify during the prosecution's case-in-chief. The remainder appeared in rebuttal after the presentation of the defense's case. Zeigler began by calling Mary Ann Coyle, the mother of the defendant and the closest witness to the murder.

Although she did not witness the murder first-hand, Mrs. Coyle was the first person to see John after the shooting and was the most qualified to explain what occurred that morning at the ferry. She was also the last to see Emily alive, at 5 o'clock in the morning on May 30. After hearing three sounds like blows of an ax, she went downstairs and encountered her son on the front porch. He told her she needn't call Emily as he had shot her and she was lying dead in the barn.

On cross-examination, defense attorney Henry Fisher concentrated more on the appearance and actions of the prisoner immediately after the shooting. He wanted to plant the idea in the jury's mind that Coyle was not mentally sound and in control of his actions. Upon questioning, Mrs. Coyle recalled how John's eyes were large and glaring as if he were crazy and that he was haggard and wild-looking with blood running down his ears and chest.

On re-direct, the District Attorney was able to get Mrs. Coyle to admit that John was fine on Saturday, two days before the murder, when he went across the river on an errand for her. She also testified she had not seen John between Wednesday and Saturday and that he had been in his room the entire time.

The next three witnesses confirmed the basic facts of the case and described the events the morning of the murder. Frank Magee, the Justice of the Peace who was the first person summoned to the ferry following the shooting, described finding the body with the pistol lying nearby. He produced the small Smith and Wesson .22 caliber seven-shot revolver and it was entered into evidence.

Drs. George Rebman and John Thompson testified they helped carry Emily from the barn and assisted in the coroner's inquest. After Rebman was finished on the stand, Thompson gave his opinion of John's wounds. The defense objected, and questioned whether Zeigler could ask the witness about the character of the prisoner's wounds since no evidence pertaining to them had yet been entered.

Judge Wickes ruled the evidence was permissible since Coyle's wounds had already been brought out by the defense during the cross-examination of Mrs. Coyle. Zeigler explained his purpose was to show that Coyle's injuries were not dangerous and he was not unusually excited following the shooting. The defense once again objected that the testimony was irrelevant, but the objection was overruled and Thompson was allowed to continue.

Thompson was one of the doctors who examined John in his bedroom after the shooting, and described Coyle's injuries as slight surface wounds, not penetrating the bone or causing significant bleeding. After giving his opinion that the defendant's breathing was free and easy and his pulse nearly normal, the defense began their cross-examination. Detailed questions were asked concerning the method in which Coyle's pulse was taken and the extent of his injuries. On re-direct, Dr. Thompson admitted he had not specifically counted Coyle's heartbeats but was of the opinion it was normal. When asked if Coyle's appearance indicated a sound, healthy person, the defense objected and was sustained.

Zeigler's next witnesses documented Coyle's murder confession. William Thompson, Alexander Thompson and Daniel Moore had all been present at the ferry on the morning of the shooting and heard Coyle freely admit to the killing. Thompson also testified he heard Coyle say he had fired on Emily on Saturday, two days before the murder. On cross-examination, the defense attempted to discredit Thompson, who admitted Coyle did not say which Saturday, or where and when the alleged warning shot was fired.

Next the prosecution needed to prove Emily had in fact been killed and to identify the cause of death. Dr. M.J. McKinnon, the physician in charge of her autopsy, testified he was present when the body was exhumed and he had removed her heart. He stated that her heart was in malposition and therefore the bullet pierced it and caused immediate death. The defense objected that the body he examined had not been positively identified and Ziegler promised the next two witnesses would establish that fact.

John Bastian, the undertaker who retrieved Emily's remains from across the river the morning after the murder and prepared it for burial the following day, identified the body as being that of Emily Myers, with whom he was acquainted. John Deppeler, the sexton who dug the grave in the Samaritan Cemetery and subsequently disinterred the body for the autopsy corroborated the identification as Emily Myers. Dr. John Thompson was recalled to testify that it was indeed Emily he had seen dead at the ferry and subsequently at graveside when the post-mortem examination was conducted.

Dr. Rebman was also recalled to provide a positive identification of the body, as he had been present at the coroner's inquest the day of the murder. The last witness to provide details of Emily's death was Dr. John Ahl, the York County Coroner in charge of her autopsy. He verified her heart was too far to the right and not in the normal position. In a dramatic display of evidence, he produced the glass jar in court containing Emily's heart preserved in alcohol.

John Coyle's confession clearly proved he committed the murder, and his guilt was not in question by either the prosecution or the defense. However, Ziegler called five additional witnesses to reinforce the fact that Coyle admitted to the killing. W.S. Sweeney, who was present at the ferry the day of the shooting, testified he heard John, in the presence of Daniel Moore, Dr. Rebman and Mr. Coyle, say that he shot Emily. As persons of authority who also heard Coyle's confession, officers William Houck, Edwin Dietz, and John Shenberger were next on the stand.

On the morning of the murder, after the initial facts of the crime had become apparent, Justice of the Peace Frank Magee had turned Coyle over to the custody of Officer Edwin Dietz from Hellam and John Shenberger, a constable from Wrightsville. Coyle was loaded into a wagon and taken to Hellam, where Shenberger exchanged places with Justice of the Peace William Houck. During the ride to the York County Prison, Coyle had several conversations with the Dietz and Houck and freely admitted to shooting Emily.

During the trip, Coyle confessed to the officers, "I shot Emily Myers, love was the cause of it; I asked her to marry me; she said she would not be my wife or any other man's; I said if she did not marry me, I would shoot her, she said 'shoot me right here', and I shot her."[2] He complained of his hard life, the trouble with his hand injured as a result of a hunting accident, and the fact he was hurried away from the ferry without the opportunity to change clothes. Each of the three officers corroborated the testimony of the others and the defense cross-examination centered on the fact that no arrest warrant had been issued before Coyle was taken to prison.

Following the testimony of the officers, the District Attorney felt he had successfully proved Emily had been violently murdered by John Coyle, Jr. He had one more witness to call concerning Coyle's confession before moving on to establishing premeditation. As promised in his opening statement, Zeigler was arguing the Commonwealth's case as briefly as possible, as he felt the facts spoke for themselves. Before he was able to call Philip Altland, Judge Wickes adjourned court for the day.

The trial resumed Friday morning at 9 o'clock. Mrs. Coyle was present at the beginning of the proceedings, but Mr. Coyle did not enter the courtroom until sometime later. In speaking to reporters before court began, Mr. Coyle told them John was deeply affected by the way things had gone the first day of the trial and had broken down in his cell the previous evening. John told his father that his friends had already said their good-byes, and asked if he would be executed immediately or have time to get religion.

First to the stand was the sheriff's son, Philip Altland, a deputy sheriff who lived at the York County Prison. During the course of Coyle's imprisonment, Philip took meals to Coyle and spoke with him frequently. He testified John told him four or five weeks after his arrest that he had shot Emily. After Altland asked why, Coyle told him it was because she had tormented him. Altland also testified that he heard Coyle tell his mother the same thing on several occasions. After Altland was dismissed, Zeigler was now ready to begin the last phase of his case, showing that the murder had been premeditated.

The Commonwealth's next series of witnesses were friends and neighbors who frequently visited Coyle's Ferry to eat in the tavern or be taken across the river to Marietta. In the weeks prior to the murder, they all heard John threaten to shoot Emily and were asked to relate their conversations with him. First called was John Warfield from Hellam Township, who had seen John on the Wednesday, Thursday and Friday immediately before the murder.

On Friday, May 27, Warfield went to Coyle's Ferry to be taken across the river. After Mrs. Coyle called John from his room, Warfield and Coyle started towards Marietta and John confided that he was having some trouble. When Warfield asked about the trouble, Coyle hesitated, afraid that he would tell someone. Eventually, Coyle said he wanted to marry the maid, but she had refused twice, and he was going to ask her only one more time. If she again refused, he exclaimed "by God, I will shoot her, before anyone else will have her."[3]

On cross-examination by the defense, Warfield indicated Coyle looked as usual and was not broken down, although he looked a little rougher than he did in court. He stated Emily Myers was the only girl John talked about and nothing was ever said about love. He looked sober to Warfield, but he didn't think Coyle's talk was in earnest and therefore had not mentioned it to anyone else. One of the jurors, Henry Deitch, interrupted and asked Warfield to confirm the day he had the conversation with John.

Warfield reiterated he had seen Coyle on May 25, 26, and 27. He was sure of the dates, as Thursday was Ascension Day and he had been in Marietta on bank business and had ridden back to York County with John. And, he was sure the conversation concerning the threats occurred the following day, on Friday. This testimony flatly contradicted that of Mrs. Coyle, who stated John was locked in his room from Wednesday through Saturday the week prior to the murder. This was only one of Mrs. Coyle's many inconsistent statements throughout the trial, and must have shed some doubt in the jury's mind about her honesty.

The next witness, William Hetrick, was at the ferry on Saturday, May 22, a little over a week before the shooting. After eating dinner at the Coyles, he took a walk with John and stopped to sit with him by the creek for a conversation. He described Coyle as unshaven and dirty, and said he listened to Coyle tell him of his trouble with Emily for about an hour. Coyle told Hetrick he read and destroyed love letters from some of Emily's other suitors and would shoot her if she didn't have relations with him. After Hetrick told Coyle he would most certainly be hanged for shooting Emily, the subject was dropped. On cross-exam, Hetrick testified John wasn't laughing when he said he would shoot her and that he told both Coyle's mother and Emily's grand-uncle Simon Myers of their conversation.

John Burg testified he was helping to plant corn at the Coyles when John told him Emily had promised to marry him and he would shoot her or get her out the way if she didn't. Burg's opinion was that he looked a little troubled about it, but did not seem angry.

The last witness concerning Coyle's threats was John P. Thompson from Liverpool, a canalman whom John had rowed across the river two weeks before Decoration Day. A comparative stranger to Coyle, Thompson had been surprised when John talked of his personal problems with the hired girl. Coyle declared he was in love with Emily but his parents were opposed to the relationship, and if he could not have her no one else would. On cross, Thompson said Coyle appeared to be serious and was sober at the time.

By this point, the Commonwealth was confident they had firmly established their case and the District Attorney took the opportunity to enter some other relevant items into evidence. Albertus Hibner, a local surveyor, produced a draft of the ferry property indicating the position of the house and barn. The document was passed around to the jury and then entered as State's evidence. Kate Hinkle, Coyle's aunt, presented a package containing the clothing worn by Emily at the time of the murder. Mrs. Coyle was then recalled to identify the dress. She stated the lack of blood on the clothing was due to the fact it had been washed.

It seemed as if the prosecution was ready to rest their case, but Zeigler decided to call several other witnesses in an effort to discount the sincerity of John's attempted suicide the day of the murder. The issue of Coyle's superficial, self-inflicted wounds was brought up in court earlier that day, and Zeigler wanted to make sure the jury understood his position on the matter. If John's attempt to commit suicide appeared genuine, the jury might believe Coyle was indeed insane – what sane person would take his own life? The Commonwealth felt John's injuries had been staged for the purpose of faking a suicide, and Zeigler thought he could prove that Coyle was in fact sane and rational enough to stage a believable deception.

Dr. John Thompson was recalled, prompting the defense to ask why the witness was being brought back to the stand. Zeigler stated his intention of showing that Coyle's wounds might have been simulated. An objection was raised by defense attorney Fisher since Coyle's injuries were not yet in evidence by the Commonwealth. Judge Wickes again overruled, stating again that the issue had already been brought out in the defense's cross-examination of witnesses. After Thompson indicated he had removed bullets before, Fisher asked if he had ever treated gunshot wounds to the head, to which Thompson replied no, he had not.

Zeigler asked Thompson if Coyle's injuries could have been made by a paper wad or a blank cartridge, which was objected to by the defense as a leading question. The objection was sustained and Zeigler rephrased the question, asking in what ways Coyle's wounds might have been made. Thompson replied the slight marks on the prisoner may have been caused by paper loads, blanks, or even a blunt instrument.

On cross-examination, Thompson explained that if the injuries were in fact caused by paper or blanks, the pistol must have been held close. This would have created black powder marks around the wounds, which he affirmed were present on Coyle. Thompson was asked if he ever attempted such an experiment, and he answered no, he had not.

The prosecution re-directed, asking if Coyle's manner shortly after the murder seemed staged, and an objection raised by defense counsel was sustained. Upon restating the question, Thompson replied that "the prisoner's actions, when pulled out of bed, after the shooting of Emily Myers, were perfectly rational – there was little if any nervous excitement about him."[4] On re-cross, he could not say whether a lack of excitement would indicate Coyle was insane.

Dr. I.C. Gable testified to treating gunshot injuries the previous month and the year prior to the trial. The defense questioned the witness's qualifications as an expert, having only treated gun wounds twice before. Although it seemed a reasonable objection, it was overruled and the testimony was allowed. On re-direct, Gable stated that if the load had contained shot, it should have penetrated the bone. Since it did not, the injuries may have been produced by a blunt instrument. On re-cross, he admitted that if the pistol was held obliquely, the ball would have glanced and been less likely to penetrate.

Following Gable's testimony, court adjourned and reconvened after lunch. Sheriff Altland was late in returning with the prisoner and received a sharp reprimand from Judge Wickes. Proceedings resumed at 1:45 p.m. with Dr. S.J. Rouse.

Dr. Rouse had considerable experience with gunshot wounds during his service in the Civil War, as a surgeon at the York Hospital, and as the attending physician at the York County Prison. He had examined Coyle after he was brought to jail and thought his injuries might have been caused by a blunt instrument or a pistol ball. On cross-exam, Rouse said the extent and depth of a gunshot wound would depend on the quality and quantity of powder used.

Dr. Rebman was recalled to testify concerning his knowledge of gunshot injuries. He examined Coyle the morning of the murder, and his opinion was that the wounds may have been produced with another instrument. However, he conceded that if the pistol had been loaded improperly, the ball may not have gone into the bone. He confirmed Dr. Rouse's opinion that it would depend on the quality and quantity of powder used.

The last witness for the prosecution was Dr. M.J. McKinnon, who also served as an army surgeon in the Civil War and had extensive experience in dealing with gunshot wounds. He stated that if the cartridges had been prepared normally, the shot would have passed through the bone. On cross-examination, the defense asked how much powder would have to be in a round in order for it to penetrate and McKinnon replied it would depend on the distance from which the shot was fired.

The two balls Coyle allegedly fired at himself were not entered into evidence during the trial. It would seem they either were not found in the barn, were not in the pistol to begin with, or no search had been conducted for them.

A few minutes after 2 o'clock, almost exactly one day after his opening statement, District Attorney Edward Zeigler rested the Commonwealth's case against John Coyle. On the surface, it seemed to be an airtight case. The prosecution had proved the three points in their opening statement, demonstrating Emily Myers was dead, killed by the hand of John Coyle in a premeditated cold-blooded murder. Coyle's mental state as testified by the witnesses thus far was inconclusive and it would be up to Henry Fisher and William Chapman to convince the jury he was insane and should not be held responsible for the murder.

Chapter 17

York County Courthouse, York, Pa
Friday, October 21, 1881

"Honesty is the best policy. But insanity is the best defense"
                                                                    ... Mark Twain

Henry Lee Fisher, lead attorney for John Coyle, Jr., opened for the defense shortly after the Commonwealth rested. His statement to the jury was concise, and he asked for an acquittal on the grounds that the prisoner was insane at the time the crime was committed. Fisher outlined his various theories on the cause of Coyle's insanity, with the promise of bringing forth witnesses to substantiate them.

Fisher boasted that he had gained acquittals in nine of the ten murder cases he previously defended. In a moment of humbleness, and perhaps in an attempt to gain sympathy with the jury, he admitted he was approaching the Coyle case with fear as he had never tried a case in which the defense was one of insanity. After acknowledging the esteemed associate counsel of the Commonwealth, George McElroy, he announced the defense had engaged the assistance of William Chapman in order to insure that Coyle received a fair trial

In order to establish a rapport with the jury, Fisher commented on how natural a reaction it was for everyone, including the jurors, to form an opinion upon hearing of the crime for the first time, but warned that initial impressions could often turn out to be completely wrong. He appreciated the difficulty in empanelling the jury in the case at hand, but attributed it primarily to false public sentiment. Blaming the newspapers for biased reporting, he expressed his confidence that the jury would try the case justly and with an open mind, and not be unduly influenced by the one-sided reporting.

Fisher read through a long list of symptoms which indicated Coyle's insanity, beginning when John was a young boy and learned to read and write but never mastered arithmetic like the other children. As Coyle grew older, he "showed a weakness of the mind, imbecility, and want of a sense of moral obligation."[1] At the age of fifteen, Fisher claimed John's brain had been affected by an accidental discharge of a duck gun close to his head and a subsequent bout of typhoid fever.

According to the defense, Coyle's insanity worsened at age twenty and he became a "monomaniac on the subject of women," further amplified by his "unnatural and filthy habits, until he lost all sense of self respect."[2] Although his parents attempted to get him medical help for habitual masturbation, nothing seemed to work and John became withdrawn, frequently locking himself in his room or disappearing into the woods along the river for long periods of time.

Fisher recalled several occasions when Coyle attempted suicide but had been prevented by his parents and relatives. Furthermore, John had a propensity for stealing children's playthings and had an uncontrollable temper. He was unreliable in his work habits, became melancholy and withdrawn, was irregular in his meals, and suffered from intense headaches. As a final symptom of Coyle's insanity, Fisher told of John's marriage proposals to respectable women, which was completely out of character given his terrible condition.

Summarizing his strategy, Fisher informed the jury he would produce witnesses to substantiate Coyle's insanity and would prove that the act of will necessary to sustain a charge of first degree murder was not present. The presumption of law was that all men were sane, and Fisher emphasized that if he proved Coyle insane, the prosecution would need to establish his sanity in order to win a guilty verdict.

Fisher opened his case with the same witness as the prosecution, Mrs. Mary Ann Coyle. For the Commonwealth, she had been called to give the basic facts of the crime and to recount the events on the morning of the murder. For the defense, Fisher hoped that Mrs. Coyle's personal familiarity with the defendant would serve as compelling testimony in demonstrating Coyle's insanity.

The Commonwealth immediately challenged the validity of calling Mrs. Coyle. Fisher contended she was the person most acquainted with John's mental condition since he lived in her home his entire life, and was uniquely qualified to prove he was unsound. McElroy objected on the grounds that the evidence provided by Mrs. Coyle would be misleading and irrelevant, and hardly up to the standard required by law to exempt John from being responsible for the crime or to establish his insanity. He argued the Commonwealth had already characterized John as a normal and rational person, and quoted several precedent cases to defend his point.

In the case of Brown v. Commonwealth, 28 P.F. Smith 123, McElroy cited, "To make the opinion of a witness that a person is insane, he must state some facts fairly indicative of insanity."[3] He further argued that in People v. Klein, American Law Register, N.S. 602, "a mere impulse of passion was not sufficient to acquit on the ground of insanity."[4] McElroy asserted the defense must prove that Coyle's insanity existed at the very moment he pulled the trigger, and could not simply claim that every indication of abnormality during his life rendered Coyle irresponsible for his actions.

Judge Wickes interrupted McElroy's objections, ruling it was hardly the proper time to debate Coyle's insanity since the testimony had not yet been given, and assured the prosecution team they would be given ample opportunity to argue its value after hearing the evidence. Mrs. Coyle took the stand and proceeded to give a detailed history of her son's problems and incidents throughout his life that she felt contributed to his mental instability.

Predictably, the defense crafted their questions to portray Coyle as unstable, while cross-examination by the prosecution focused on showing that his activities were normal. Mrs. Coyle described her son as unreliable with an uncontrollable temper and disposition, and described his moods as being better or worse as the moon changed. Although John was addicted to alcohol, she stated his problems had begun long before he began drinking. As far as Emily Myers was concerned, John never mentioned that he hated her or loved her, and talked to her like a sister.

Mrs. Coyle went on to detail several incidents when John attempted to commit suicide. When he was nineteen, she discovered him in the barn pointing a pistol at his breast with his eyes rolled back in his head, looking haggard and crazy. After her brother William called out to him, John dropped the pistol and she retrieved it and hid it in a drawer. About a month later, John began carrying a razor and threatened to cut his throat, but Mrs. Coyle was able to sneak the blade away from him. Shortly afterwards, John threatened to hang himself.

In order to get her son help for his melancholia, Mrs. Coyle had taken him to Dr. Brenneman in Middletown a year after he had typhoid fever, but the medicine did not help. She then sought advice from Dr. Hinkle in Columbia, but John's depression soon returned worse than ever. She had also discussed with Dr. Alexander in Marietta the possibility of sending him to a hospital for the insane, but never pursued it any further.

On cross-examination, Mrs. Coyle said she first realized something was wrong with her son from the time he first went to school, and felt he was foolish and different from the other children. He was often short-tempered and ill-natured when he played, and as he grew older he preferred the company of much younger boys. She thought he was responsible enough to go hunting alone, but once shot himself accidentally in the hand while crawling under a log while out for ducks. McElroy then asked about John's duties around the ferry in an effort to demonstrate his ability to function as a normal person.

Mrs. Coyle described John's responsibilities as minor, doings things such as planting corn, potatoes, and tobacco. He tended to the cows and horses, but never helped keep the tavern books. As she explained, he did not stick with any particular piece of work very long and was unreliable. But, she admitted, John frequently rowed people across the river, sometimes several times a day, and on the Saturday before the murder, he had gone across the river to sell some butter and returned later with the groceries she had requested.

Far from portraying John as chronically insane, Mrs. Coyle ended up describing her son as a basically functional, yet immature simple-minded young adult. Due to the aggressive cross-examination by George McElroy, the defense would have to come up with stronger witnesses if they had any hope of convincing the jury of Coyle's insanity. Next on the stand was John's aunt, Mrs. Kate Hinkle.

Mrs. Hinkle did not consider John to be of sound mind since he sometimes acted silly. The court pointed out that "the witness must confine herself to the words and actions of the prisoner, not merely saying that he acted or talked foolish."[5] Pressed for specific examples, she recounted one Christmas where he had teased her children by taking their playthings and cakes, and after she scolded him, John had laughed. Other times he asked for pie but refused to take it, or would offer to cut firewood and then say the ax was too dull. The only other instances she could recall were the many times John talked of marrying different girls.

She corroborated the events the day at the ferry when her husband William discovered John in the granary with a pistol, threatening to shoot himself. She thought John never seemed right after the injury to his hand and his sickness with typhoid. He complained to her of his headaches, and with wild eyes often said he wished he was dead. She and her husband thought John should be put in an asylum before something dreadful happened, and although they spoke of it to his parents, nothing was done.

On cross-examination, Mrs. Hinkle admitted the incident when John had teased her children happened eleven years earlier, and he was often drunk when visiting her. She judged John unsound due to his wild looks and his constant talk about getting married. All in all, Mrs. Hinkle proved to be a less than effective witness for the defense, as the proof she offered consisted of mostly isolated trivial incidents.

The last witness of the day was Nicholas McDonald, who had known the Coyles for about seven years. He thought John had a weak mind and everything about him was a little different from other people. He was then asked to relate some examples from which he had formed his opinion.

McDonald said he had spoken with John hundreds of times, and his talk was mostly of a cranky and trifling nature. Many of their conversations centered on marrying, and McDonald never paid much attention to them. On one occasion, John talked about proposing to a schoolteacher from Lebanon who was staying at the Coyles. McDonald thought it crazy, as the girl was a "lady of fine appearance and more than ordinary intelligence,"[6] and much above John's station in life.

McDonald cited another example when John said he had gone to Philadelphia in a sleigh by way of Baltimore and Washington and thought it was a direct route. John also told McDonald of the frequent quarrels with his father and related several occasions when he had attempted to shoot him, laughing about it like it was a joke. McDonald also detailed conversations where John talked about his addiction to masturbation and that he was seeing a doctor for it.

On cross-examination, McDonald admitted he frequently saw Coyle drunk on both sides of the river, and during the conversations concerning the fights with his father, Coyle always seemed like he had been drinking. He believed that Coyle was silly, sober or not, but was especially foolish on the subject of women.

At 5:30 p.m., Judge Wickes ended the third day of the trial. Thus far, Fisher and Chapman had offered a weak case for the defense, producing witnesses who gave inconclusive and vague statements about Coyle, with no compelling testimony proving that he was insane. Their evidence consisted mostly of personal impressions based on inconsequential conversations and incidents, and did not go far in helping to demonstrate Coyle was not in control of his actions at the time of the murder.

Saturday morning at 9 o'clock, court resumed with the cross-examination of Nicholas McDonald. The prosecution hoped to show Coyle's irrational behavior was caused more by his bad habits than any weakness of his mind. McDonald admitted that Coyle had been drinking when he spoke of going to Philadelphia in a sleigh by way of

Baltimore and Washington. The defense, hoping to salvage the testimony of the witness, got McDonald to clarify that Coyle was not completely drunk when the statements were made.

The next witness, Thomas Scott, turned out to be yet another disaster for the defense. Scott, a hotelkeeper in Marietta, said he never noticed anything that unusual about John, except for his carelessness and the fact he never was concerned whether he did anything or not. Scott did not take notice to anything particularly odd about Coyle on the streets of Marietta, although he had seen boys making fun of him.

As his only example of Coyle's weak mind, Scott cited an instance the previous winter when John left a package at his hotel and asked him to care for it. In about a half hour, Coyle came back and retrieved the package. A little while later, he came back again and asked for the same package. When Scott told him he had already given it to him, Coyle became angry and had to be thrown out of the hotel.

At this point, Fisher asked "From all you have seen and know of John Coyle, generally, from his actions, was he in your opinion a few weeks before the shooting of sound mind?"[7] Scott asked for some clarification on the definition of an unsound mind, and the court stated that to be considered insane, a person would have to be unconscious of what they were doing at the time of the crime.

Much to Fisher's disappointment, Scott answered that given the definition he would have to consider Coyle of sound mind and that some foolish actions would not necessarily justify him as being crazy. On cross, Scott admitted that Coyle was sober when he left the package at his hotel, but when he came back for it he was slightly intoxicated, and when he returned the second time, he was even more so.

The defense continued to call witnesses who offered only inconsequential examples of Coyle's alleged insanity, while the prosecution was able to show that most of these incidents occurred while Coyle was drunk. Fisher decided to change his tactics and address Coyle's many unreasonable marriage proposals and called Miss Emily Rollins from Marietta.

Rollins testified John had passed by her house two years previous and proposed to her from the street. He was fixated on the subject and appeared to be serious but eventually left. The Christmas before the murder, he again asked her to marry him, which she refused. Coyle was insistent, and in an attempt to get him to leave, Rollins jokingly said she wouldn't consider marrying anyone unless she had a silk dress. Instead of being discouraged, John said he would go get his mother's dress and return that afternoon to be married.

Rollins testified that Coyle seemed sober when he proposed, but she did not consider him sane. On cross-examination, Rollins said her opinion was not merely because of the proposals, but also because she had seen him playing marbles with young boys the previous year.

Henry Deitch, one of the more vocal jurors who frequently interrupted with questions of his own, wanted to know what Coyle's appearance had been when he proposed. She said his eyes were large and glaring and he looked quite different than he did in court. As with the previous defense witnesses, Rollins' testimony was ineffectual and gave no substantial evidence to prove Coyle's insanity.

Next called was Melchior Harline, who thought John often talked silly, telling him Stratton[*] was at the ferry when it was not true. Harline said Coyle preferred the company of young boys, and he often saw him play marbles with both white and black boys. He had last seen Coyle in March, when he came into his shop red-faced and began dancing around in the store. From his language, conduct and general appearance, Harline considered Coyle to have an unsound mind.

Predictably, McElroy's cross-examination centered on Coyle's drinking, and Harline admitted John was often drunk in Marietta, and acted like a drunken man when he came in the shop dancing. Fisher then decided to call Mr. Coyle to give further details on John's upbringing, which he hoped would provide some credible evidence of his son's insanity.

---

[*] *Coyle may have been referring to Charles S. Stratton, a.k.a. General Tom Thumb, a midget entertainer with P.T. Barnum.*

Mr. Coyle confirmed the basic facts given by his wife concerning John's troubles growing up and the circumstances the day of the murder. His son loitered around most of the time, was very hard to teach, and could never make out a board bill at the inn correctly. Once he found him in the woodshed crying and John complained to him that his head was all wrong. He told John if he would be a good boy it would be all right, but he continued to get worse. After the shooting, he described his son as "wild and crazy, just like a madman that had broken out of a mad house."[8]

On cross-examination, Mr. Coyle elaborated on his son's education. John did not want to go to school, but attended until he was about thirteen, when he was removed due to constant quarreling with the teacher and the other children. He admitted that John could do basic arithmetic, and occasionally was able to get the tavern account book correct. Mr. Coyle concurred with his wife that John had been locked in his room most of the week before the murder.

On re-direct by the defense, Mr. Coyle stated John never said a word to him about marrying Emily Myers, and denied his son shot at her the Saturday before the murder. Assistant prosecutor McElroy challenged Mr. Coyle on re-cross about the incident, point-blank asking him "Didn't you say in the presence of Elizabeth Mack, in the yard of Simon Myers, in the Borough of Marietta, the day of the funeral that John shot at Emily Myers on Saturday before she was shot, and that you took the pistol and hid it?"[9]

Mr. Coyle vehemently denied knowing Emily Myer's aunt, Elizabeth Mack, or the fact that John even possessed a pistol. Mrs. Coyle was briefly recalled to the stand to corroborate her husband's testimony, and reiterated that she and Emily were home all day working and no shooting occurred. This flatly contradicted the testimony of William Thompson, who said John told him of firing at Emily two days before the murder.

Fisher needed to get the defense back on track, as he had not been able to put together any compelling evidence of Coyle's insanity.

However, he had no better luck with his next witnesses and the defense case continued to unravel.

H. G. Beatty formed his opinion of Coyle based on trifling conversations and his general appearance and conduct on the street. His felt Coyle's dress was not that of a sane man, and although there were other men careless in their dress, a sane man would occasionally wear something other than work clothes. Beatty admitted he had only seen him on the streets three times, but each time Coyle had been walking carelessly.

The next witness was Percy B. Shock, the publisher of the *Marietta Register*. Coyle would come to his office regularly and talk silly, saying there were flocks of ducks on the river when there were none and speaking loosely about women. Judge Wickes interrupted and explained that conversations entered as evidence must indicate mental unsoundness and the ones just related did not qualify.

Shock testified that on the day of the murder, Coyle said to him "Shock, my God I wish I had shot and killed myself first and then shot the girl."[10] Since it was an impossibly backwards statement, he felt Coyle did not understand the gravity of the situation. At other times, he had seen Coyle playing marbles with white and colored boys and frequently saw him taunted. From these incidents, he considered him unsound. However, on cross-examination, Shock admitted he did not consider Coyle insane, and conceded that Coyle's statements about the shooting the day of the murder may have been just a slip of the tongue. When pressed by juror Henry Deitch to clarify his opinion, Shock reiterated that he considered Coyle unsound but could not swear he was insane.

John Campbell, a hotel keeper in Marietta, then took the stand. He testified Coyle would often come in and attempt to help himself to food and drink and would have to be told to leave. Coyle would come from the post office with love letters he claimed were from girls who had previously lived at the ferry, and would ask Campbell to read them out loud. He was very silly and foolish and often talked of how splendidly he would live when he got married. By his movements and eyes, Campbell did not consider him a sound-minded man.

During McElroy's cross-examination, Campbell admitted that John was often under the influence of liquor and became abusive when drinking. His opinion of Coyle was formed because he thought a man of strong mind would never show his love letters to a stranger, and he often thought Coyle had written the letters himself. He also acknowledged he had been given an extra five dollars to testify, in addition to the witness fees and mileage he was being paid.

Next to testify was George Spangler from Marietta, who knew John since childhood. Although he had been away the previous three years, he frequently associated with John when younger and related an incident which occurred while they were hunting together. Spangler had been about ready to shoot at a rabbit when Coyle pointed his gun at him and yelled, "Damn you, if you shoot, I will shoot you, come here."[11] Coyle, with eyes standing out like fists, ordered Spangler to feel his forehead, but there was no fever and they continued hunting. From this incident, Spangler formed his opinion that Coyle was unsound. Juror Deitch wanted to know if John had been drinking at the time of the gunning incident, and Spangler replied that he had been sober.

The poorly organized defense continued to shift from one strategy to another. Dr. Alexander was Fisher's next witness and was brought to the stand to provide medical testimony. After he stepped down, several more of Coyle's casual acquaintances were called to give anecdotal opinions of John's mental state. Fisher then returned to calling additional medical experts.

Dr. H. M. Alexander had been present at the ferry the morning of the murder, and after classifying John's injuries as superficial surface wounds, had declared him well enough to be taken to jail. He acknowledged treating Coyle several times over the previous ten years, including seeing him for impotence in 1879. Alexander considered Coyle's general appearance to be normal, except for his downcast look. He categorized Coyle as slow and dull, and felt his impotence was caused by his addiction to unnatural vices.

On cross-exam, Alexander said he couldn't tell the extent of Coyle's impotence since he had not made a physical examination, but only treated John based on his statements. When asked what effects habitual masturbation would have on someone, he stated it would weaken the body. On re-direct, he testified that continued practice would not produce insanity, an opinion which would not have been welcomed by the defense.

The last witness before court recessed for lunch was Mrs. Susan McCann, who briefly lived with the Coyles and saw John frequently at the ferry and in Marietta. She thought he had a soft, innocent mind and had seen him playing marbles and bathing in the river with much younger boys. About three weeks before the murder, John told her he could not stay at home because he and Emma Myers wanted to marry but his mother was opposed to it. He was crying and visibly upset, and made Mrs. McCann promise not to say anything about their conversation.

McCann was the only witness to testify that John and Emily had an intimate relationship. She said that when Mrs. Coyle was not around, they would put their arms around each other and make love. On cross-examination, she admitted it was not unusual for a young man to put his arms around a young girl, but John and Emily acted in a loving and affectionate way, even though there was no "billing and cooing."[12] She felt Emily drove Coyle mad and as a result could not have been sane at the time he shot her.

On re-direct, Mrs. McCann asserted she had seen John and Emily embrace dozens of times and was within ten feet of them on several occasions. Her testimony added some credibility to John's claims that Emily loved him and had pledged to marry him. Although not helping to prove Coyle's insanity, it gave the jury the impression there was actually a relationship between the two, and that Emily may have been tormenting John by professing her love and then repeatedly rejecting his continued marriage proposals.

At 2 o'clock, the defense resumed with John Stall, a childhood friend of Coyle. His few encounters with John in the previous ten years were limited to seeing him walk down the street being tormented by other children and playing marbles with boys, both black and white. Sometimes John chased the boys in return, and other times he associated with them, which did not seem normal to Stall.

He related a conversation overheard in Bower's barroom when John boasted that he was running rafts down the river without ever touching a rock. Coyle clamed "that he could lay any of the other pilots of Marietta in the shade,"[13] but Stall knew Coyle had never been a raft pilot. In another instance, John talked immorally about women and prostitutes, and told Stall he visited Mammy Howard's in Irishtown. In Stall's opinion, Coyle was of unsound mind during the time he knew him.

When asked on cross-examination whether he had ever seen boys torment anyone else other than Coyle, Stall acknowledged that he had. When challenged about the rafting conversation, he admitted he never saw Coyle attempt to take a raft down the river and may have done so without his knowledge. Stall turned out to be yet another ineffective witness for the defense.

James Hogan had known Coyle for more than eighteen years, but had not associated with him for the last five. He felt something was wrong with Coyle's mind, basing his opinion on John's motions and conversations. When asked what motions, Hogan explained Coyle continually slung his arms back and forth when walking down the street which proved he wasn't normal. Although he had never seen Coyle drunk, he thought his notions were queer and conversation flighty. Hogan believed John had no common sense.

Next on the stand was John Sargent, another of Coyle's boyhood friends. He felt Coyle's mind had changed in the last four or five years and he acted strangely, throwing stones at the men and boys who teased him. According to Sargent, John "acted like a man that hasn't got a full row of buttons, hasn't got his good sense."[14] Coyle once spoke to him about marrying Sargent's cousin, a school teacher from Lebanon who was staying at the ferry, but Sargent had no such cousin.

When asked by McElroy on cross-examination how he formed his opinion that Coyle was unsound, all Sargent could say was that Coyle was constantly teased and acted foolishly on the streets of Marietta. Yes, he admitted, the boys in Marietta teased plenty of other drunken men, but he hadn't considered Coyle drunk since he didn't often see him stagger.

Realizing the futility of bringing more ineffective personal acquaintances to the stand as witnesses, Fisher called three physicians to testify concerning Coyle's masturbation and the possible effects on his sanity. The first was Dr. John Ahl, a practicing doctor of thirty-six years and the York County Coroner who had performed the autopsy on Emily Myers.

Ahl stated that in his medical practice he had never personally seen insanity produced by habitual masturbation, but had done extensive reading on the effects produced by it and had "a knowledge of the tendency of unnatural vices to produce weakness of the brain."[15] He had observed a patient at Bayview Hospital[†] in Baltimore, Maryland, whose insanity was diagnosed as being caused by masturbation. That patient had looked pale and had run about in his cell like he was crazy.

During an aggressive cross-examination by George McElroy, Ahl admitted that a man might practice the vice all his life and be able to transact ordinary business. He described other symptoms, including physical lassitude, dull eyes, loss of memory, and back pain. Ahl felt that anyone who regularly masturbated would avoid female company, seek solitude, and would not be the kind of man who would talk of marriage. Yes, he had read of men who were impotent yet of sound

---

[†] *Founded in 1773, Bayview is one of the oldest continuously operating heath care institutions in the United States. Now part of Johns Hopkins Health System, it began as an almshouse and evolved into an asylum before becoming a municipal hospital.*

mind, and acknowledged masturbation would produce physical symptoms long before imbecility.

On re-direct, Ahl said he treated Coyle at the beginning of May for his impotency, three weeks before the murder. Coyle was under the influence of whiskey and asked to be admitted to the almshouse hospital. Ahl thought he looked like a tramp and told him he might be admitted with the permission of the resident director, but Coyle did not go to the hospital as far as he was aware.

Next on the stand was Dr. J.T. Perkin, who testified he had treated persons with impaired minds caused by masturbation. He thought they were essentially harmless individuals, who preferred solitude and roamed about aimlessly. He felt dementia would be produced only after a long continued practice, and agreed with Dr. Ahl that symptoms would include dullness and discoloration of the eyes, epilepsy, back pain and lethargy. However, during cross-examination he admitted that "the appearance of the prisoner at the bar does not indicate a long continued practice of this vice."[16]

The last medical witness, Dr. J.W. Kerr, had seen a few cases of masturbation in his practice, and observed several patients in Blockley's[‡] Hospital in Philadelphia. He concurred that long practice of masturbation would produce memory impairment, weaken the mind and produce an aversion to society. However, Kerr was willing to go a step further and stated that according to studies performed at Blockley's, 100 of 4000 cases of insanity were caused by habitual masturbation, or 2.5%.[17]

During cross-exam by George McElroy, Kerr was asked "to look at the prisoner and say whether his appearance would indicate physical prostration or mental alienation produced by masturbation, for the purpose of proving that the prisoner is not a victim, nor made insane, by masturbation."[18] Defense counsel objected and Wickes ruled the question was improper and disallowed it. However, based on

---

[‡] *The Blockley Almshouse, a poorhouse and charity hospital opened in 1723, later became the Philadelphia General Hospital, which closed its doors in 1977.*

the physical signs described by all three doctors, it was obvious to the jury by looking at Coyle in the courtroom that he did not exhibit any of those symptoms. McElroy had achieved making his point.

The final two witnesses for the defense were called to give their opinions concerning the likelihood of Coyle shooting paper wads or blanks at his head and breast on the day of the murder in an effort to simulate a suicide attempt. These witnesses were in response to those produced by the prosecution who implied that John had not actually made a sincere effort to kill himself.

Professor S.B. Heiges related his experience in testing the effects of pistol cartridges when fired against hard objects. He had experimented in the courthouse yard during the summer, shooting shells of the same caliber at a wooden plank. Depending on the amount of powder in the cartridge, some shells penetrated the plank and others bounced off, sometimes two or three in succession.

Removing the ball from the unfired shell in the murder weapon, Heiges exhibited the contents to the jury, showing that it was charged with ordinary pistol powder of the normal quantity. He stated that this particular type of pistol could not easily be loaded with a paper ball without taking apart one of the cartridges, removing the ball, and replacing it with a paper wad. On cross-examination, he admitted that blanks were sometimes made, but he had never seen one the same caliber as the murder weapon.

F. G. Metzger was the final witness for the defense and was summoned only for the purpose of corroborating the testimony of the previous witness. He had been present during the experiments made by Professor Heiges and verified the results. At this point, Coyle was asked to show the jury his hand injured in the duck hunting accident, as well as the wound on his breast made the day of the murder.

The defense rested at 4:15 p.m. The twenty-two witnesses called by Fisher had attempted to prove Coyle insane only by describing his unusual actions, appearance or conversation. Other witnesses for the defense included several doctors whose purpose was to show that Coyle's addiction to masturbation had contributed to his insanity, and a firearms expert to demonstrate that Coyle's attempt at suicide had been genuine.

Compared to the Commonwealth, Fisher and Chapman presented a weak, disorganized case with no compelling witnesses to convince the jury Coyle was insane at the time of the shooting. Their testimony was insignificant and easily discounted during cross-examination by the prosecution. It was reported that "the family and friends of the prisoner were more hindrance then help. In seeking to point out traits that would prove the insanity of John Coyle, Jr., and not, in the majority of cases even understanding the meaning of the word, the evidence they gave was hopelessly contradictive."[19]

After Fisher rested his case, it was the District Attorney's turn to call rebuttal witnesses to counter the evidence produced by the defense. The witnesses called during the initial presentation of the prosecution's case-in-chief had only established the basic facts of the crime. Now that the defense had finished offering evidence to demonstrate Coyle's insanity, Zeigler could call witnesses to testify that Coyle was indeed sane and should be held responsible for the murder.

George Rebman was the first defense witness called in rebuttal and stated he had been the family physician of the Coyles since early 1880. He held intelligent conversations with John concerning the knitting of fish nets and the clearing of ground for tobacco, and John had come to his office on one occasion to pay on his mother's bill. Rebman paid close attention to John's mental state and never saw him say or do anything that would indicate there was any abnormality. John had confessed to Rebman he was a masturbator and a drinker, and the doctor had told Coyle those were the causes of his impotence.

At 5 o'clock, Judge Wickes pounded his gavel and adjourned court for the weekend.

Chapter 18

York County Courthouse, York, Pa
Monday, October 24, 1881

"The law presumes intelligence in jurors."
           ... Massachusetts Supreme Judicial Court, 1829

On Monday morning, court was brought to order at 9 o'clock. Present for the first time was Emily's sister, Annie Myers, who was scheduled to testify later in the day. Before calling additional rebuttal witnesses to show that John was indeed rational, District Attorney Zeigler recalled Coyle's parents to clarify their previous testimony.

Mrs. Coyle was asked for specific details concerning John's prior suicide attempts. She also recalled another incident when John tried to eat rat poison. She was mixing strychnine to put on bread and John had tried to grab it, but Kate Hinkle prevented him from eating it. Mrs. Coyle felt John could have taken it if he had pushed Kate aside.

Apparently the issue of whether Mr. Coyle publicly stated that John shot at Emily two days before the murder was a key point to the prosecution. If true, it demonstrated premeditation in the days immediately prior to the crime. Zeigler recalled Mr. Coyle and asked "Did you say in the presence of Miss Annie Myers, in Simon Myers's yard, that John had shot at Emily on Saturday before the shooting, and you took the pistol away from him, or words to that effect?"[1] Mr. Coyle once again vehemently denied, in no uncertain terms, ever having said such a thing.

Later in the prosecution's rebuttal case, Zeigler would call seven others who would flatly contradict Mr. Coyle's testimony, but he first called additional witnesses to provide evidence that John Coyle was in fact a common, reasonable man, capable of transacting business and acting in a rational way. First on the stand was Henry Matthews.

Matthews testified that he saw Coyle on Ascension Day, the Thursday before the murder, and talked with him about farming and horses. He stated John took him across the river frequently and his conversations were never incoherent, nor did they concern women. From Coyle's manner, Matthews did not think him to be unsound. The next witness, Thomas Wilson, was also ferried by Coyle many times and saw him working in the tobacco fields, hauling rails, currying horses, cutting firewood and performing other normal chores. He too never observed anything that led him to think Coyle was not sane.

John Raymond was a river pilot who conversed with Coyle during frequent trips across the river and had seen him driving wagons and hauling manure. He loaned John money several times to pay for freight to haul whiskey barrels back to the tavern or to get a shave. On another occasion, John asked to borrow money to pay for a pair of shoes. He promised Raymond he would repay him when the tobacco was sold, and had made good on his word.

John Harris observed Coyle working at a lumber mill in Wrightsville and rafting in the spring. He also witnessed him conducting business at the ferry, and Coyle would often talk about river conditions and tell Harris whether it was rising or falling. Harris's testimony was echoed by George Wilson, who talked with John at his blacksmith's shop about raising tobacco. Neither had ever seen Coyle do or say anything that led them to the conclusion he was unsound.

One of Coyle's school teachers, William Crumbling, was called to the stand to provide details concerning John's education. Mr. Coyle had indicated in previous testimony that John was not a good student and had to be taken from school due to constant quarrels and fights. Crumbling, however, painted a much different picture of his former student. John was in his schoolroom in 1868-1869 during a winter session and had studied reading, writing and geography.

Coyle's progress was described as mediocre, and although he would follow instructions, he had not been very regular in attendance. Crumbling did not notice anything in particular that made John different from any of the other students during the time he attended his school. On cross-examination by Fisher, Crumbling could not produce Coyle's records, as they had been turned over to the school board.

The next rebuttal witness was John Haines, a former laborer who briefly worked at the Coyles, five years before the murder. Along with typical conversations concerning the ferry or crops, he recalled an occasion where John had been upset at the lack of shad in the river. Coyle had organized and circulated a petition to have the Columbia dam removed, and obtained a fair number of signatures by canvassing the neighborhood.

Joseph Wilson testified he once saw John hurriedly climb from a front porch window of the inn. Coyle told Wilson his father was angry at him and that he "was damn near caught, I was after the old man's bitters."[2] Wilson said he told John he should be a better boy, and Coyle replied he would try. The witness testified he never felt the prisoner was unsound.

Christian Woods and William Houck crossed the river with Coyle many times and thought that he was an accomplished ferryman. They stated John could handle rough and dangerous conditions and knew how to avoid rocks. Houck cited an instance when Coyle had helped take a raft to Wrightsville when the river was running high and fast. Both men felt that Coyle's manner and appearance was that of other men.

In order to discredit the prior testimony of Mr. Coyle, the District Attorney planned to call several witnesses who would contradict the facts concerning John shooting at Emily two days before the murder. Zeigler again recalled Mr. Coyle and asked him once more: "Did you not say in his [Frank Magee] presence and others that John had shot at Emily Myers on Saturday before the murder and that was the first you knew he had a pistol?"[3] Predictably, Mr. Coyle flatly again denied saying anything of the sort.

Justice of the Peace Frank Magee was then asked the same question: "Did you not hear John Coyle, Sr., say on the day of the inquest that John had shot at Emily Myers on the Saturday before the murder, and that was the first he knew that John had a pistol or words to that effect?"[4] The defense objected to the question as leading, but after Zeigler stated that his purpose was to contradict the testimony of the prior witness, the court overruled the objection. Magee assertively answered that he heard Mr. Coyle say those things.

The District Attorney then called six more witnesses who corroborated the testimony of Frank Magee, indicating they too heard Mr. Coyle tell of the shooting incident two days before Emily was killed. William and Alexander Thompson were called before the noon recess, and were followed after court resumed at 2 o'clock by D.H. Moore and William Sweeny. Mrs. Elizabeth Mack, the widowed aunt of Emily Myers and step-sister of Mrs. Coyle, along with the victim's sister Annie Myers, also confirmed they heard the exact same thing.

During the afternoon session, Zeigler called eleven more witnesses who saw nothing unusual about Coyle and who gave examples of his ability to conduct business in a normal manner. The first was H.L. Roat, a lawyer from Marietta, who recalled a visit from Coyle in April, a month before the murder. John had come to him for an order to be admitted to the hospital, but Roat told him he couldn't provide it since John was from York County and would need to be examined by two doctors.

On one occasion, Roat testified that Coyle borrowed money to rent a boat to return home because someone had stolen his, and the money had been repaid. In another conversation, John had pointed out the course of the river for a picnic party Roat was organizing. He had observed Coyle's conduct and manner, and nothing indicated to him that the defendant was insane.

George Windolph, a merchant in Marietta who was acquainted with Coyle for twenty years, recalled an occasion when John came into his shop wanting to buy a new suit but did not have any money. After Coyle's tobacco was harvested and sold, he returned and bought the clothing, struck a good bargain, and paid for his purchases. It seemed to Windolph that Coyle was like all other men who attended to their own business.

Another merchant, John Lindenmuth, stated Coyle came into his store to order goods and always seemed rational. Adam Reynolds, a hotel owner in Marietta, testified John would frequently stop in to buy beer, and once had witnessed him purchase straw from some other men. Reynolds also saw John ferry a thirty-five-foot raft loaded with people across the river safely. Neither man noticed anything in John's expressions, manner, or actions that seemed unusual.

Reynolds had also discussed with Coyle the merits of the ferry property as a picnic resort. He expressed some interest in purchasing the property and asked if the Coyles were looking to sell. John said no, but renting it might be possible, and suggested that Reynolds speak to his father. On cross-examination by the defense, Reynolds said John came in at least once every week, and he refused him liquor many times because he was already drunk. He never saw Coyle in the company of boys and never repeatedly called him a crazy fool. However, he admitted that he had been notified by the constables in Marietta not to sell John liquor because they considered his mind to be not quite right.

Alexander Buchannon testified he helped Coyle buy tobacco plants and he had always seemed well behaved. Captain George Atlee said he once gave John paper to cover his tobacco plants, and John indicated he could handle the task. Atlee frequently took his family across the river for picnic excursions and went fishing with John, and their conversations seemed normal to him. Both witnesses were repaid money they had loaned John and felt Coyle acted responsibly.

The next three witnesses each lived with the Coyles at some point over the previous ten years. Mrs. Sallie Hendricks worked intermittently at the ferry since 1879, and helped Mrs. Coyle with the gardening and housework. She recalled the incident in May when John and Emily had fought at the garden gate. She also remembered the warning Mrs. Coyle had given Emily, telling her if she continued to be impudent towards John "he would put out her light."[5] After hearing this testimony, Emily's sister Annie broke down and began weeping uncontrollably in the courtroom.

Hendricks testified John occasionally read newspapers on the weekend and was the same as any person when sober, but drank frequently and would become quarrelsome. To the best of her knowledge, she could not see anything that led her to believe he was unsound. On cross-examination, she recalled several times when John went off by himself for days at a time when he was cross at his father. She said John teased her until she called him a crazy fool, but she did not mean it literally. Ironically, John objected to Hendricks and Mrs. Coyle reading *Saturday Night* and *The National Police Gazette*[*] because he felt they were enough to turn anyone's mind.

Harriet Emsweiler worked at the inn five years before the murder and saw John frequently around the house. John had proposed to her several times, but she had not taken it seriously. Rath Emsweiler was also employed at the ferry for a short time in 1879 and talked with John about cows, chickens, and gardening. He sometimes fished with Coyle on Sundays and helped him with the heavy shad nets.

Both Harriet and Rath Emsweiler testified that John frequently wrote letters to lady friends. Samples of Coyle's writing were produced in court and identified by both witnesses as being written by the defendant. They were entered into evidence to show Coyle's soundness of mind, over the objections of the defense counsel who claimed they were not proper rebuttal evidence.

In one letter written just two weeks before he murdered Emily for not accepting his marriage proposal, Coyle wrote to Harriet (Hallie) Emsweiler's sister Annie, mentioning the schoolteacher Sue Hartman to whom he had previously proposed. He seemed somewhat jealous of Annie's friend Howard Erman and encouraged Annie to stop seeing him. The letter is full of small talk concerning the weather and crops, and includes some short poems. The correspondence, including the many misspellings and grammatical errors, was published verbatim in the next morning's paper.

---

[*] *Saturday Night and The National Police Gazette were popular tabloids of the era, filled with lurid, detailed stories of murder, crime, sex and sport.*

"Wrightsville, York County, Pa.   May 15, 1881

My esteemed Friend,

I Take The pleasure This morning To inform you That I receved your very kind and welcome letter as was very much surprised To see That You Thought worth wile To Answer It as You Where so long winded.

Your leeter Found Us all well at Present time. Hoping These few Lines may find You in the Same State of Injoying Health. But I wish you would Tell me what you ment when you Sayed You saw me On Saturday Evening and how Did Howard Erman Get to Wrghtsville. But I suppose you can Tell me That

That is A Little to Thin Annie. You had better give Howard up if you wish to corspond with me. One is Company to Is a crowd. I wish you where up hear Now you and Hallie as they call hear. Johns Brother is hear at present and says he would like to see the Wrightsville Ladies

His Name is William Hartman very Fine young man to. He brought his sister sue along down with him on saturday again Just three weaks since sue was down hear. Will and miss Ella Weaver and I had miss sue Hartman On the round top[†] a sunday to see the fine views. Miss Sue Hartman Is a very fine Young Lady I have got several letters from Hear.   She is a school Teacher by Trade a very good scholar I suppose.

Hallie will have to look a while Before she gets a letter from John For I wrote a letter to him and received no answer. his sister says he cannot compose a letter so that is a poor sort of a Beau. Will and I are going to York on Saturday it may

---

[†] *Round Top referred to the rocky ridge behind Coyle's Ferry overlooking the river and the town of Marietta, and was a popular location for picnics.*

be possible that we may come to Wrightsville in the eving Just accordel we get along in York But if possible we will come down a Saturday Evening.   I would like you to see that young man

I am very sorrow a Bout poor Hallie But it may come all right yet. Give hear my love enayway & Best Respects. The weather hear at present is very weat. Miss Annie I could talk to you all day. But you know how it is your selfe. I have not the time only on Sunday then I ought to Go to church.

I have got my corn all planted now and potatoes. But I had very bad Luck with my Tobacco plants. thay all Frose so I gave up Tobacco planten for this season. I planted my ground all in corn so I wont have so mutch stupen over the dam Tobacco this summer. It is only for nigrs to rase enaway. I Suppose your Father is goin to raise Tobacco this summer a gain. Annie give me all the news from Wrightsvil and vicinity.   I suppose I have come to a close For this time

Remaining Your True loving Friend

John Coyle Jr.

I suppose Annie you have read Miss Candles Lectures if you have not read them then think over those things

Remember me In your wedding Day
Remember me when Far away
O For ever Dear Annie

Good night Annie with meny pleasant Dreams
Wishing you will come up soon
Write Soon Write Soon" [6]

The last witness of the day was a schoolmate, James Nagle. He recalled a business transaction with John and Mr. Coyle after they had retrieved some stray logs on the river during the spring rafting season. When Nagle and his partner went to the ferry to purchase them, John asked if they had paid for two logs and was told they had. John then joked with his father "Old man, give me half of that money if you are paid for both logs,"[7] after which they all sat down and carried on a normal conversation about the lumber business.

At 5:45 p.m., the Commonwealth was almost done presenting their rebuttal case and planned to call only four additional witnesses. However, since the hour was late, Judge Wickes ended the fifth full day of the trial and adjourned court. It was just as well that he did, for one of the witnesses the following morning caused a protracted controversy in court between the counsel for the defense and the District Attorney.

On Tuesday, the first two rebuttal witnesses were Mrs. Kate Hinkle and Annie Myers, who were recalled to testify concerning a conversation between the two of them the day of the shooting. It seemed a minor point, but for some reason it was important to Zeigler to question the credibility of Coyle's aunt, Mrs. Hinkle, who had been a witness for the defense and claimed she thought John was insane.

The afternoon of the murder, Mrs. Hinkle and Annie Myers rode across the river with Simon Myers to Coyle's Ferry. While in the boat, Hinkle allegedly made a comment that she "pitied old Mr. and Mrs. Coyle, but did not pity John Coyle, Jr., for he was no more crazy that I am."[8] As this would have contradicted her prior testimony concerning John's insanity, Mrs. Hinkle predictably denied making the statement. Annie then testified that the comment had definitely been made. For an unknown reason, neither Simon Myers or John Bastian, who were also present in the boat that day, were ever called as witnesses during the trial to corroborate the statement.

Sheriff Samuel Altland was the last rebuttal witness called for the prosecution. The District Attorney offered to prove that Coyle's response of "I don't know anything about it," when asked to plea at his arraignment, had been dictated to him by his lawyer, Henry Fisher. The prosecution contended that Coyle had been instructed to give the vague scripted response when he met privately with his lawyer in the petit jury room before the proceedings on June 9. Zeigler asserted "that the seemingly insane answer of the prisoner is simulated and was put in his mouth by his counsel, for the purpose of exonerating the prisoner of the fearless crime which has committed."[9]

Henry Fisher, astonished by the accusation, immediately asked for a word with the court. He reminded Judge Wickes that during the June sessions, he had asked for permission to consult with his client privately and was granted the request by the court. The Sheriff had escorted them to the petit jury room and left them alone, only to return in a few minutes at the court's request. Fisher said he allowed Altland to remain, but told him he was not to speak of the conversation outside of the room, and the Sheriff had agreed.

William Chapman asserted that asking such questions would violate the confidentiality of conversations held between counsel and the prisoner and should not be allowed. District Attorney Zeigler vehemently disagreed and addressed the court:

"May it please the court: In the course of my professional career there has been no professional duty which I have felt called upon to perform with greater reluctance than this. The bill of indictment in this case is record evidence, and will go out with the jury during their deliberations. On the back of the bill is the plea of 'not guilty', placed there by the direction of your honor after repeated questions put to the prisoner at the time of his arraignment, and after repeated answers of 'I don't know anything about it.'

The words 'I don't know anything about it' appear on the bill as part of the plea, and shall not the commonwealth be permitted to show how the prisoner came to make such an answer on the bill. Suppose your honor, that during the deliberations of the jury, their attention is called to the peculiar manner of the prisoner's plea. May they not consider it evidence of unsoundness of mind? Is it not rebutting evidence to explain away this fact and shall the people possibly suffer because the Commonwealth failed to explain away this fact by evidence in its possession.

Will I have done my full duty as the prosecuting officer of this County if I were to fail to offer all the evidence which throw light on this important trial? This, your Honor, is not within the class of privileged communication. The offer in my opinion and that of my colleague is evidence in this trial, and proper at this stage of the case to introduce. We ask your Honor to admit the offer; the purpose is clearly stated, and we ask to be permitted to proceed with the examination of the witness on the stand."[10]

The court asked Henry Fisher if he had any objection to the Commonwealth asking the questions of the witness. Fisher angrily responded he would allow the Sheriff to tell his story, but wanted an opportunity to make his own statement. Chapman again objected that it was a privileged question and should not be allowed. After a moment, Judge Wickes sustained the objection and did not allow the witness to be questioned about the conversation that occurred between Fisher and Coyle in the presence of the Sheriff. But, he expressed his opinion and hope that Fisher would take it upon himself to "investigate such a serious charge against his fidelity to the court."[11]

Given the legal interpretation of the attorney-client privilege[‡], Sheriff Altland should have been required to testify concerning the conversation he overheard between Coyle and his attorney, as they chose to speak openly in his presence. According to a commonly accepted definition, "if the client chooses to make his communication in the presence of third persons, is ceases to be confidential, and is not entitled to the protection afforded by the rule."[12] Also, "any presence of third parties who are not agents of the attorney for the purpose of

---

[‡] *Case law existed at the time of the Coyle trial to substantiate the admission of the testimony, including (Ala. 1880) Mobile & M. Ry Co. v. Yeates, 67 Ala. 164, (Conn. 1859) Goddard v. Gardner, 28 Conn. 172, and Jackson v. French, supra.*

assisting the attorney in giving legal advice negates the requisite element [for conversations to qualify as privileged]."[13]

However, District Attorney Zeigler chose not to press the issue with the court and the Commonwealth formally rested their rebuttal. The defense team would now have one more opportunity on surrebuttal to challenge any new testimony given by the prosecution.

Fisher recalled only one witness, Mrs. Kate Hinkle, who testified she did not hear Mr. Coyle say that John shot at Emily the Saturday before the murder. As Hinkle had already contradicted herself several other times during her various appearances on the stand, there was little value in asking her about this issue. Predictably, the only other witnesses who had corroborated Mr. Coyle's version of the story were his wife and sister-in-law.

However, since the District Attorney had produced eight witnesses who testified Mr. Coyle made the statement, perhaps the defense wanted to even things up by having one more witness deny it was said and have it be the last testimony on the matter heard by the jury before deliberations. It was left to the jury to decide whether Mr. Coyle actually made the statement.

After three-and-a-half days of testimony, the evidence phase of the trial was formally over and the witnesses were discharged and allowed to return home. The twenty-two witnesses produced in Coyle's defense were mainly relatives, old acquaintances and childhood friends who were only able to relate isolated anecdotes concerning Coyle's unusual behavior. In contrast, the District Attorney had called thirty-four extremely credible witnesses, including professionals such as doctors, merchants, co-workers, a lawyer, and a Justice of the Peace. These witnesses painted a completely different picture of Coyle than had been portrayed by his defense counsel.

Shortly after 10 o'clock, District Attorney Zeigler began his closing statement to the jury, "speaking with much ability and earnestness two hours and one minute."[14] Zeigler reviewed the details and facts of the case, citing evidence produced to show any insanity or unsoundness. According to accounts, his convincing arguments "had the undivided attention of the jury."[15] Wickes allowed Zeigler to continue uninterrupted and adjourned court when he was finished.

After lunch, Henry Fisher had his opportunity to speak to the jury for the final time and his two hour address "evinced careful participation and much ability."[16] Fisher attempted to convince the jury that although Coyle had admitted to the crime, he should not be held criminally responsible due to his inability to control his actions as a result of his chronically unsound mind.

Fisher was followed by William Chapman who spoke until almost 6 o'clock, after which court was adjourned for the day. Chapman made a powerful plea on Coyle's behalf and his address "contained a vast amount of information on the subject of insanity in all its phases and degrees. It was pronounced as one of his best efforts."[17] To all those present, it was obvious that Coyle had been aggressively prosecuted, and received an equally skillful defense.

Chapter 19

York County Courthouse, York, Pa
Wednesday, October 26, 1881

> *"A jury consists of twelve persons chosen to decide*
> *who has the better lawyer"*
> ... *Robert Frost*

At promptly 9 o'clock, Court was called to order and George McElroy, special counsel for the Commonwealth, delivered the final closing argument in the Coyle trial. He spoke for one-and-a-half hours, "in his usual eloquent manner, eliciting the closest attention on the part of the jury and the large number of persons present."[1]

Following a short recess, Judge Wickes began his detailed charge to the jury. "Gentleman of the Jury, Without pausing to dwell upon the very serious character of the business in which you and I are engaged, for that has been sufficiently been pressed upon you already, I shall proceed to address you as clearly and briefly as possible upon what I conceive to be the necessary questions of law arising in this case, and in regard to which you are entitled to instructions from the court that you may intelligently apply them to the facts, which are more especially for you determination."[2]

The judge commended the lawyers who argued on behalf of the Commonwealth as well as those who defended John Coyle, Jr. In his opinion, they had "carefully analyzed the evidence, brought to the foreground like skillful artists the facts they considered, and desire you to consider, most important and perhaps left in the shadow other facts not so essential to their views, but altogether the result has been that the evidence produced on both sides has been thoroughly canvassed – its contradictions been pointed out - its weak points exposed."[3]

Wickes first defined the indictment of murder in the first degree and the proof required to sustain such a charge. Next, he explained the law as it related to the prisoner's defense of insanity. Finally, he informed the jury the extent of proof required to excuse Coyle of criminal responsibility.

The Act of March 31, 1860, defined first degree murder as: "All murder which shall be perpetrated by means of poison or by lying in wait or by any other kind of willful, deliberate and premeditated killing, or which shall be committed in the perpetration of or attempt to perpetrate any arson, rape, robbery or burglary."[4]

Since Emily was not poisoned, murdered by lying in wait, or killed in the commission of a felony, premeditation had been the key issue for the prosecution. The importance of proving it explained the District Attorney's motivation and persistence in calling witnesses to substantiate the fact that Mr. Coyle said his son had shot at Emily two days before the murder, as well as the others who testified John told them he would shoot Emily if she refused to marry him.

Under Pennsylvania law, all homicide was presumed to be second degree unless proved otherwise. Wickes defined second degree murder as all unlawful killing where "there is wickedness of disposition, hardness of heart, cruelty, recklessness of consequences, and a mind regardless of social duty."[5] Since the Commonwealth charged Coyle with first degree murder, their evidence had to satisfy the jury the killing was willful, deliberate and premeditated.

Wickes then explained manslaughter to the jury, which was defined as a murder committed "not under the influence of malice, but where the blood is heated by provocation and before it has time to cool."[6] Ultimately, if the jury found Coyle guilty of murder, they would have to determine if the facts dictated a conviction of first degree murder or one of the two lesser charges.

In summarizing the prosecution's case, Wickes reviewed the basic facts of the crime. It had been proven that on May 30, Emily Myers was murdered and John Coyle had repeatedly confessed to the crime. Neighbors were alerted, authorities notified, and a Coroner's inquest was held, which determined the cause of death to be a single pistol ball piercing Emily's heart. Further evidence proved that on several occasions prior to the murder, the defendant had threatened to shoot Emily if she refused to marry him.

Since the fact that Coyle murdered Emily was not in dispute, the primary question was whether he was sane at the time he fired the fatal shot. Therefore, Wickes spent an inordinate amount of time explaining the interpretations of insanity to the jury. He recognized Coyle's mental state as the pivotal issue of the case, and one that would cause the most difficulty for the jury. "This is an extremely delicate question to deal with, and is entitled to receive at your hands and mine the most serious consideration."[7] He then proceeded to describe the various forms of insanity - general insanity, partial insanity and homicidal mania.

In an attempt to define general insanity in plain terms, Wickes quoted a Chief Justice of Pennsylvania: "A man may be mad on all subjects and then though he may have a glimmering of reason he is not a responsible agent ... but if it not be so great in its extent or degree as to blind him to the nature and consequences of his moral duty, it is no defence to an accusation of crime. It must be so great as entirely to destroy his perception of right and wrong, and it is not until that perception is thus destroyed that he ceases to be responsible."[8]

The capacity of the prisoner to distinguish right from wrong was the crucial test for general insanity. Wickes reviewed the M'Naghten Rule, the standard against which the jury would need to weigh the evidence presented. He quoted from the British opinion on the subject: "To establish a defence on the ground of insanity it must be clearly proven that at the time of the act, the accused was laboring under such a defect of reason from a disease of the mind as not to know that nature and quality of the act he was doing; or if he did know it, that he did not know what he was doing was wrong."[9]

Wickes acknowledged that a defendant might be able to distinguish between right and wrong but still not be held accountable for his actions. He went on to define partial insanity as being confined to a particular subject, but sane on all others. For example, if a defendant were laboring under a delusion that someone was attempting to kill them, and they in turn killed in what they perceived to be self-defense, they might be exempt from responsibility. The test the jury was to consider was whether the prisoner truly believed in the real existence of facts which were actually entirely imaginary.

However, Wickes explained, "if his delusion was that the deceased had inflicted a serious injury to his character and fortune, and he killed him in revenge for such supposed injury, he would be liable to punishment."[10] What the jury may have inferred from the judge's example was that if they felt Coyle had been seeking revenge for Emily's repeated refusals to be his wife, he should be held accountable for her murder.

The third form of insanity, homicidal mania, was not generally recognized in 1881, and not widely accepted until the mid-twentieth century. It was defined as an irresistible, uncontrollable urge to kill. Wickes was ahead of his time in presenting it to the jury, citing "There may be an unseen ligament pressing on the mind, drawing it to consequences which it sees but cannot avoid, and placing it under a coercion, which, while its results are clearly perceived is incapable of resistance."[11]

Wickes did acknowledge that instances of true homicidal mania were rare and could only exist in the clearest of cases. He warned the jury if they were to consider this type of insanity, they would need to take care to examine the facts to make sure no underlying circumstances such as revenge or anger were the real motives. The test would be the presence of clear evidence that the defendant was utterly unable to control his will and was not motivated by evil passions.

Wickes pointed out that merely being perceived insane by others was different than actually suffering from insanity. He quoted an author who said "The mind is always greatly troubled when it is agitated by anger, tormented by an unfortunate love, bewildered by jealousy, overcome by despair, haunted by terror or corrupted by an unconquerable desire for vengeance. Then, as is commonly said a man is no longer master of himself; his reason is affected, his ideas are in disorder, and he is like a mad man."[12]

Admitting he was a bit confused by the strategy of the defense, Wickes confessed he had taken so much time to define the various forms and manifestations of insanity to the jury because he did not "understand the particular kind which is set up as a defence in this case."[13] Since the judge was confused, the jury must have been even more bewildered.

On one hand, Wickes said, Henry Fisher had called it an "insane delusion at the time the act was committed."[14] In another instance, William Chapman said Coyle's "insane desire to marry was doubtless produced by his secret habit, and this was a mania – a monomania."[15] The defense had also indicated they "didn't mean to say the prisoner was frantic or a maniac at the time he shot the deceased, but that his mind was so diseased that he didn't know or comprehend what he was doing."[16]

Depending on interpretation, the defense counsel's descriptions could have been describing homicidal mania, partial insanity or general insanity. Wickes handed the decision over to the jury, indicating they adequate information and tests to use, and it was now up to them to apply these facts to the evidence presented and decide for themselves.

The most important issue Wickes needed to define was the measure of proof required to excuse Coyle of criminal responsibility for the murder. He explained that the law presumed sanity as the normal condition of man and it was up to the defense to satisfy the jury that insanity existed when the crime was committed. The proof must be satisfactory and clear, and if the evidence left any doubt as to Coyle's insanity, it would not justify an acquittal.

Wickes knew it was a difficult matter to quantify the degree of proof needed, and chose instead to cite multiple examples of how it had been expressed by others in prior cases. The Supreme Court had used phrases such as "the evidence must be sufficient to fairly and reasonably satisfy you" and "evidence must fairly convince." Other cases used the terminology "it must be clearly proven by satisfactory and clearly preponderating evidence," "it must be clearly proved," and "the weight of the evidence must be preponderate."[17]

In summarizing the defense's case, Wickes reviewed the witnesses who testified concerning Coyle's mental condition and the observations which caused them to form the opinion he was unsound. They provided examples of Coyle's attempts at suicide and his habitual masturbation as additional evidence of his insanity. Wickes cautioned the jury that attempted suicide should raise no presumption of insanity, and just because some spoke of Coyle as "weak minded, a simple, foolish fellow,"[18] those things should not be considered as traits that excuse murder.

Wickes acknowledged the Commonwealth had produced a large number of witnesses to contradict those of the defense; including the schoolmaster, people Coyle had transacted business with, and employees at the ferry. These witnesses had voiced their belief Coyle was of sound mind, and the jury would need to decide what value should be attached to those opinions and which witnesses should be deemed truthful.

In an almost apologetic tone, Wickes admitted to the jury that the possibility existed that he had not fully explained the law as it pertained to the charge, the defense of insanity, or the extent of proof required to sustain such a defense. He conceded "If I have erred in any particular way to the prisoner's injury, it is an infinite satisfaction to me that the appellate tribunal of the Commonwealth can and will correct my error."[19]

Wickes closed his charge to the jury with a summary of their responsibilities in determining a final verdict. "And now, gentlemen, I submit to you the case of the Commonwealth v. John Coyle, Jr. You and each of you have sworn that you have no convictions unfavorable to capital punishment, you have said that you have no bias or prejudice for or against the prisoner and that you had formed no opinion as to his guilt or innocence that would for a moment influence or control your verdict. You were therefore fit to enter the jury box and listen to the evidence and the law. You have heard both, and now your sworn duty is to render a true verdict upon them.

You are not to be frightened from your duty from rendering a fair and impartial verdict by any fear of what the punishment may be. With that you have nothing to do. It follows the crime and not the verdict. It is pronounced by the court and not the jury. You will therefore follow whatever the evidence may lead, calmly considering it in the light of the principles of law which have been given to you, and render such a verdict as will satisfy your own consciences, and do justice to the prisoner and society, which is the Commonwealth.

If after you considered it with all the seriousness and care the momentous issue involved requires, and shall be of the opinion the prisoner is guilty in manner and form as he stands indicted, your verdict will be 'guilty of murder in the first degree.' If you find that he is not guilty of murder of the first degree, but guilty of murder in the second degree or manslaughter, you will render a verdict with such finding. But if you shall be of opinion that the prisoner was of unsound mind at the time the offense was committed and to a degree that renders him irresponsible for his acts, then your verdict will be not guilty because of insanity."[20]

At 12:16 on Wednesday, October 26, a week after it had begun, the trial of John Coyle, Jr., for the murder of Emily Myers was over. Wickes excused the jury, and the tipstaves escorted them from the courtroom to the petit jury room to deliberate the case.

The afternoon session began promptly at 1:30 p.m. with the ringing of the courthouse bell. Word had been circulating outside the courthouse that the Coyle jury was in deliberations and would return after lunch. As soon as the bell was rung, crowds came flooding into the courtroom from all directions, filling it to capacity. Judge Wickes requested tipstaff David Myers to check with the jury and ask if a verdict had been reached.

Myers returned a moment later, indicating the jury had reached a decision. He returned to the petit jury room and escorted them back into the courtroom, where they took their places in the jury box. After each juror was called, a brief silence ensued, heightening the suspense of the moment.

Clerk:	"Prisoner, stand up"
Clerk:	"Gentlemen of the jury, have you reached a verdict?"
Jury:	"We have"
Clerk:	"Who shall answer for you?"
Jury:	"Our foreman" [Thomas Ramsey, Justice of the Peace from York Borough]
Clerk:	"What say you in the issue joined between the Commonwealth of Pennsylvania and John Coyle, Jr., the prisoner at the bar, whom you have in charge? Is the prisoner at the bar guilty of in the manner and form as he stands indicted, or not guilty?
Foreman:	"Guilty of murder in the first degree."[21]

A perceptible murmur ran through the courtroom, and several spectators and reporters in the gallery immediately left to spread the news of the verdict. Coyle did not appear to be visibly affected, although "his lips quivered as he was waiting to hear the verdict. His aged mother sobbed, while his father labored to restrain his feelings."[22]

Wickes directed the verdict to be entered into the record, but Henry Fisher immediately requested that the jury be polled. Each juror was called by name and asked the same question as the foreman, and each responded, "Guilty of murder of the first degree." The court recorded "the prisoner at the bar is guilty in manner and form as he stands indicted of Murder of the first degree,"[23] and remanded Coyle to prison until further ordered by the court.

As soon as the verdict was recorded, Henry Fisher gave notice to the court he would be filing motions for a new trial and an Arrest of Judgment.[*] The court discharged the jury, thanking them for their service and the manner in which they had performed their duties, and court adjourned until the next day when the defense motions were scheduled to be filed.

In the course of the Coyle trial, almost 91,000 words were recorded by Mr. Murdoch, the court stenographer. The testimony was also meticulously transcribed by John Metzel, a special detective for the Commonwealth, who had been seated at the prosecution table the entire trial. Metzel had done most of the preliminary investigative work for the prosecution's case, including finding and subpoenaing all the witnesses for the Commonwealth.

The morning paper the following day announced the verdict as "one of remarkable interest and will be remembered as one of the most important trials which has ever occupied the attention of courts."[24] It went on to praise the efforts of the attorneys and the jury. "The labors of all concerned in this case have been arduous, and we have no doubt great relief is experienced by the court, lawyers and jury in the termination of the trial."[25] However, Coyle's legal battle had only begun, and would drag on for another three years before finally coming to a conclusion.

The following afternoon, Fisher filed his motion for a new trial, alleging twelve errors of the court, and Judge Wickes ordered formal arguments to be presented to the court in mid-December. A week before the scheduled date, Fisher added eight additional errors to his motion. Several days later, he attempted to add yet another error related to the alleged insobriety of certain members of the jury.

Judge Wickes was becoming frustrated and impatient with the defense team and their continual attempts to invent new reasons why

---

[*] *A Motion in Arrest of Judgment is an application by the defense to stop a guilty verdict from being entered and is usually made in conjunction with a motion for a new trial.*

Coyle should be granted a new trial. Despite Fisher's objections, he refused to allow the last error to be included in the motion because the defense was out of time, and he stated it had never been proven that "the jury or any member of it was at any time under the influence of liquor or their impartiality affected by it."[26]

On Friday, December 16, the date scheduled for the presentation of arguments on the motion, the defense counsel requested a continuance until the next day. The court granted the request "at the insistence of the Prisoners counsel."[27] The following morning, arguments relevant to the points stated on the motion were presented, and Wickes said he would consider the motion over the weekend and rule on it Monday morning.

Court commenced at 9 o'clock Monday morning and Judge Wickes announced he was prepared to rule on the defense motion for a new trial, and voiced his opinion that the defense had done a poor job arguing their case. "It is difficult to deal with the numerous reasons filed for a new trial in this case. Some were abandoned on the argument - some not alluded to at all – and those relied on, with one or two exceptions, argued in such general terms that it was not easy to tell precisely to what reasons the argument applied."[28]

Wickes first ruled on the twelve points filed by Fisher on October 27. Seven had either been abandoned by the defense or no arguments had been presented to substantiate them. Wickes felt the issues could not be taken advantage of after the trial was over and the verdict had already been rendered. Without further information, Wickes was not able to "discover the error which lies hidden in them."[29] The other five reasons pertained to points of law and Wickes believed he had addressed them correctly based on previously adjudicated Pennsylvania court cases and had kept within the limits of precedent cases decided by the Pennsylvania Supreme Court. "If we are wrong, the Supreme Court is also in error, and that error can only be set straight by that tribunal."[30]

The original twelve alleged errors of the court filed by Henry Fisher consisted of the following issues:

1st, The writ of venire[†] was not proper as it did not indicate the specific number of jurors summoned, nor did it specify the day, month, or year they were to appear.

2nd, The writ did not include the words "from the body of the county" and was not authenticated by the court seal.

3rd, The verdict was against the law.

4th, The verdict was against the weight of the evidence.

5th, The court erred in referring to the specific witnesses called by the commonwealth during the charge to the jury.

6th, The court erred in stating that homicidal mania could only be recognized in the clearest of cases.

7th, The court erred in their answers to the three points the defense had requested be included in the jury's charge.

8th, The court erred defining the test for partial insanity.

9th, The court erred defining the test for homicidal mania.

10th, The court erred when admitting it did not understand the type of insanity being used as a defense and pointed out contradictory defense statements.

11th, The court erred in charging the jury by saying that if the evidence left any doubt as to the prisoner's insanity, it would not justify an acquittal.

12th, The court erred in describing the extent and manner of proof required to establish the unsoundness of mind of the prisoner during the charge to the jury.

[†] *A writ of venire is a court order directing the Sheriff to summon a jury.*

Judge Wickes then ruled on the eight additional points filed by the defense on December 7. The first point had not been discussed during arguments and Wickes felt no further comment was necessary. Several other points alleged that Wickes did not correctly address various aspects of law during his charge to the jury. The judge overruled them, stating that he had cited the applicable authorities and felt no need to refer to them again.

Three of the allegations dealt with the admissibility of testimony from several prosecution witnesses. The defense contended that Dr. Thompson was not qualified to testify concerning the prisoner's gunshot wound, and Wickes ruled that the value of Thompson's opinions were for the jury to decide. Another alleged error objected to the contradictory nature of Frank Magee's testimony, but the judge reminded Fisher that he had also called witnesses to contradict prosecution testimony on the same issue.

Another point claimed that jurors heard comments about Coyle's guilt before the proceedings began. Wickes flatly dismissed that any expression heard by a juror prior to the trial could be used as a reason for a new trial after the case had been settled. He chastised defense counsel for suggesting the jury would be so easily swayed and again commended them for their service. "Their conduct was marked by the utmost propriety and solemnity, and their verdict entirely justified by the law and evidence upon which it was based."[31]

The last of the eight additional points addressed the issue of public sentiment and its possible affect on the trial. Although acknowledging that there had been adverse publicity, Wickes cited the case of the Commonwealth vs. Flanagan (7W. & S., 415), which stated that public excitement, or ill-will against an accused, is not justification for a new trial.

The eight additional points presented by the defense in their motion for a new trial court pertained to the following issues:

<u>1st</u>, Peter Heiges, one of the jurors, stated before he was sworn, "That man must be a rascal; he ought to be hanged, and if I was on the jury I would hang him."[32] This statement was not made known to the defendant or his counsel until after the verdict was returned.

<u>2nd</u>, The court erred in explaining the general insanity test and should have included the words "and to adhere to the right and avoid the wrong"[33] at the end of the definition.

<u>3rd</u>, The court erred in the charge to the jury when stating the evidence of insanity must be satisfactory, and nothing less than satisfactory could convince a reasonable mind.

<u>4th</u>, The court erred in stating that attempted suicide would not be evidence of insanity, but only a circumstance to be taken into consideration with other facts.

<u>5th</u>, The court erred in overruling defense objections to the admission of evidence from Dr. Thompson, who testified on the cause of Coyle's self-inflicted wounds.

<u>6th</u>, The court erred in overruling the defense objections to the leading questions asked of Frank Magee regarding statement he allegedly heard Mr. Coyle make about John shooting at Emily the Saturday before the murder.

<u>7th</u>, Peter Bievenour, one of the jurors challenged for cause during the second special venire, said in open court in the presence of other prospective jurors "I say hang him"[34], the jury was prejudice against the defendant.

<u>8th</u>, The prisoner was deprived of a fair and impartial trial due to public rumors and hostile discussion in the newspapers up to and during the trial.

In his ruling on the defendant's motion for a new trial, Judge Wickes commented, "I am not unmindful of the momentous consequences to the unfortunate defendant involved in the view we have taken in this application, but we have no power to avert the shadow of that doom into which he is so rapidly passing, without trampling underfoot the declared principals of law upon which the welfare of society so firmly rests. He has 'sown the wind,' and unless there shall be some interference in his behalf elsewhere, he must 'reap the whirlwind.' And now to wit, December 19th, 1881, motion for a new trial and in arrest of judgment overruled."[35]

After the judge ruled on the motion, District Attorney Ziegler requested the court to pronounce sentence on the prisoner. "May it please the court: in the case of the Commonwealth of Pennsylvania against John Coyle, Jr., under indictment No 58 of June Term, 1881, for murder, the jury have returned a verdict of 'guilty in the murder of the first degree.' The reasons for a new trial filed by the prisoner's counsel have been argued and the motion based on the said reasons has been overruled. There is at this time a duty for the prosecuting attorney to perform. It is a painful duty, but one which cannot be avoided. The Court is therefore moved to pass the sentence of the law upon the prisoner."[36]

The courtroom fell silent and Judge Wickes directed the prisoner to stand, asking him if there was anything he wanted to say. Coyle replied in a quiet voice, "There has been too much said already about me by the jury and the witnesses."[37] The judge agreed, citing the fact that Coyle had not testified in his own behalf. Coyle indicated he had nothing more to say, and Wickes proceeded.

"John Coyle, Jr., under an indictment presented by the grand jury inquest inquiring for this county, you have been fairly and impartially tried by a jury of your peers for the murder of Emily Myers, and notwithstanding the earnest efforts of able counsel in your behalf, the jury has found you guilty of the highest crime known to the law, the penalty of which is death. The court, in view of the law and evidence cannot disapprove of that verdict, and nothing more remains, but to pronounce the sentence which follows. That you, John Coyle, Jr., be taken hence to the County prison from whence you came, and thence to the place of execution, and that you be hanged by the neck until you are dead. May God in his infinite goodness have mercy on your soul."[38]

Coyle seemed composed while his sentence was read, "evincing no fear or nervousness during the solemnity of the scene."[39] He was immediately removed from the courtroom and escorted back to his cell by Sheriff Altland, who promised that a strict watch would be maintained over the prisoner.

A record of the trial was sent to Governor Henry Hoyt, who issued the death warrant on January 24, 1882, a little over a month after Coyle's sentencing. The warrant specified that Coyle was to be executed sixty days later on Friday, March 24, 1882, between the hours of 10 a.m. and 3 p.m. by the Sheriff of York County. Sheriff Altland notified Coyle that he had received the warrant, but did not read it to him since his case was in the process of being appealed.

Mr. and Mrs. Coyle continued to hold out hope and "did not give up the fight to save the life of their only son after he was sentenced to be hung."[40] They already had plans in place with their attorney to redouble efforts to secure a new trial, and defense attorney Henry Fisher announced his intent to appeal the decision to the Pennsylvania Supreme Court.

Chapter 20

Pennsylvania Supreme Court, Harrisburg, Pa
Wednesday, October 4, 1882

*"An appeal is when you ask one court to show
its contempt for another court"*

... Finley Peter Dunne

While John Coyle spent the next ten months in the York County Prison, his attorneys worked feverishly on his appeal. Two weeks after sentencing, on January 2, 1882, a writ of error* was presented in open court and filed by the clerk of York County. The Pennsylvania Supreme Court agreed to review the case for errors as alleged by the defense, and on May 12, a certified copy of the Coyle trial case record was sent to Harrisburg.

The abstract submitted by Fisher for consideration by the Supreme Court contained four specifications of error, as compared to the twenty presented in his motion to the York County Court the previous December. Each dealt with a specific point in the charge to the jury made by Judge Wickes, citing alleged errors in wording or in the interpretation of the law. Three of the specifications had been previously argued during Fisher's original motion for a new trial, and had been overruled by Judge Wickes the previous December.

Arguments before the Middle District Supreme Court began on May 15. Present for John Coyle, the plaintiff in error, were his lawyers Henry Fisher and William Chapman. York County District Attorney Edward Zeigler and special counsel George W. McElroy represented the Commonwealth. The case was heard by Chief Justice

---

* *A writ of error is a request to a trial court, demanding that the record of a case be sent to the appellate court so it can be reviewed for alleged errors of law committed during trial proceedings.*

George Sharswood and Justices Ulysses Mercur, Isaac Gordon, Edward Paxson, John Trunkey, and Henry Green. The defense and the prosecution were each given an opportunity to state their positions, and the court deliberated for six months before returning their ruling. On October 4, Justice Mercur gave the court's opinion on each of the four points included in the Specifications of Error.

1st Specification of Error. During his charge to the jury in York County, Judge Wickes quoted former Chief Justice John Gibson, Commonwealth v. Moser, 4 Barr 264, in describing homicidal mania: "There may be an unseen ligament pressing on the mind, drawing it to consequences which it sees but cannot avoid, and placing it under a coercion, which, while its results are clearly perceived is incapable of resistance. The doctrine which acknowledges this mania is dangerous in its relations, and can be recognised only in the clearest cases. It ought to be shown to have been habitual or at least so envinced itself in more than a single instance."[1]

Henry Fisher objected to the wording Wickes used in his statement to the jury, but was taking a chance before the Supreme Court challenging citations made by a former Chief Justice of the same court. Fisher stated that the remainder of the charge pertaining to homicidal mania was extremely unfair to his client, and cited three precedent cases as evidence.

Ruling: "The able argument of counsel has failed to convince us that this was not a correct declaration of the law ... it is certainly not requiring too much to hold that it shall be shown in more than a single instance. We know of no later case in this State where the precise question has been ruled otherwise."[2]

Although the court admitted the legitimacy of using homicidal mania as a defense in certain cases, they agreed with Justice Gibson that care must be taken not to confuse it with reckless frenzy, and that it must be clearly proven by prior acts of violence. The ruling seemed somewhat insufficient since it ignored the fact that there would have to be a first time for someone to display homicidal mania.

2nd Specification of Error. Fisher disagreed with the evidential value the lower court placed on Coyle's suicide attempts. Wickes said in his charge "It is perhaps proper to say to you as matter of law, that even if you believe the prisoner really intended to take his own life, this would not be of itself evidence of insanity. It would only be a circumstance in the case to be considered by you in connection with other facts and circumstances, for the purpose of enabling you to determine the mental condition of the prisoner. The fact of the attempted suicide raises no presumption of insanity."[3]

Ruling: In his jury charge, Wickes quoted a Supreme Court case in which the court ruled a jury could not infer insanity simply from the heinous nature of a crime. Using the same logic, insanity could not be presumed by the mere fact of attempted suicide. However, Justice Mercur agreed that these circumstances could lend weight to the evidence which constituted the other proof. The justices ruled that the lower court's language was acceptable and Wickes' instructions to the jury were acceptable.

"Suicide may or may not be evidence of insanity. Sometimes it may be evidence of a wicked and depraved heart, familiar with crime; at others, of despondency and discouragement; but perhaps more frequently of cowardice and a lack of courage to face ignominy or public disgrace, or to submit to the punishment likely to be imposed on him."[4]

3rd Specification of Error. This allegation caused the most difficulty with the Supreme Court. At issue was the statement made by Judge Wickes in his jury charge: "The law of the state is, that when the killing is admitted, and insanity or want of legal responsibility is alleged as an excuse, it is the duty of the defendant to satisfy the jury that insanity actually existed at the time of the act, and a doubt as to such insanity will not justify the jury in acquitting on that ground. The law presumes sanity when an act is done, and that presumption can only be overthrown by clearly preponderating evidence."[5]

Ruling: With the exception of the last sentence, specifically the word *clearly,* the Supreme Court agreed that Judge Wickes' statements were a correct interpretation of current case law. Wickes had cited Brown v.

Commonwealth, 28 P.F. Smith 122 in his charge, quoting the phrase "clearly preponderating evidence." The Supreme Court indicated this was not an accurate representation of the language used in that case, and felt Wickes must have read an erroneous brief.

The question remained as to the degree of proof required to overcome the legal presumption of sanity. Justice Mercur ruled that *fairly* preponderant would have been the appropriate wording, as *clearly* demands a higher degree of proof than was required. In addition, "To require it to be 'clearly preponderant' is practically saying it must be proved beyond all doubt or uncertainty."[6]

District Attorney Edward Zeigler and special counsel George McElroy argued that the specific wording used by a judge was not the important factor. They cited a ruling in a prior case by Justice Mercur himself, in which the statement "proof of insanity must be satisfactory and not merely doubtful"[7] was used. They contended it should make no difference whether the specific word used by a judge was *clearly*, *fairly*, or *satisfactorily*.

In a final effort to convince the Supreme Court to overrule this specification, Zeigler emphasized "The burden being on the prisoner to satisfy the jury that insanity existed, how can the jury be *satisfied* except where the evidence of insanity clearly preponderates over the presumption of sanity? No distinction can be drawn between the expression '*clearly* preponderating evidence', as used in this case by the court below, and '*fairly* preponderating evidence', as used by the this court in Pannel v. Commonwealth, supra. The *meaning* in each case is that the evidence must preponderate sufficiently to satisfy the jury. A judge is not required to use any particular formula of words, and we submit that the meaning conveyed to the jury by the expression complained of is in harmony with the decisions of this court; and the mode of expression, whether standing alone or taken in connection with the context and other parts of the charge, could not have been misunderstood by the jury."[8]

Citing several other precedent cases, the Supreme Court ruled it was not necessary to provide evidence so conclusive to remove all doubt of sanity, and that evidence fairly demonstrating insanity would be sufficient for the jury to be able to render a verdict of not guilty. Since Coyle was on trial for his life and special care had to be taken to ensure due process, the court sustained this specification of error.

4th Specification of Error. Fisher objected to Judge Wickes instructing the jury "you are not to be frightened from your duty from rendering a fair and impartial verdict by any fear of what the punishment may be. With that you have nothing to do; it follows the crime, and not the verdict. It is pronounced by the court, and not the jury."[9]

Ruling: The court ruled that Wickes was correct in charging the jury not to be fearful of their duty based on the possible punishment and overruled this specification.

━━━━━◁◁◁▷▷▷━━━

York County Courthouse, York, Pa
October - December, 1882

Due to the improper use of the single word *clearly* instead of *fairly* in Judge Wickes' charge to the jury, the Supreme Court of Pennsylvania granted John Coyle, Jr. a new trial for the murder of Emily Myers. Wickes, although unhappy the opinion of the higher court had been based on his own error, acquiesced to the Supreme Court's decision. "The wisdom of this decision it would be unbecoming in us to question. We can only say of the higher court, what Lord Holt said of Parliament, 'it can do no wrong.'"[10]

The quote was in reference to a statement made following a judgment rendered in City of London v. Wood in 1702, when Lord John Holt said "An act of Parliament can do no wrong, though it may do several things that look pretty odd..."[11] After being challenged on his ruling in the Wood case, Holt took the opportunity to question the omnipotence of Parliament and their narrow views which questioned the experience and autonomy of local judges.

Likewise, Judge Wickes apparently did not agree with Justice Mercur and the Supreme Court in their granting a new trial for John Coyle, but was not quite as vocal as Lord Holt in voicing his opinion. The mild sarcasm in his use of the quotation would not have been lost on anyone intimately familiar with British case law, but probably not understood by those who heard it in the York County courtroom.

The remittitur[†] was returned to Judge Wickes and filed in York County Court on October 23. Since the original judgment was reversed by the Supreme Court, a *venire facias de novo*[‡] was awarded, which began the process of a second trial. Henry Fisher immediately filed a petition with the court for a continuance of the new trial until the January 1883 term due to the illness of the defendant's parents.

Judge Wickes denied the motion because Fisher had not obtained the necessary doctor's statement. "The practice is to require the affidavit of a physician when a motion is made for a continuance upon the grounds of the sickness of a witness. We suggested this to the defendants counsel when they were about to present the papers a week ago. As no such certificate is before us we overrule this motion and fix Wednesday November 1st for the trial thereof."[12]

Three days later, on October 26, John Coyle and his lawyers were back in court with the proper paperwork. An affidavit from Dr. Alexander of Marietta was presented, certifying the illness of John Coyle, Sr. and Mary Ann Coyle. The court relented and granted the motion, scheduling the trial date for the January 1883 term.

Only a week after the continuance was granted, rumors were already circulating in the local papers concerning a possible change of venue for Coyle's second trial. In the Gettysburg, Pa. *Star and Sentinel* on November 4, an article predicted "the next move in the Coyle

---

[†] *A remittitur is the formal transmittal of the ruling of an appeals court back to the trial court indicating a new trial was granted.*

[‡] *A writ meaning "may you cause to come anew," issued by the court to summon a new venire, or jury pool, to retry a case.*

Murder Case will be, it is said, an effort to have the new trial in the case removed to another county. On account of publication of the evidence throughout York County at the time of the first trial would make it most difficult to obtain a jury for a second trial."[13]

John Coyle, Sr. and Mary Ann Coyle presented the change of venue petition in court on November 21. Affidavits from defense lawyers Fisher and Chapman were also filed the same day, claiming that undue excitement caused by the publication of unfavorable editorials and testimony taken in the first trial had biased public opinion to the point that a fair and impartial trial could not be obtained in York County. The petition asked the trial to be moved to "some adjoining, or other, county, where these prejudices and excitement do not exist."[14]

The application was made under the provisions of the Act of March 18, 1875, P.L. 30, which allowed for a change of venue "when it is made to appear to the satisfaction of the court, that from undue excitement against the prisoner, in the county where the offense was committed, a fair trial cannot be held, or that there exists in that county so great a prejudice against him that he cannot obtain a fair trial."[15] Following the filing of the petition, the court granted a Rule to Show Cause[§] and ordered arguments to be presented on December 4.

Coyle was present in court for the change of venue proceedings and the local papers remarked that he "looks remarkably well considering the fact the he had now been in prison for more than a year."[16] Both his parents had suffered emotionally, but despite their declining health, they continued to appear in court whenever possible to support their son and do whatever they could help save his life.

A number of affidavits were presented by the defendant's counsel on December 4 to support the assertion that public opinion against John Coyle would prevent a fair trial if he were retried in York County. For the prosecution, District Attorney Edward Zeigler frankly

---

[§] *An order of the court following a motion by one party, calling the other party to explain why the motion should not be granted.*

admitted that he was "unable to procure counter-affidavits, having studiously endeavored to secure them."[17]

Zeigler conceded that prejudice did indeed exist against the prisoner due to the publication of testimony from the first trial which contained details of the "shooting of a defenseless orphan girl, because she refused to become the mistress or the wife of her slayer."[18] In his opinion, these causes "intensified the hostile feeling this singularly revolting crime at first awakened."[19]

Zeigler argued that changing the venue immediately would ultimately save the county money. Based on the difficulty experienced in seating a jury in the first trial, he felt that if the new trial was scheduled for York County, it would be inevitable that a change of venue would eventually be granted. If that were the case, he said, why not move to another county now and save York County the expense of preparing for a trial which would most likely end up being held elsewhere.

Since both the prosecution and defense counsels agreed that justice would best be served by moving the trial, the decision should have been straightforward. However, even though Judge Wickes was probably not anxious to try the case again in his courtroom and in all likelihood had already made his decision, he deferred ruling on the motion until Wednesday, December 6.

On Wednesday morning, Judge Wickes filed his opinion on the application by the prisoner's counsel for a change of venue. John Coyle, along with his lawyers and parents, were present in court to hear the ruling. Without specifically questioning the upper court's decision, he did agree it would be impossible "to deny that public sentiment has been deeply stirred."[20] Acknowledging that a second trial in York County would cause "... possible peril to this defendant, should he be again tried in this jurisdiction,"[21] Wickes felt compelled to grant the petition and ordered the trial to be moved to an adjoining county.

Taking one last opportunity to show his displeasure with the Supreme Court's decision, Wickes commented "The hardships of sending this case so far from the homes of the witnesses, most of whom are poor, has been brought on their behalf to the notice of the court. But we have no power to avert it. We can only administer the laws as we find them, and follow the decisions of the Supreme Court wherever they may lead."[22] The following order was then read in court:

"And now, to wit, December sixth, 1882, on due consideration of the application for a change of venue in this case – to wit, the case of the Commonwealth v. John Coyle, Jr., indicted in the court of Oyer and Terminer of York County for the murder of Emily Myers, being indictment No. 58 of the June sessions, 1881, and being satisfied from the evidence produced that a fair trial cannot be obtained in this county because of prejudice existing against the said prisoner, we do order that the venue thereof be changed to the adjoining county of Adams, where the cause alleged for this change does not exist. And we do further order that a warrant shall issue directed to the Sheriff of York county, commanding him to safely convey the prisoner, John Coyle, Jr., to the jail of the county of Adams, there to be safely kept by the jailor thereof until discharged by due course of law."[23]

No time was wasted, and the warrant to relocate Coyle to Adams County was issued the same day. Six days later, on December 12, the York County Clerk of Courts personally delivered a complete record of the case and all the evidence to his counterpart in the Court of Oyer and Terminer in Adams County. York County was officially finished with John Coyle.

Before leaving the York County Prison, Coyle penned a letter to Sheriff Altland and his family, expressing his thanks for the good care he was provided and the respect he was offered during his nineteen month incarceration. It was reproduced verbatim in the local paper a few days before he departed for the Adams County Prison to await his second trial.

"York Dec 10th 1882

To Mrs Altland and Family

I am very sorry to have to leave my Home but I have not forgotten My Duty to Give my Kind and Affectionate Motherly friend Mrs altland Meny Meny Thanks and God Bless her and her Whole family for Theare Trouble and Love Kindness Shown to Theare old Prisoner while In theare care   I shall always Remember Mrs altland and family I was Cast in Prison away from every Person even my Poor old father and ould mother got sick and was not able to come see me   Still made my Case a hard one for I never was In Prison But Thank God I came across a nice family and I shall always talk well of mrs altland and her family hopeing we may all meet together In Heaven   I would Like to write a nice card to the family but I have no Chance in Prison out if I have Luck I Hope to Remember the family with something Boantiful to Remember Theare Prisoner John Coyle Jr   I will never be able to speak well enough about the family even Jerry H. altland for a young man has shown Respect to me and gave me more Libberty then eny other Prisoner would ever get and I shall Remember Jerry when I say Libberty I mean to give me free access of the Hall and prisnors Kitchen the same as other Prisnors, and he always Talked to me nice and with Respect we never had eny trouble In what ever I only Pray and Hope to get under as good Turnkey In adams county I will be perfectly satisfied I feel sorry to have to leave my Kind young friend Jerry H altland Turnkey of York   I now Come to a Close by hopeing the family will always Remember there Prisnor wheare ever he goes and I Hoipe the Family will speak well of me on account of my Dear Love Parents it will be all the better for my Poor old Parents if the family speaks will of me Please Excuse all mistakes and bad writing my pen is very bad

> From the care of
> Prisnor John Coyle
> York Penn"[24]

Chapter 21

Adams County Prison, Gettysburg, Pa
December, 1882

"America is the land of the second chance - and when the gates of the prison open, the path should lead to a better life."

... George W. Bush

At the beginning of December 1882, Sheriff Samuel Altland led a manacled John Coyle out of the York County Prison for the final time. The trip to the Adams County Prison took most of the day, and after conveying custody of their prisoner to Sheriff Jacob Plank, Altland and his son Philip, who was acting as an additional guard during the transfer, found a room in the nearby Eagle Hotel. Meanwhile, Coyle was led to one of the fourteen small cells in the jail where he settled in for his first night.

The prison, located at 59 East High Street, was built on land donated by the town's founder James Gettys. When Adams County was formed from York County in 1800, a state selection committee was appointed to choose a location for the county seat, and New Oxford, Hunterstown (the county population center), and Gettystown (the county geographic center) were the top candidates.

Gettys offered the committee land to build a county jail in an attempt to sway the decision towards his newly laid out Gettystown. In addition, a group of nine prominent local residents put forward a $7,000 bond, which was earmarked for the construction of a court house and administration buildings.

This was apparently enough to convince the selection committee, and Governor Thomas McKean signed the bill in January 1800, placing the courts for the newly formed Adams County in Gettystown. In the wording of the "strong and effective bond, effective in making this the county seat,"[1] the town was referred to as "Gettysburg" for the first time.

In the deed from James Gettys to the trustees appointed for the newly formed Adams County in 1799, and subsequently in the deed from the trustees to the County Commissioners in 1801, Gettys legally transferred his "right, title, interest and claim to a suitable lot of ground for the purpose of building a Gaol thereon, ... forever, on condition that Gettystown aforesaid be fixed as the seat of justice."[2]

The original prison was constructed around 1802, but burned to the ground in 1850 in a fire apparently started in one of the cells by an inmate suffering from dementia. The prison was rebuilt on the same lot the following year. The new two-story brick jail was built to resemble a fortress with a rear cell block and yard surrounded by a sixteen-foot-high stone wall. The front building contained offices and living quarters for the sheriff. A third story was added to the prison in 1889 and the facility continued to be used as the county jail until 1948.[*]

On July 2, 1862, Confederate commander Robert E. Lee used the jail for a council of war with his generals. Based on their minor victories in the first two days of the battle, a course of action was decided for the following day, including the infamous Pickett's Charge. After the Battle of Gettysburg, the Union Army regained control of the prison and the Provost Marshall used it to hold citizens and soldiers charged with martial law violations.

The cell block contained fourteen cells arranged in a single tier along a sixty-six-foot long by ten-foot-wide corridor, seven cells to a side. Sheriff Jacob Plank and his family, including his son who acted as deputy, lived in the apartments on the second floor of the front building. The prison was small by Pennsylvania standards with an average population of only eight prisoners, most of whom were awaiting trial. The majority of convicted criminals serving sentences

---

[*] *The following year it was purchased for use as the Adams County Library, and in 1991 it became the home of the Gettysburg borough offices.*

were sent to the Eastern State Penitentiary, as there was no room, and only minimal security, in the Adams County facility.

Escapes were not uncommon and were accomplished by prisoners breaking through the outer walls of their cells, with two occurring in 1883 while John Coyle was an inmate. According to the annual prison report the following year, the prison "is by no means strongly built, and affords but little protection against a frequent repetition of these occurrences, which are only prevented by the exercise of personal vigilance on the part of the keepers."[3]

At seven-feet wide by fourteen-feet long by nine-feet high, Coyle's cell in Gettysburg was smaller and more confining that the one he occupied in York by a foot in every dimension. Instead of solid brick, most cells were partitioned with lathe and plaster walls, which were inspected and whitewashed regularly. The brick floors were covered with wood planking in order to provide some insulation to prevent dampness, and although all cells had toilet facilities, they did not have running water.

Each cell had two doors, one solid wood and the other iron lattice, and contained only sparse furnishings. The straw mattress on the small bed was lice-infected, and the thin woolen blankets provided little protection against cold weather. The small window in each cell was drafty and did not admit much light. The prisoners were only allowed a candle or lamp if they could afford one, as long as it was extinguished by 9 o'clock each evening. Tobacco was provided by the county, but not alcohol or clothing.

The rules in Adams County were very similar to what Coyle was accustomed to in the York County Prison. There were no employment opportunities, and prisoners were allowed to congregate in the corridor during the day. Breakfast and lunch consisted of bread, coffee and molasses, and for dinner the prisoners were served soup, vegetables and meat. The punishment for breaking the rules was confinement in a dark windowless cell. No education or vocational instruction of any kind was provided, but inmates who could read were given bibles to keep in their cells.

Old County Prison, ca. 1865
Excerpt of Tyson Studio Stereo #564
Adams County Historical Society, 5071.001

Adams County Prison, ca. 2010
Collection of Author

Recommendations resulting from the yearly inspections of the Adams County Prison cited the same issues from year to year. Although the cells, kitchen and basement were kept clean and orderly, discipline was not strictly enforced, no separate infirmary facilities were provided, and there were inadequate arrangements for the separation of women prisoners. When necessary, repairs to the heating and drainage were promptly made, and overall the prison got fair marks. The report for 1883, as a result of a visit made on June 11, noted the presence of John Coyle, a prisoner who "had been tried for murder, who it was alleged was insane."[4]

<hr>

Adams County Courthouse, Gettysburg, Pa
February, 1883

The second trial of John Coyle was scheduled to begin during the January 1883 Quarter Session of the Court of Oyer and Terminer of Adams County in the courtroom of Judge William McClean. McClean, a native of Gettysburg and a graduate of the Harvard Law School, had been admitted to the Adams County Bar in 1854.

According to procedure, the jury pool was selected in January with actual trial proceedings to begin in February. However, before *voir dire*[†] could begin, Adams County District Attorney Samuel M. Swope moved to nullify the entire panel. Swope alleged the jury commissioners had neglected to take the proper oath required by Section 1 of Article VII of the Pennsylvania Constitution before drawing jurors. Swope notified Henry Fisher and William Chapman, the same lawyers who represented Coyle during the first trial in York, that a motion would be made in court on Monday, February 5 to quash the entire jury pool.

[†] *Voir dire is the formal examination of potential jurors where the prosecution and defense can ask questions to determine their impartiality.*

The motion alleged that since the required oath was not taken prior to selecting jurors, grave doubts were raised as to the legality of the panel. Swope did not want to take any chances that there would be any reason for an appeal in the second Coyle trial.

According to The Act of April 9, 1849, a list of trials and jurors for each upcoming session was required to be published in at least three local newspapers, three weeks before the meeting of the court. As trials were to begin February 26, the motion to quash the jury was made just in time to stop the list from being published.

The motion was granted and the entire panel of jurors was voided and taken out of the jury wheel. The Coyle trial was granted a continuance until the March 1883 term and the Commissioners were ordered to "make a new selection of four hundred sober, intelligent, and judicious persons and deposit their names in the wheel for the remainder of the current year in the manner directed by law."[5]

Ever mindful that York County was paying the expense for the second Coyle trial in Gettysburg, the *York Daily Record* commended the efforts of Adams County District Attorney Swope. "The prosecuting officers are determined to force the case to as early a trial as possible. The discovery of the defect in drawing the jury in time to notify witnesses not to attend court in Gettysburg will save the county many dollars of costs."[6]

Adams County Courthouse, Gettysburg, Pa
Monday, April 23, 1883

The first Adams County courthouse was located in the middle of the Gettysburg center square. By 1858, the county had outgrown the facilities and a new building was completed the following year. The original courthouse was eventually torn down and the lot turned over for public use. The new, larger structure where the Coyle trial was being held was located on the southwest corner of Baltimore and West Middle Streets, one block south of the square.

Four years after it was built, Confederate troops occupied the courthouse prior to the Battle of Gettysburg. The clock tower later served as a Union flag station in support of General John Buford's First Calvary Division, and following the three-day battle it was utilized as a hospital for both Union and Confederate troops. The courthouse still appears much the same as it did during the Coyle trial in 1883.

Adams County Courthouse, ca. 2010
Collection of Author

At 10 o'clock on April 23, the courthouse bell rang and the case of the Commonwealth vs. John Coyle, Jr. was called to order, Judge William McClean presiding. "The novelty, or rather rarity, of a trial for murder in the courts of this county attracted a large number of persons to the court-house. The court-room was filled, both inside and outside the bar, all eager to hear and see what was being done."[7]

The Commonwealth was represented by Adams County District Attorney Samuel M. Swope and his counterpart from York, Edward Zeigler, the prosecutor from the first trial in December 1881. Although Sheriff Plank and John Coyle were present, defense lawyers Henry Fisher and William Chapman were not yet in court, as they had missed boarding the morning train in York. Court was recessed until they arrived and Coyle was escorted back to his cell.

The distance from the jail, located one block south of the courthouse on Baltimore Street and one block east on High Street, took them only a few minutes to walk. As was to be the case for the rest of the trial, Coyle was friendly to the crowds that stood along the streets to watch them pass. Although noted for his "hard looks," Coyle was not publically hated in Gettysburg as he had been in York. During the second trial, an aged schoolteacher in town "often saw the murderer on his trips from the jail to the courthouse. She said that he was a handsome man, who greeted the people and jokingly referred to his handcuffs as 'my pretty bracelets.'"[8]

"Birds-eye view of Gettysburg, Pennsylvania," ca. 1888
showing the locations of the Courthouse (3) and County Prison (4)
Library of Congress Geography and Map Division

With all counsel present, Judge McClean began the process of impaneling a jury. A venire of sixty had been pulled from the jury wheel for "twelve free and lawful men of said County; by whom the truth of the matter may be better known and who are not of kin to the said John Coyle, Jr., to recognize on their oath whether the said John Coyle, Jr. be guilty of felony and murder in the said indictment specified and set forth; or not guilty."[9]

The first juror called was George Lady. Before questioning could begin, Henry Fisher interrupted the proceedings and filed a special plea questioning the jurisdiction and validity of the Adams County court. The plea was filed as a precautionary measure so it would be included in the court record. If the case were taken before the Supreme Court on appeal, the higher court would have to first rule on the constitutionality of the Adams County court. Fisher felt that the jurisdiction was unconstitutional and might be a reason to be granted another trial if needed.

Technically, Fisher was correct. According to the Pennsylvania Constitution of 1874, "whenever a county shall contain forty thousand inhabitants it shall constitute a separate judicial district, and shall elect one judge learned in the law."[10] However, when the Forty-Second Judicial District was established in 1874, Adams County had only approximately 31,000 inhabitants. In 1870, the population was 30,315 and grew to only 32,455 by 1880.[11] In fact, Adams County did not exceed a population of more than 40,000 until the early 1940s, being 39,435 in 1940 and 44,197 in 1950.[12] At the time of the Coyle trial, Henry Fisher was correct in stating that Adams County did not appear to be a valid judicial district. District Attorney Swope demurred, or objected, to the plea and the Court sustained the objection.

In his response, Judge McClean stated "Judge Purviance, the author of the constitutional provision on which the plea was based, had expressed the opinion that a district constituted such as Adams was clearly constitutional and that Governor Hoyt in his veto message of the Judicial Apportionment bill and ex-Senator Buckalew in his recent work on the Constitution had expressed similar opinions."[13]

Defense council took exception to the ruling, and their objection was noted. It would be up to the Pennsylvania Supreme Court to determine the constitutionality of the Adams County court should the case be appealed. However, before Judge McClean could move on to jury selection, Fisher made another motion and asked that Coyle's "not guilty" plea from York County be removed from the record.

The Commonwealth objected, and McClean ruled "it seems to be unnecessary and we take the record as sent us [from York County] with the plea of not guilty,"[14] and refused to have it withdrawn. This motion was entered into the record along with the Commonwealth's objection. Like the first motion, this issue would have to be left for the Supreme Court should Fisher appeal the verdict.

Finally, with no more motions to be entered, the process of choosing a panel for the Coyle trial began. In York County, jury selection required the questioning of 111 potential jurors over two days, in one regular venire and three special venires, before a panel of twelve was chosen. In Adams County, only one venire of sixty was needed and forty-seven were questioned over a three-hour period before a jury was selected.

Clearly, the jury pool in Adams County was not as familiar with the Coyle case as those questioned in York, and the defense must have felt better about their chances of getting a fair trial. In the first trial, most jurors were challenged for cause due to preconceived opinions, but in Adams County, only fourteen were dismissed for cause. The defense used nineteen of their twenty peremptory challenges, the Commonwealth none. Two jurors were excused for ill-health and thirteen were never questioned at all.

The twelve jurors, "who being elected, tried, and sworn in due form of law in the presence of John Coyle, Jr. here in open court, to will and truly try and true deliverance make..."[15] were as follows: George W. Lady, David Bricker, John H. Dubs, Abraham M. Waybright, Obediah S. Harner, James N. Kelley, Levi M. Plank, John

F. Bowers, Oliver F. Neely, Jacob L. Grass, Samuel H. Eicholtz, and Joseph Rebert.

Shortly after 5 o'clock, the Coyle jury was placed in the custody of tipstaves Jerimiah Martin and Lewis Myers. The twelve jurors were escorted to the nearby Globe Hotel[‡], located just off the square on York Street, where they would be sequestered for the remainder of the trial. They were instructed not to have any conversations with anyone outside the courtroom, and were told they would be allowed to take walks with their appointed guardians. Court was adjourned until the next morning, when the Commonwealth would issue their opening statement to the jury.

[‡] The Globe Inn was originally owned by town founder James Gettys and was used by Union general John Buford during the Battle of Gettysburg. Drastically remodeled over the years, it was renamed the Lincoln Way Hotel, then Hoffman's, before being destroyed by fire in 1968.

Chapter 22

Adams County Courthouse, Gettysburg, Pa
Tuesday, April 24, 1883

"They've got him – credible witnesses, documents, heaven knows what else. In all my years as a prosecutor I have never seen such an open-and-shut case."

> ... *Elliot Richardson, Attorney General,*
> *Nixon Administration*

Adams County District Attorney Samuel M. Swope opened the case for the Commonwealth with a brief address to the jury, simply stating that he intended to prove that Emily Myers had been murdered, John Coyle was responsible, and the act was premeditated. Since Swope was being advised by the District Attorney from York, his strategy was essentially the same as Edward Ziegler had used when the case was first tried.

All except six of the twenty-seven witnesses who testified for the prosecution in York were subpoenaed in Gettysburg, and none were called who had not appeared before. In addition, the witnesses were called to the stand in essentially the same order and were asked much the same questions as they had been a year and a half earlier.

Many of the witnesses were from Marietta, and in order to be at the courthouse in Adams County on time each morning, they had to take the first train at 7:10 a.m. from Marietta to Columbia. From there they needed to change trains for York and Gettysburg. Since the early train from Columbia was normally scheduled to leave at 7:05 a.m., special arrangements were made during the trial to hold the train so the witnesses coming from Marietta could be on board.

The prosecution opened with Mrs. Coyle, as they had in the first trial, and she explained the facts which occurred the day of the murder. Frank Magee, Dr. John Thompson, William Thompson, Alex

Thompson, Daniel Moore, and William Sweeny testified concerning the coroner's inquest and the statements Coyle made the day of the murder. Undertaker John Bastian and gravedigger John Deppeler related the facts concerning the burial and exhumation of Emily Myers. They were followed by Dr. John Ahl, who described the autopsy.

Court officials from York County entered into evidence the exhibits from the trial in York, including Emily's heart preserved in alcohol, the murder weapon, the dress worn by Emily when she was shot, and the draft made of the Coyle premises. Justice Houck, Constable Shenberger, and Officer Dietz testified concerning the conversations they held with Coyle on the way to the York County Prison the day of the murder. Philip Altland, the Sheriff's son, related his discussions with Coyle while in prison.

The last four witnesses for the prosecution were called to provide evidence of premeditation. John Thompson, John Burg, John Warfield and John Shutzbaugh, all related conversations with Coyle in which he had threatened to shoot Emily if she would not marry him or have sexual relations.

Shortly after 3 o'clock, after fewer than six hours of testimony, the Commonwealth rested. They had proven their case in the same clear and concise way they had in the first trial and hoped that the facts would speak for themselves and lead to another guilty verdict. Cross-examination of the prosecution witnesses by Fisher and Chapman was minimal and ineffective, as the facts of the case could not be disputed.

William Chapman was chosen to give the opening statement for the defense. He spoke passionately for thirty minutes before calling his first witness, Mr. Coyle. Over the course of the next two days, the defense would call a total of twenty-eight witnesses, six more than had testified in the first trial. Eleven had appeared in York, and seventeen were testifying for the first time in Gettysburg.

Perhaps judging Mr. Coyle to be a more credible witness than his wife, the defense chose to lead with his testimony instead of Mrs. Coyle, as they had in York. He established the facts related to John's childhood and prior incidents that demonstrated unsoundness. Due to the late hour, Mr. Coyle was the only witness to appear for the defense on the first day of the trial.

He spoke of the depression John suffered after the accident that resulted in the disfigurement of his hand. He then described the severe attack of typhoid fever his son suffered from the following year, indicating that John's peculiar attitude and eccentric actions began shortly after his illness.

Fisher:	"What had he complained of after that [hunting accident], if not before?"
Mr. Coyle:	*"He complained of pains in his head, and particularly at times more so than others ..."*
Fisher:	"...What was the result [of the injury to his hand], if anything?"
Mr. Coyle:	*"To the extent of disturbing his mind"*
Fisher:	"State what differences, if any, you noticed afterwards?"
Mr. Coyle:	*"I noticed he was not the same person in any way"*
Fisher:	"In what respect?"
Mr. Coyle:	*"In respect to going off, and complained of his head or mind."*
Fisher:	"State whether or not you ever set him about doing work, and with what result, and what did he do as regards to carrying out any instructions you gave him?"
Mr. Coyle:	*"There was very little I would send him to do after he got that way; there was no use to send him to town for anything by himself."*
Fisher:	"What, if there was anything unusual, did you ever notice about John's expression at these times when he had these spells – I mean his looks?"

Mr. Coyle:	*"If I tried to control him, he would get cross and use rough language."*
Fisher:	"What would he say to you?"
Mr. Coyle:	*"He would say many rough things, and call me names that he should not."*
Fisher:	"What would he call you?"
Mr. Coyle:	*"An 'old rascal', or something"*
Fisher:	"What business did John engage in besides what you have stated?"
Mr. Coyle:	*"Nothing else, never could send him an errand with a wagon or horse by himself, and no one ever saw him that way either."*
Fisher:	"You did not - why?"
Mr. Coyle:	*"He was not capable."*
Fisher:	"State how John was at these times when you say that he acted in this peculiar way, with regard to his being drunk or sober ..."
Mr. Coyle:	*"Well, it was very seldom he was under the influence of liquor - he wasn't under the influence at the times he got these spells, and people used to think it was the liquor."*
Fisher:	"Not what people thought, would he be under the influence of liquor?"
Mr. Coyle:	*"Why he would be sometimes, but they -"*
Fisher:	"Say whether he was under the influence ..."

Mr. Coyle:	*"There was sometimes, I believe, he was somewhat under the influence of liquor, and sometimes he was better than when the spells were on him."*
Fisher:	"From your knowledge of Johnny during this time that you have been speaking of, from what you know of him and saw of him, - was he or was he not, in your opinion, of sound mind on the morning of the 30th of May, 1881, when he shot this girl?"
Mr. Coyle:	*"No, he was not."*[1]

The second day of testimony began with the cross-examination of Mr. Coyle by the District Attorney. After asking about John's age and his hand injury, he was finished with the witness. Henry Fisher then called Mrs. Coyle to the stand. She told of John's condition following the hunting accident, his bout with typhoid fever, and his relationship with his father.

Fisher:	"What did he complain of [following his illness with typhoid], if anything?"
Mrs. Coyle:	*"Pain, constant in the back of his head, and he does to this day."*
Fisher:	"When he was suffering from that pain in his head, from that time he commenced complaining about it?"
Mrs. Coyle:	*"Well he was always complaining about pain in his head, and about having trouble, and about being – feeling worried, and such like, - such as a person melancholy and usually out of gear"*
Fisher:	"State whether you ever followed him? [when he would go off by himself]"
Mrs. Coyle:	*"Yes, frequently all over the hills already. After he got melancholy and threatened to take his life, of course I got uneasy, and would go after him"*

Fisher: "In what situation particularly would you find him at
                any of these times?"

Mrs. Coyle: "*Well, I would find him very pale and haggard and
                looking troubled, just like as some person having great
                trouble on him*"

Fisher: "What was his appearance otherwise than you already
                described – his face, as to color?"

Mrs. Coyle: "*Well, it was pale, and kind of blue rings around his
                eyes, and queer looking.*"

Fisher: "What did he say, if anything?"

Mrs. Coyle: "*Nothing more than he had trouble, and was tired of
                living, and wanted to die and such talk like that.*"

Fisher: "What, if anything, do you know about John's carrying
                any other weapon besides the pistol? [that he used to
                attempt suicide in the barn on a previous occasion]

Mrs. Coyle: "*Yes, he carried a razor, he said he was going to cut
                his throat.*"

Fisher: "Was this all before or afterward?"

Mrs. Coyle: "*It was after we took the pistol from him. The razor he
                used to shave with, we took that from him, and he
                went to Marietta and got shaved after that.*"

Fisher: "Did he give any reason for it?"

Mrs. Coyle: "*No sir, he said he just had trouble, and he could not
                live, and didn't want to live, and had no other way to
                die but to put himself out of the road.*"

Fisher: "And what did John say at the time he wanted to take
                this poison?" [rat poison]

| Mrs. Coyle: | *"He said he wanted to die, and he was tired of living, and Kate [Hinkle] and him wrestled around until I got away from him."* |

| Fisher: | "What was John's appearance at the time he talked about taking this poison?" |

| Mrs. Coyle: | *"His appearance – I can hardly express it; something like melancholy or getting crazy – something like that – when he was talking about losing his mind."*[2] |

On cross-examination, Prosecutor Swope aggressively questioned Mrs. Coyle in an attempt to discredit her testimony regarding the effect that John's hunting accident had on his mind twelve years earlier.

| Swope: | "How did John complain about his hand?" |

| Mrs. Coyle: | *"How did he complain?"* |

| Swope: | "Yes, what was his complaint – wasn't the only complaint that he made of his annoyance, or his regret?" |

| Mrs. Coyle: | *"Yes, he often complained about the impairing of his hand and worrying him, and about it bothering his mind. I think that helped to make his mind what it is"* |

| Swope: | "Wasn't the only worry that you heard him make over that, the fact that he regretted it – he was sorry he crippled himself in that way?" |

| Mrs. Coyle: | *"Yes, I often heard him say he was sorry, and wished it wasn't so."* |

| Swope: | "The only way he suffered on account of that was the pain in his hand?" |

| Mrs. Coyle: | *"Yes, certainly"* |

| Swope: | "He was not out of his mind?" |

Mrs. Coyle: *"He was not at the time."*

Swope: "He only complained about the pain in his hand, and the annoyance of being crippled?"

Mrs. Coyle: *"Yes, but the doctor said the report of the gun so close to his head would cause his mind to grow weak."*

Swope: "Who said that?"

Mrs. Coyle: *"Dr. Trout"*

Swope: "Where is Dr. Trout?"

Mrs. Coyle: *"In his grave"*

Swope: "If this discharge of the pistol was so close to his head ... " [interrupted]

Mrs. Coyle: *"It was a big duck gun"*

Swope: "... was so close to his head as to cause concussion of the brain, wouldn't it be perceived right at once?"

Mrs. Coyle: *"It might have been, but he was so weak and low down with the pain in his hand, that I didn't notice - I couldn't tell if it was or not - I wasn't doctor enough for that. The next year he had typhoid fever and after he got out of that I saw what was the matter with him."*

Swope: "Did you ever know both of them [Mr. Coyle and John] to be under the influence of liquor there and get into quarrels?"

Mrs. Coyle: *"No sir"*

Swope: "On one of these occasions, when John left the house and went away, state whether or not he and his father were not somewhat under the influence of liquor, had a fight, and that your husband raced John around the house with a gun, and chased him off?"

Mrs. Coyle: *"I don't know anything of the kind. If anybody else saw it, I didn't. No such a thing ever happened that I know of."*

Swope: "You were not at the jail at the time testified by Philip A. Altland, the deputy sheriff of the York county jail – you and your husband together – when you came to see John, and you were left in the cell, and he was standing at the doors – you didn't ask John why he did this?"

Mrs. Coyle: *"No sir, and I never spoke to John nothing about the girl, never once while he was in prison, for I thought he had enough to study without speaking of her."*[3]

Swope wrapped up his cross-examination of Mrs. Coyle by asking some pointed questions concerning an instance where she and Mr. Coyle sent John to Gettysburg under someone else's care. The prosecution's theory was that these trips were merely to prevent John from drinking, a fact which Mrs. Coyle flatly denied.

Swope: "Being of unsound mind, as you say, and having a disposition to take his own life, as you say, and needing to be overlooked and guarded by you to be prevented from committing suicide, as you say, how does it come for the benefit of his mind, and for his protection, you would send him away from home on an excursion?"

Mrs. Coyle: *"People that have only one child will do everything for his comfort that they can – that is what we were trying to do."*

Swope: "If anything was said about John going on this excursion to Gettysburg, or any other place, wasn't it to try to prevent him from getting drunk?"

Mrs. Coyle: *"No sir, it wasn't all drunk with John, it was all drunk with all these witnesses though."*[4]

Mrs. Coyle's sister, Kate Hinkle, corroborated much of the testimony given by Mr. and Mrs. Coyle concerning the hunting accident, the typhoid illness, and the several suicide attempts she had witnessed. However, on cross-examination, she admitted that John seemed good enough after those incidents, effectively negating the prior testimony.

Swope:	"When you saw him [after the hunting accident], mentally he was not disturbed?"
Mrs. Hinkle:	*"I spoke to him, and asked him how he was, he said he had hurt his hand pretty bad."*
Swope:	"He was mentally all right then?"
Mrs. Hinkle:	*"Yes sir."*
Swope:	"You talked to him [after the typhoid]?"
Mrs. Hinkle:	*"Yes sir."*
Swope:	"He talked all right to you?"
Mrs. Hinkle:	*"Yes"*
Swope:	"He was mentally all right?"
Mrs. Hinkle:	*"Yes."*
Swope:	"Don't be afraid to say yes loud, so we can all hear it, - did you say yes?"
Mrs. Hinkle:	*"Yes"*
Swope:	"Did he not come there [to your house] several times under the influence of liquor?"
Mrs. Hinkle:	*"I knew him to come there twice [drunk], and then he was more sensible than any other time, - he talked sensible then. (laughter)."*

Swope: "Those times that John came to your house so often, - did he ever hurt your children?"

Mrs. Hinkle: *"Sometimes he would come in pretty rough."*

Swope: "Rough at all times?"

Mrs. Hinkle: *"No sir, he was not all time crazy or drunk."*

Swope: "He had temporary symptoms of sanity?"

Mrs. Hinkle: *"Sometimes he was very good and nice; sometimes he caught the children and would behave badly."*[5]

The testimony of the next witness, Emily Rollins, followed the same pattern – weak questions by the defense followed by strong cross-examination by the prosecution. She told of John's many marriage proposals, but contradicted herself several times. She eventually made Coyle's proposals sound as if they were all in fun, rather than being obsessive or indicative of insanity.

Swope: "The last time when you met him at the gate, he asked you whether you would not marry him that day?"

Rollins: *"Yes, that day; it was on a Christmas day"*

Swope: "Wasn't it in a jovial way that he said he would go and get his mothers [silk dress]?"

Rollins: *"No sir"*

Swope: "Was it not a sort of jovial way that you said you didn't want to get married until you had a silk dress?"

Rollins: *"I said it in fun, he meant it in earnest"*

Swope: "So when you said you wanted to get a silk dress, you didn't mean that?"

Rollins: *"Yes sir, I meant it"*[6]

William Frane, a part-time employee of the Coyles who did odd jobs around the ferry, was a new witness for the defense in the second trial. Fisher asked a long series of questions about an excursion that Mr. Coyle had asked Frane to take with John to Port Deposit, Maryland, on the Fourth of July, 1875. John was depressed at the time and his father thought the trip would do his mind some good, but Mr. Coyle warned Frane to keep a close eye on him.

Frane, eight years older than John at the time, took the twenty-year-old John down the river. They attended several picnics while they were in Port Deposit, and one night a man was shot and killed. John was extremely frightened when he heard the gunshot and ran away. Frane was able to find John, calm him down, and convince him to return to their hotel. Apparently something happened during the night, perhaps John making some type of sexual advance, as Frane refused to answer any specific questions related to the events in the hotel room.

Fisher: "How was John at that time [of the excursion to Port Deposit] in regard to the condition of his mind?"

Frane: *"Well his mind appeared to be wild, - fierce looking."*

Fisher: "State whether or not you and he slept in the same room while you were there?"

Frane: *"Yes sir."*

Fisher: "Different beds?"

Frane: *"Yes sir."*

Fisher: "State what, if anything, John did at night that was unusual?"

Frane: *"Well, he would get up and run around the room sometimes."*

Fisher: "State whether you heard him make any complaints of his head at night?"

Frane: *"Yes sir."*

Fisher: "Describe it?"

Frane: *"He told me he had pain in his head, - he didn't know what to do."*

Fisher: "State whether or not he came into your bed?"

Frane: *"Sometimes."*

Fisher: "What would he do there?"

Frane: *"He would talk to me about the women and the girls."*

Fisher: "What, if anything else, did he do or try to do with you?"

Frane: *"Nothing."*

Fisher: "Go on tell it all, whatever it was, that he did and said?"

Frane: [hesitation]

Fisher: "Have you stated all that he did at night?"

Frane: *"Sir, - yes sir."*[7]

Under cross-examination by District Attorney Swope, Frane again refused to give details about the night in Port Deposit, but did admit that both he and John drank frequently. Swope was able to portray Frane's casual attitude about the Port Deposit shooting as an irrational response and made Coyle's reaction seem to be reasonable given the circumstances.

Swope: "He came into bed with you, and talked about different girls that he liked?"

Frane: *"Yes sir."*

Swope:	"That is all he did, - you were talking together then, were you?"
Frane:	(no answer)
Swope:	"You got down there at the Port and a pistol went off?"
Frane:	*" Yes sir."*
Swope:	"Somebody was killed?"
Frane:	*" Yes sir."*
Swope:	"He was very much frightened at the discharge of that gun, - ran away from it?"
Frane:	*" Yes sir."*
Swope:	"Like a madman?"
Frane:	*"I suppose if he had been a man of good sound sense, he would have stood still – he wouldn't have run away from one man lying dead."*
Swope:	"It didn't scare you?"
Frane:	*"No sir."*
Swope:	"Didn't disturb you in the least?"
Frane:	*"No sir."*
Swope:	"Didn't give any thought that a man was killed there?"
Frane:	*"No sir."*
Swope:	"Didn't think of it any more than any other little thing that might occur?"
Frane:	*"Not at all."*

Swope:	"Did you see John under the influence of liquor while you were there?"
Frane:	*"I have seen him under a number of times."*
Swope:	"Did you take anything to drink today?"
Frane:	*"I did take several drinks."*
Swope:	"You are accustomed to imbibing on those occasions pretty freely?"
Frane:	*"When I feel dry I generally drink"* (laughter)
Swope:	"You are accustomed to feel dry several times a day?"
Frane:	*"Sometimes, and sometimes not."*[8]

Susan McCann was next on the stand for the defense and testified about the same incidents she had in the first trial. On cross-examination, District Attorney Swope managed to get her to admit that, even though she thought him insane, she trusted him with her life.

Swope:	"You say that you worked at Mrs. Coyle's or had known them for about 5 or 6 years ...?"
McCann:	*"Yes sir."*
Swope:	"When you went there, did you see John return from Marietta at any time?"
McCann:	*"Oh, yes; he often took me over the river; his mother sent him, and I went over with him."*
Swope:	"You had no fear going across the river with him?"
McCann:	*"Oh, no; I wasn't a bit afraid of him; I was well acquainted with him, and I had no fear of him."*
Swope:	"He enjoyed a reputation as a ferryman?"

McCann:	*"I didn't see anything that I should be afraid of in him."*
Swope:	"And he rowed you across?"
McCann:	*"Yes sir."*
Swope:	"You were never cautioned by Mr. or Mrs. Coyle not to go with him?"
McCann:	*"Oh no, they knew I knew him well; I wasn't afraid to go with him."*[9]

Before leaving the stand, McCann testified about the romantic relationship between John and Emily. She was the only witness in either trial to mention they were even on friendly terms. In fact, the prosecution had portrayed Emily as being murdered by an unrelenting suitor that she continually, and consistently, rejected. John's comments that Emily had frustrated him because she teased him about marriage were mostly discounted, but if McCann's testimony were to be believed, they may have been based on fact.

Swope:	"That is all you know about John?"
McCann:	*"No; any place that him and her would meet other than his mother's presence, they made love to each other – him to her, and her to him ..."*
Swope:	"What did they do?"
McCann:	*"She would put her arms around his neck and kiss him, on the porch and sometimes in the house – no matter where, - I came here to tell the truth and nothing but the truth. I was there until Christmas, and after Christmas I was also until Spring. We went out in the wood-house, me and her, and another little boy, and he was there, and she sat down on his knee and kissed him – they sat down on the saw-buck."*
Swope:	"Where were you?"

McCann: *"I was standing as close to her as to this man (indicating stenographer about five feet off)."* [10]

John Stahl was the first of many witnesses to attest that John was commonly known as "Crazy John Coyle" in Marietta. He testified that he had seen Coyle talking and playing with small boys, both black and white, and that John was constantly teased and tormented by them. He was called to the stand primarily to relate a conversation he overhead when John told Captain Ettla that he had piloted rafts down the river.

On cross-examination by District Attorney Swope, Stahl eventually stated that Coyle associated with people other than small boys, and admitted his opinion that John was unsound was based only on the rafting conversation.

Swope: "Now give us some evidence of his cranky conversation?"

Stahl: *"No matter what you spoke about, there was no sense in his conversation at all, - he would get off the subject altogether."*

Swope: "... have you not heard him talk to boys and also to men?

Stahl: *"Yes sir. When he was talking to Mr. Ettla he was talking to a man."*

Swope: "Have you heard him talk to other men?"

Stahl: *"I have."*

Swope: "Then his conversation was not entirely confined exclusively to boys?"

Stahl: *"O, no, - I don't pretend to say that - but his associates."*

Swope:	"The only reason you told the Court and jury that you did not think he was telling the truth [about piloting a raft] was the fact that he was too young to be a raftsman?"
Stahl:	*"Yes sir, - that is a trade by itself."*
Swope:	"And that is a trade, to ferry across the river, is it not, only less extended?"
Stahl:	*"Yes sir."*[11]

Jacob Hanlon, a saloon keeper and a new witness for the defense, testified about John's offer to sell his father's property. He claimed that John's wild and visionary talk about converting the old saw-mill into a fashionable resort, and the fact he wanted to sell it for one-fourth what it was worth, proved he was unsound.

Fisher:	"Did you ever buy anything from him, and if so, what?"
Hanlon:	*"I never bought anything from him except the property that his father lives in; he sold me that several times."*
Fisher:	"Was it in writing or not?"
Hanlon:	*"No sir, all verbal."*
Fisher:	"Who commenced it?"
Hanlon:	*"I did, I said "It will make a right nice summer resort, John." He said it would, and spoke along that way, and finally he offered it to me for sale - and he said he would sell it to me, and he wanted me there. I said "What will become of the old folks?" He said "I will build them a house." And I asked him where he would build them a house. He said "Up on the hill." I didn't buy at that time. A short time afterwards - about 10 days - he approached me, and I bought the*

property for $1500. There was no writing or paper, or anything, about the place. And I saw him some time afterward and he asked me about it, and he said he was going to run a railroad from Wrightsville to run summer boarders to the place. I told him that if he did, I would take the place. He agreed to do it, and it stands that way to this day."

On cross-examination, District Attorney Swope attempted to portray John as a scheming drunk. Although Hanlon had no problems in transacting business with Coyle, he did have a problem with selling him liquor.

Swope: "John frequently came there, [to Hanlon's saloon] didn't he?"

Hanlon: *"Not frequently, occasionally."*

Swope: "You wouldn't sell him anything to drink?"

Hanlon: *"No sir."*

Swope: "Do you think he wasn't capable of taking a drink?"

Hanlon: *"Yes, he was capable, but I considered him unsound; the law prohibits giving any to such a man, and I gave orders to that effect."*[12]

Jacob Hanlon's wife, Elizabeth, also proved to be an ineffective witness for the defense. Her opinion that John was unsound was solely based on an incident at Coyle's Ferry when John wanted her to ride a horse bareback. On cross-examination, Swope trivialized the importance of the riding incident and made Mrs. Hanlon's testimony seem insignificant.

Swope: "He asked you to get on his horse?"

Hanlon: *"No sir. Yes sir."*

Swope: "There was nothing improper about that?"

Hanlon:	*"I don't think a smart, intelligent man would ask a lady to get on a horse without a saddle."*
Swope:	"You don't think a smart, intelligent man would do that?"
Hanlon:	*"Not a man of his age, unless out of his mind."*
Swope:	"They [Miss Rollins and another married lady] both got on?"
Hanlon:	*"They both got on."*[13]

Another first-time defense witness, George Blessing, told of his experiences when Coyle was in his employ doing odd jobs. One winter, John was sledding wooden cross-ties across the river on the ice, but Blessing had to discharge him because he would go to Marietta and not return to work. Another time he saw Coyle throw stones at his father from behind the barn, and formed his opinion that he was unsound based on these experiences.

Percy Schock, the editor of the *Marietta Register,* could give no compelling reason why he formed his opinion that Coyle was unsound. The questioning of Schock by both the defense and prosecution was adversarial and sharp at times, and did not add significantly to either side.

Fisher:	"Well, be good enough to state any conversation, or the subject of any conversation that you can remember having with him?"
Schock:	*"I wouldn't be positive of the subject of any conversation, or state any time."*
Fisher:	"What was the manner of it?"
Schock:	*"Very disjointed as a usual thing; he would go from one subject to another, and never stick long at one thing."*

Fisher: "From what to what would he go?"

Schock: *"That I can't tell you, sir, - I can't tell you from what to*
                 what he would go, I know it was disjointed, to tell you
                 exactly what it would be impossible; one would have to
                 have a very good memory."

Fisher: "State what you have seen him engaged at in
                 Marietta?"

Schock: *"I never saw him engaged at anything but polling and*
                 rowing back and forward across the river, or I have
                 seen him occasionally go into a store and purchase."

Swope: "How many times have you seen him in that condition
                 [drunk]?"

Schock: *"I may have seen him ten times, but I would not be*
                 positive about the exact number of times."

Swope: "May he not have been under the influence of strong
                 drink, to the paralyzing of his system, and you not
                 have noticed it ...?"

Schock: *"Certainly, if he was a couple of miles off."*[14]

        Edwin Lewis described various arguments and fights he
witnessed between John and his father, and that he had heard people
in Marietta say "There comes that damned crazy fool, Johnny Coyle."[15]
Overall, Lewis portrayed Coyle as simply an extremely rebellious
teenager as opposed to an insane man.

Fisher: "And how did he behave ...?"

Lewis: *"Sometimes he would behave very vulgar about the*
                 table."

Fisher: "Describe it?"

Lewis: *"Well, I have known him to get in a very high rage at*
                 the table with his parents, who would ask him to do

> *certain things after meal-time about such and such work; he would rip and tear that he would not do this, and would not do that, and so on."*

Fisher: "What provocation was there?"

Lewis: *"None that I could see, no more than he would disobey his parents."*

Fisher: "Just go on and fully describe what you have seen on such occasions, in regard to his mother?"

Lewis: *"I have known him at different times to ask his father or mother for money; he would want to go across the river to Marietta, and Wrightsville, and they wouldn't give it to him, and told him "Johnny, you stay at home," and he would get into a great passion; I have heard him threaten to shoot his father."*

Swope: "Now recollect properly [a conversation overhead in the tavern]?"

Lewis: *"I don't remember properly what he asked him to do, and his father said he should do it; he said – the father said "You must do it, John." He said "You damned old son-of-a-bitch, I will shoot you!" Those were the words he used."*[16]

     Mrs. Margaret Reichard was next on the stand. Her testimony was short and inconsequential, consisting primarily of an instance where she heard Mrs. Coyle tell John, "Go away, you know you're not right."[17] James McFarland was the last witness to appear for the defense on Wednesday. He had not appeared in York, and like many of the other new witnesses, added little value. He spoke of John's laziness and portrayed him as obstinate, but by no means insane.

Fisher: "What else, if anything, did you see unusual in his conduct about the house with his parents?"

McFarland: *"I never heard him speak in a way a child should speak to his parents at all whatever."*

Fisher: "Describe?"

McFarland: *"He was cursing and swearing around there, - around the house; disobedient in everything they would tell him; use his own pleasure whatever in doing work."*

Swope: "How is it about seeing him under the influence of liquor over there at times?"

McFarland: *"I can't say that I saw him more than once drunk on that side."*

Swope: "You mean by "drunk," visibly - decidedly under the influence of liquor?"

McFarland: *"Well what do you call drunk?"*

Swope: "Well, what I want you to say is what you call "drunk" - what do you mean by drunk?"

The Court: "Is it really important, Mr. Swope?"[18]

Chapter 23

Adams County Courthouse, Gettysburg, Pa
Thursday, April 26, 1883

"Never, never, never, on cross-examination ask a witness a question you don't already know the answer to ... Do it, and you'll often get an answer you don't want, and an answer that might wreck your case."
                                                                          ... Harper Lee

The defense resumed their case-in-chief on Thursday morning. The first four witnesses were physicians who had examined both John and Emily the day of the murder, and they recounted much the same testimony given in the first trial. Dr. Alexander, Dr. Thompson, Dr. Ahl, and Dr. McKinnon, were all questioned about any physical evidence that was found at the scene of the murder or on the body of the deceased.

Fisher:	"Did you or not see any search made for a pistol ball – for any missile?"
Thompson:	*"No sir."*
Fisher:	"Do you know of any having been found of your knowledge?"
Thompson:	*"I do not."*
Fisher:	"In conducting the autopsy, state whether or not there was a pistol ball or any other missile found in the body of the deceased?"
Ahl:	*"No sir."*
Fisher:	"Did you make a thorough search?"

Ahl: *"Yes sir. I do not think we opened the cranium, that I recollect. We made a thorough search of the abdomen."*

Fisher: "In what way – what instruments – describe particularly?"

Ahl: *"We used the scalpel, and we used our hands in searching – or Dr. McKinnon, who was the post mortem physician."*

Fisher: "State what, if anything, was found in the body of the deceased, as a missile, to indicate how death was produced."

McKinnon: *"There was no missile found in the body."*[1]

Next on the stand was Harry Child, who testified that John bragged to him about a shooting incident with his father. On cross-examination, Child admitted that he had not believed John about the shooting and his opinion of Coyle was largely based on his shabby appearance. Mr. Coyle was briefly recalled to the stand and denied the shooting incident ever happened, and stated that the conversation between John and Child was another example of his son's crazy talk.

Fisher: "On what subject, if any, did he talk to you?"

Child: *"... I was standing in front of my door, and he says 'Did you hear of the shooting match?' I said 'No, Johnny, what is that?' He said 'The old man and I had a shooting match;' and he said 'I was trying to shoot him, and he was trying to shoot me.' ... I paid no more attention to it, as I usually did, and walked into the house."*

Swope: "You said that John would be called by the people "Crazy son-of-a-bitch?""

Child:	*"I heard him called crazy son-of-a-bitch. I heard them say "There comes that crazy son-of-a-bitch, lousy John Coyle."*
Swope:	"It didn't make a special impression upon you, that expression [the shooting match]?"
Child:	*"No sir, I didn't take any stock in him, I didn't consider him my equal whatever."*
The Court:	"Why did you say you did not consider him your equal?"
Child:	*"Why, from evidence that I heard there once, setting around saloon steps close to me, and what I seen of him along the street. He was clousy, and dirty-looking, and I didn't want to associate with such a person."*
Swope:	"What did you mean by clousy?"
Child:	*"A man that has no respect for himself, and don't keep himself clean."*[2]

Amos Myers, a carpenter who occasionally did work for the Coyles, testified concerning John's foolish talk about fixing up the ferry to be used as a summer resort. Coyle had borrowed two dollars from Myers and had not paid him back, and Swope took the opportunity on cross-examination to turn the situation around and actually make John appear clever.

Swope:	"And after Mr. Coyle had engaged you to do that work, - you knew you were going to Coyle's to fix up the house at that time?"
Myers:	*"Yes sir."*
Swope:	"John met you there, and borrowed two dollars?"
Myers:	*"Yes sir."*

| Swope: | "And told you he would pay you back when you did the work?" |

Myers: *"Yes sir."*

Swope: "Referring to the work that you did there. You would never have loaned him the two dollars, would you, if it had not been for the fact that his father had engaged you to do that work, - that was the inducing cause to do it, wasn't it?"

Myers: *"Well, I should think so, yes sir."*

Swope: "So that was a little smart in John. He beat you out of two dollars, - he never paid you back?"

Myers: *"He never paid me."*[3]

The next witness, W.P Cummings, presented articulate testimony regarding an incident at Coyle's Ferry when he and some friends rented the saw-mill for a party. He believed Coyle's language, manner, and mental quality were below normal, and had formed his impression partially because people in Marietta referred to him as "Crazy Johnny Coyle."

Fisher: "Under what circumstances have you made those frequent visits [to Coyle's Ferry]?

Cummings: *"That is what I am coming to. I went there with a party of young men for the purpose of camping out, - in the first place to get Mr. Coyle's permission to camp in his old saw-mill, and Mr. Coyle permitted us to fix it up for that purpose. So we boarded up one part for the purpose of making a kitchen and dining room, and took possession of it for a camp for about ten days, and during that time I saw Johnny frequently, - not at all some days, and others three or four times a day, depending on whether I wanted to see him or not."*

Fisher: "What was the character and manner of his conversation?"

Cummings: *"I was always in the habit of looking on Johnny as below the average in intellect, and didn't expect anything from him."*

Fisher: "From what?"

Cummings: *"From the general rumor concerning his conduct and abilities."*

Fisher: "What was it?"

Cummings: *"That of being simple or crazy."*

Fisher: "About how many of you were there, altogether?"

Cummings: *"Ten or twelve, and on some occasions, when we had visitors, there may have been 40 or 50, but in the regular party there were ten or twelve."*

Fisher: "Do we understand that all the persons who were there permanently, or the occasions, were lodged in the saw-mill?"

Cummings: *"Yes, and in the barn, and in Mrs. Coyle's grass patch, and wherever they chose to stop and encamp, - the mosquitoes were so bad we couldn't stay long in one place – a delightful place for a summer resort!"*

Fisher: "About what, if anything, did he talk to you about, or in your hearing, during the time?"

Cummings: *"Particularly about women and girls."*

Fisher: "What about them, - why inquiring?"

Cummings: *"Well, little delicate matters."*

Fisher: "Well, I think you will have to answer, or as much as the Court will admit. Go on, if you please, and describe what the character of his talk about women?"

Cummings: *"During the time we encamped there, we usually had one or two pic-nics, - that is occasions where we invited friends of both sexes to visit us, - in that way we pic-niced. Then we danced, and enjoyed ourselves – as we usually do; and probably some of the young men would take walks with the young folks or ladies, sometimes single couples would go on walks through the hills of perhaps an hour, or half an hour, and then return. I was among the parties that did that sort of thing; and after I had returned John would usually interrogate as regards what I had been doing, and began by insinuating that I had had close intimacy with the ladies I was with."*

Fisher: "Give us the language, if you recollect it?"

Cummings: *"No, I cannot give you his language."*

Fisher: "What were the words?"

Cummings: *"It was as low as you could possibly – "*

Fisher: "How low?"

Cummings: *"He would say have you been fucking that girl in the hills?"*

Fisher: "State whether or not he would use that sort of language in the presence of other persons?"

Cummings: *"O, yes."*[4]

After several witnesses appeared who gave essentially the same information as they had in the first trial, Nicholas McDonald was called to the stand. Coyle had confided to McDonald that he wanted to get married but could not, and he was very candid about his reasons.

Fisher:	"What did he say to you in conversation – did he ever say anything to you about his own habits?"
McDonald:	*"Yes sir."*
Fisher:	"What?"
McDonald:	*"He said he was addicted to the habit of masturbation."*
Fisher:	"What did he call it?"
McDonald:	*"He called it by its vulgar name."*
Fisher:	"What was it?"
McDonald:	*"Dubbing off."*
Fisher:	"What, if anything, did you ask him, or say to him about it?"
McDonald:	*"I asked him why he didn't stop."*
Fisher:	"Well?"
McDonald:	*"He said he couldn't."*[5]

On cross-examination, Swope established the fact that Coyle was aware that his habitual masturbation was wrong, and Swope wanted the jury to infer he would also be capable of knowing that murdering Emily was wrong.

Swope:	"We understand you to mean that you do not think he had as good a mind as some persons had?"
McDonald:	*"He had not the power to resist a bad act."*
Swope:	"You refer to the secret vice?"
McDonald:	*"Yes."*
Swope:	"He knew it was wrong?"

McDonald: *"He confessed to me that it was ruining him."*

Swope: "He knew it was wrong to do it?"

McDonald: *"Yes sir."*[6]

Fisher recalled George Blessing, who provided additional evidence about John's eccentric actions. John once asked Blessing if he could marry his ten-year-old daughter and was apparently in earnest. Blessing also related an incident that occurred while John was working for him chopping and hauling wood. Clearly embarrassed, Blessing finally told the court what had happened.

Fisher: "State any conversation that took place within the period that we have been speaking of, that you witnessed on the part of John Coyle, that was out of the usual way of talking, if you remember anything – when the chopping was going on?"

Blessing: *"He did sometimes, but I wouldn't like ---"*

Fisher: "Sir?"

Blessing: *"I wouldn't like to expose myself."*

Fisher: "Speak out, you are in Court, and under oath?"

Blessing: *"I did see some bad habits of him."*

Fisher: "What was it that he did - go on?"

Blessing: *"Must I say it?"*

Fisher: "You have been sworn to tell the truth and the whole truth, - do not detain us – go on with it?"

Blessing: *"He took his horse and shook it at me."*

Fisher: "Took out what?"

Blessing: *"His horse."*

Swope:	"You mean his – (Indicating)?"
Blessing:	(a nod)
Fisher:	"What did he say, if anything?"
Blessing:	*"He asked me whether I could beat that, - he shook him around, and asked me whether I could beat that."*
Fisher:	"Were there any other person present or not?"
Blessing:	*"There were working men around there."*[7]

On cross-examination, District Attorney Swope attempted to make the incident seem like just a prank, and not something indicative of Coyle's insanity.

Swope:	"Where was it then he shook his person at you?"
Blessing:	*"Down on the wood-workings."*
Swope:	"He had urinated?"
Blessing:	*"I came out of the shanty, and he came out of the road."*
Swope:	"And before he buttoned himself up, he shook it at you, and asked whether you could beat that?"
Blessing:	*" Yes sir."*[8]

Fisher was adopting a different strategy in the second trial by calling witnesses to demonstrate how John's more salacious tendencies contributed to his insanity. Dr. H.E. Norris was a new witness in Gettysburg, and provided information on John's habit of frequenting with prostitutes as well as his treating Coyle for impotency.

Fisher:	"State any conversations you had with him that you recollect particularly?"
Norris:	*"He would generally, in leaving the shore of York County, ask me to furnish him with 10 cents, or*

                    something of that kind, to provide him with something on the other side by way of drink, or would probably turn the conversation in another channel."

Fisher: "What?"

Norris: *"That he would expect to meet a lady at the other end of town, and would need means to be accommodated."*

Fisher: "What did he want for that purpose?"

Norris: *"I believe he told me they charged from 50 cents up."*

Fisher: "Did you ever furnish him with any?"

Norris: *"I often gave him 10 cents. I never provided him with fifty for anything of that kind."*

Fisher: "What did he tell you, if anything [regarding Coyle's attempts to get admitted to the Lancaster and York County hospitals]?"

Norris: *"I asked him what he applied for treatment for, and he said he wanted to be treated for loss of manhood."*

Fisher: "Give us his words."

Norris: *"Well substantially as follows: That he had on several occasions very recently attempted to perform the sexual act, but he could not reach his climax."*

Fisher: "Are you using his words?"

Norris: *"Not verbatim."*

Fisher: "Give them verbatim, as near as you can?"

Norris: *"That he had tried to do it on several occasions but couldn't; and I told him that I often had patients of that kind, and should do for him what I had for others under similar circumstances, and did so."*

Fisher: "What did he say to that?"

Norris: *"He said that he had a great desire to be cured, and that he was so desperate in his affliction that if he wasn't cured within a week, he would kill himself."*[9]

On cross-examination by the District Attorney Swope, Norris was asked whether he felt Coyle was able to distinguish right from wrong. Norris was not able to give a conclusive answer, and held to his opinion that John's masturbation would naturally lead to weakness of the mind.

Swope: "At other times he would want to borrow more, would he?"

Norris: *"For a different purpose."*

Swope: "That purpose, as he would name it, would be?"

Norris: *"He wanted to visit Irishtown to visit Mabel."*

Swope: "A bad woman there?"

Norris: *"Yes, and I would ask what it would be for and he said it could be had for 50 cents."*

Swope: "Sometimes reports of the kind go around, - I want to ask you whether, when he came to your office – when you saw him on the ferry, ferrying you across the river, and from your knowledge of him, and your acquaintance with him, whether, in your judgment, John Coyle was not able to distinguish right from wrong?"

Norris: *"I would have to preface that with my estimate of the man. He was always a weak, vacillating, dimless, purposeless man; and from my intimate knowledge of him, he might be; I could not say positively that he was."*

Swope: "You would not answer it in the negative?"

Norris: *"I couldn't, nor in the affirmative. Well, that might be qualified, of course, - according as he understood what the right and wrong was. As far as my dealings have been concerned with him, he seemed to have an idea of the difference; but whether he had an absolute idea of the difference, I couldn't absolutely say."*

Swope: "Don't you believe John Coyle knew that he was violating the laws of both God and man if he killed – took life?"

Norris: *"In the same way, I believe he would – judging him as I said before, of course – from my acquaintance with him, in that way I believe he would have that knowledge, but his secret intents, of course ..."*[10]

The next four witnesses for the defense, William Krueger, E. W. McElroy, John Bink, and John Staub, were all testifying for the first time. However, they had little new information to add and only served to corroborate previous testimony related to John's foolish talk, impractical business schemes, visits with prostitutes in Irishtown, and his partiality to playing with small boys.

Edward Stahl testified that be believed John to be unsound based on an incident when he had tried to sell him a boat and Coyle had offered to pay him more than his asking price.

Fisher: "What was that [business transaction]?"

Stahl: *"It was a transaction about a boat. I had a boat lying up nearly to my place then, and he wished to buy it; and he asked me what I would take for it, and I said I will take $10 for the boat. He said "I will not give you ten, I will give you five." I said "$5 will not buy it." He said*

> *"I will give you eight." I said "I will not take nine dollars and ninety-five cents for the boat." And he stood a while and said "I will give you twelve for it." I said, "I am satisfied." It was in the evening, and on Tuesday night about half past nine o'clock, after I had come from band practice."*

Fisher: "You asked $10 for it?"

Stahl: *"Yes sir."*

The Court: "He finally offered you twelve?"

Stahl: *"Yes sir."*

Fisher: "What did you say to that?"

Stahl: *"I told him I would take $12 of course."*

Fisher: "What did he say?"

Stahl: *"He said he would take the boat; and he got a piece of paper from one gentleman and a pencil from another gentleman, and wrote something down on it, and the next morning he called over for the boat. Says he "I came for the boat." Says I "You failed to pay me." He says "I paid last night." Says I "O, no." He said "that is the way you Marietta people do with us over there," to take the advantage of them. So that is all the business transaction I ever had with him – first and last."*

Fisher: "State whether you have ever been acquainted with his general reputation in Marietta as to his condition of mind?"

Stahl: *"I heard them repeatedly call him the "crank," or "Crazy John Coyle."*[11]

The final defense witness was Professor S.B. Heiges. His answers to the last few questions were representative of the weak nature of the witnesses called by Coyle's lawyers. If Fisher intended to produce witnesses who would clearly and confidently state they felt Coyle was insane and unable to tell right from wrong, he failed in his attempt. Heiges was not able to do so, and his inconclusive statements left the impression with the jury that there was some doubt as to whether Heiges himself even believed it. The Court seemed to agree.

Swope: "From your acquaintance with John Coyle, the prisoner, - from your intimacy with him by reason of these ferry rides that you had, and the ride from the station, state whether or not, in your opinion, he was of sound or unsound mind, - I mean was he able or not in your opinion, to distinguish right from wrong?"

Heiges: *"O, I could not form an opinion. Upon one occasion he did not speak at all, - I have given the opinion as to other occasions, his language was silly, - that is, when talking of women, his language was silly."*

Swope: "Only when talking of women?"

Heiges: *"Yes sir."*

Swope: "What I mean in this, - from that conversation, and the conversations you had with him, when you had them, state whether or not in your judgment, he was able to distinguish right from wrong, - that is, if he went to steal, he would know whether he was violating the laws of God and man – whether he knew it was wrong to do it?"

Heiges: *"I could not form an opinion from such a basis, - I could not form an opinion."*

The Court: "The facts are too meager?"

Heiges: *"Yes sir."*[12]

At 3:35 p.m., the defense rested. Although they called a significant number of new witnesses in Gettysburg, the nature and weight of their testimony was inconclusive, as it had been in the first trial. The questions asked by Henry Fisher and William Chapman were unimpressive and ineffectual compared to the sharp and competent cross-examination by Adams County District Attorney Samuel Swope.

According to the *Gettysburg Star and Sentinel,* "The witnesses for the defence seem all to dread going to the stand to testify on account of District Attorney Swope's severe cross-examinations. He (Swope) is determined to have the case made plain to the jury. One of the defendant's witnesses yesterday attempted to teach him (Mr. Swope) some law points, to the amusement of the spectators. There seems to be a deadly enmity between the witnesses for the Commonwealth and the Defendant."[13]

Edward Ziegler, the District Attorney from York County, opened the rebuttal for the Commonwealth with a forty-five minute opening statement in which he "very clearly and forcibly presented a summary of the evidence which would be adduced by the prosecution on the subject of sanity and also in contradiction of some of the prisoner's witnesses."[14] One witness, Dr. George Rebman, was called and briefly testified before court was adjourned for the day.

The following morning, the prosecution began their aggressive rebuttal in earnest, with nine witnesses called to the stand for the Commonwealth. Over the course of the next six days, a total of fifty-three would be called to the stand to challenge the testimony of the defense witnesses. The majority of those appearing were from Wrightsville near Coyle's Ferry, and included medical experts and many others who had not appeared in the first trial in York.

Only six testified on Saturday, and Court was adjourned early at 1 o'clock to allow witnesses adequate time to travel home to spend Sunday with their families. However, the law required a daily session to be held every day during a criminal trial in order to keep the court record complete, so a short session was held on Sunday. No business was transacted and Judge McClean adjourned court at 9 o'clock.

The following week was consumed until Thursday by the rebuttal witnesses for the prosecution. Twelve appeared on Monday, fifteen on Tuesday, seven on Wednesday, and four on Thursday. Many had appeared for the prosecution in the first trial in York, and testified to essentially the same facts. Much of the testimony directly opposed that of the defense, and at one point "a little commotion was created by the prisoner interrupting and saying that the testimony was false and that he would so swear, but a scene was prevented by the prompt interference of the Court."[15]

When asked their opinion of Coyle's sanity, the rebuttal witnesses gave answers that were predictably similar. They thought Coyle knew the difference between right and wrong, felt he was of sound mind, and thought "his general conduct, appearance and conversation, when they saw him, did not indicate any mental unsoundness."[16] However, most of the witnesses admitted never seeing John in a fit of melancholy or in the process of attempting suicide.

Coyle was thought to be a skillful ferryman and had rowed many of the witnesses across the river, and showed one witness how to make fishing nets. Others observed him driving a team of horses to and from the mill, even though his father asserted under oath "John never went away from home with the team for neither his mother or I would permit such a thing."[17]

One of the witnesses, John Sultzbach, claimed John's motive for killing Emily was not one of love, but of lust. He related a conversation with Coyle in which John said he would kill Emily unless she had sexual relations. Although the prosecution theorized she may have died defending her virtue, no other testimony was presented supporting the allegation that John had attempted to rape Emily.

Medical witnesses were called by the Commonwealth to contradict defense testimony concerning the alleged damage to John's brain as a result of his hunting accident and his bout with typhoid. In their opinion, "shock, or concussion of the brain, would not be caused by the discharge of a gun so close to the head as to produce no other external effect than blackness of the face from powder."[18] As for the typhoid, "a severe and protracted attack of typhoid fever in 1871, so as to greatly reduce the prisoner in flesh and require him to be handled like a child, but having recovered so as to enable him to ferry people across the river, etc., would not in their opinion be any evidence, or the cause of producing insanity in 1881."[19]

By mid-morning Thursday, after six grueling days of rebuttal testimony, the state rested its case. The defense called only four witnesses in surrebuttal. Mr. and Mrs. Coyle angrily denied much of the testimony made by prosecution's rebuttal witnesses, and "branded as false and untrue the testimony of those who claimed to have seen their son attending to the accounts of the Coyle Ferry Tavern."[20]

Since many of the rebuttal witnesses claimed John's mental and physical capabilities were not impaired, the defense felt it necessary to contradict their testimony on surrebuttal. Both Jacob Hanlon and Mr. Coyle were recalled and stated that the crossing at Coyle's was one of the safest and easiest on the river and "very little skill is required in rowing boats or steering rafts across the Susquehanna River at Coyle's Ferry."[21] They implied John would have been able to handle the job, even though he was unsound.

The final two witnesses, Dr. John Weist and Dr. T.J. Perkins, were new medical witnesses for the defense in the second trial. Perhaps Fisher saved them for last so their testimony would be fresh on the jurors' minds as they began deliberations. The doctors spoke at length describing the actions and mannerisms exhibited by insane persons. Both declared John Coyle to be, in their opinion, unsound.

Overall, the second trial in Gettysburg mirrored the first one in York, with the prosecution presenting a decidedly more thorough and convincing case than the defense. The general feeling was that Judge McClean "conducted the trial with great care, impartiality and ability. No question of admissibility of evidence or other legal point has been presented during the trial which he did not promptly decide."[22]

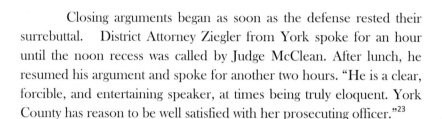

Closing arguments began as soon as the defense rested their surrebuttal. District Attorney Ziegler from York spoke for an hour until the noon recess was called by Judge McClean. After lunch, he resumed his argument and spoke for another two hours. "He is a clear, forcible, and entertaining speaker, at times being truly eloquent. York County has reason to be well satisfied with her prosecuting officer."[23]

William Chapman was next, and took the balance of Thursday afternoon and an hour on Friday morning to deliver his closing argument for the defense. "He has evidently given the subject of insanity and its different phases close thought, as his remarks on this very subject were by no means dull or uninteresting. His argument was a masterly one from his standpoint and hid in it ingenious points that proved Mr. Chapman's reputation as a lawyer to be well-founded."[24]

Other parts of Chapman's closing remarks were not received as favorably. His argument was "marred by his unjust, unfair and sarcastic assaults upon the sister of Miss Myers, and District Attorney Zeigler. This portion of his remarks was severely criticized, because Mrs. Goodyear had conducted herself with modesty and propriety during the trial and was remarkably calm and undemonstrative during the severe ordeal which she was compelled to undergo. Every intelligent person knew that Mr. Ziegler was only present during the trial of the case from a high sense of public duty, and not, as alleged, as 'the leader of the inflamed, damnable, diabolical fury of the citizens of York county.' As a sworn officer of the Commonwealth, he deserves praise, and not censure, for the conscientious discharge of his duty."[25]

Apparently the defense felt it inappropriate for the District Attorney from York to participate in the second trial and took the opportunity for a parting shot at both Ziegler and Judge Wickes. "Both Fisher and Chapman, in their addresses, roundly assailed District Attorney Zeigler, styling him the representative of the insane mob fury of York County, following John Coyle, Jr. out of his jurisdiction and seeking his conviction in Gettysburg. The Judge who tried his case in York County, said Mr. Chapman, was influenced by that same spirit, and committed an error on the side, not of mercy, but of severity. District Attorney Zeigler took the attack good-naturedly."[26]

For the next four hours, Henry Fisher delivered his closing argument for the defense. He was followed by District Attorney Swope from Adams County, who spoke for about three hours. Swope's argument contained impassioned readings from the Bible, and was regarded as "a dignified and dispassionate appeal to the jury to render a verdict which would protect and serve society, and not be influenced in their deliberations by a mistaken and injurious sympathy."[27]

Coyle's mood during the trial depended on the witness on the stand, sometimes looking disinterested, and at other times troubled. Seated next to his counsel, he did not appear to be a criminal, and "apparently paid close attention to all the testimony, his usually stolid, sullen look being relieved occasionally by a smile when a witness says something which conflicts with the theory of the defense."[28]

Emily's sister Annie sat at the prosecution table and showed a deep interest in the case as it progressed. "Considerable sympathy was at first experienced for the murderer, but this gradually passed away as the testimony disclosed the brutality of the crime. The sister of the deceased Emily Myers who sat by the side of the Commonwealth's counsel attracted much attention and elicited much sympathy."[29]

However, not all of the papers were as kind to Annie, and commented that "The sister of the slain Emily Myers apparently enjoyed her role of tragedy queen – she was at all times in the court room – seated at the Commonwealth table. She remained mute – but her presence alone was enough to prejudice any jury. There is no evidence to indicate that she was deeply attached to her unfortunate sister but did enjoy her day in court."[30]

Most felt the jury did a commendable job in absorbing the eight days of testimony. "The jury have paid the closest attention to the testimony and their dignified demeanor shows that they fully appreciate and realize the solemn duty imposed upon them and that they are conscientiously endeavoring to discharge it. The intimations, in some of the newspaper reports of the case, that there had been indications from some of the jurymen of their opinions, are entirely groundless ... Notwithstanding their close confinement and change of regular habits, the jury look well and do not show any evidence of fatigue."[31]

The newspapers credited both Fisher and Chapman for the defense, and Swope and Ziegler for the prosecution, saying "The counsel for the Commonwealth, although both comparatively young men, have both shown thorough familiarity not only with the facts of the case, but an intimate knowledge of the law of homicide. The marked skill with which they have tried the case, examined and cross-examined witnesses, argued law point, &C., has elicited complimentary opinions from all who have been present. The counsel for the prisoner are leading members of the York bar, of long experience and large practice, and it is due to them to say that, whatever the result of the trial, they will have the consciousness of knowing that every honorable and legal means has been exhausted by them in behalf of their client."[32]

The trial was long and arduous for all the participants, and according to the court stenographer, Mr. Demming, "the record of the trial is three times as great as York, proving how much more exhaustive this was. The cost of the trial must run up to several thousand dollars, which also falls to York County to pay."[33]

During the course of the trial, the editors of various local newspapers took the opportunity to pass along moral advice to their readers. Their Victorian views on the effects of reading scandal sheets and tabloids foreshadowed more modern arguments on the effects of rock-and-roll music, violence on TV, video games, and the Internet.

"The old man said his son did read some – was accustomed to reading novels and "The Day's Doings." Such publications as "The Day's Doings" and "Police Gazette" have a demoralizing effect upon the minds of their readers, and their pernicious effects, we fear, crop out all too often in furnishing the incentive to murder. Parents should carefully prevent their children from having access to such publications, and societies for the prevention of vice and immorality should turn their attention to the prevention of the promiscuous circulation."[34]

<u>Chapter 24</u>

Adams County Courthouse, Gettysburg, Pa
Saturday, May 5, 1883

*"You have been tried by twelve good men and true, not of your peers
but as high above you as heaven is of hell, and they have said you are
guilty"*

... Judge Roy Bean

The weather Saturday morning took a decided turn for the worse, but the courtroom was at capacity nonetheless. The Coyle case was going to the jury, and everyone anticipated a quick verdict. Judge McClean's charge to the jury took almost five hours and had to be interrupted several times by the jurors, who needed periodic breaks from the monologue.

The address was exhaustive, covering all the intricacies of law as it related to first-degree murder and the interpretation of insanity as it pertained to criminal responsibility. He reviewed the detailed testimony of a large number of both prosecution and defense witnesses, and the lawyers felt obligated to point out to the judge key pieces of testimony they felt were not covered adequately.

Fisher:	"There was a portion of that testimony, if your Honor please, we think important, as to what John said to Nicholas McDonald regarding his trip to Philadelphia by way of Baltimore."
Swope:	"There are a great many other things of importance that your Honor has overlooked."
The Court:	"I did not intend to omit anything important."
Fisher:	"In this instance I should not have interrupted, only because you have invited it to be done."

The Court: "And I hope, Mr. Swope, that you will do the same thing, and not be satisfied until it is done. The jury ought not to go out to their room until they fully understand all the facts in this case. I have no doubt that I am wearying you, but it must be done. I am not willing to submit this case to you, until all the facts are reviewed, or all the important facts of the case."[1]

Judge McClean repeatedly asserted his neutrality, and reminded the jury it would be up to them to interpret the evidence. "I have no opinion upon the all important question in this case - I wait for yours - and, gentleman, be assured - let me be positive with you on the subject - that I at no time intend to express or intimate any opinion, if I have any in my mind, of the guilt or innocence of the defendant, or of the question of sanity or insanity. John Coyle, the prisoner, is to be tried by his peers - by his countrymen - not by a judge, and I would be overstepping the bounds of my office, if I attempted to influence you by an opinion of my own, one way or the other. I will not do it, gentlemen."[2]

Several of the judge's statements seemed to favor the defense, and McClean's opinion was that the Commonwealth had not done an adequate job during their closing arguments in reviewing the important testimony made by some witnesses. McClean stated he would take the time to make up for their lack of detail, an in one instance, he felt it necessary to tell the jury that some of the witnesses for the Commonwealth had misled them concerning what the valid causes for insanity might, or might not, be.

"And gentleman, with all due respect to the testimony of the medical experts who have testified before you, I think I am warranted in saying that it is authority in medical books that acute febrile diseases, as typhoid, are causes of insanity. I find it so recognized in medical works of standard authority. Also that sexual excess, and unnatural vice, from inducing a perverted condition of the mind and nervous system, as well as from their weakening effects, are not uncommon exciting causes of insanity."[3]

The judge instructed the jury to pay extra attention to the testimony of Mrs. Margaret Reichard, who testified she witnessed Mrs. Coyle tell John, "Go away, you know you're not right." McClean told the jury that if John's own mother felt her son was mentally deranged, she would be the last one to admit it; therefore they should carefully consider her opinion.

On several occasions, McClean seemed to imply that some of the prosecution witnesses were not totally reliable. He referred to the testimony of William Arnold, who claimed he had been at the Coyles the Sunday before the murder and spoke to Mr. Coyle for two hours while John was reading newspapers. Mr. Coyle vehemently denied that Arnold had even been there. Although the judge told the jury they would have to decide who was telling the truth, he thought it seemed unreasonable that Arnold had been there for two hours, but could not recall a single word of the conversation he had with Mr. Coyle.

Although his charge seemed to favor the defense, Judge McClean was careful in his statements concerning the determination of Coyle's insanity. He told the jury, "I have, at the expense of wearying and fatiguing you, endeavored to impartially review the facts, and especially the testimony of the witnesses who have undertaken to express an opinion on the subject of the sanity or insanity of John Coyle, so that you may take them up – that you may recall all the facts of the case, and reach your own conclusion."[4]

McClean did not want to make the same mistake Judge Wickes had made in York County at the first trial, and did not want to leave any chance for the defense to challenge the verdict. He specifically left out the word *clearly* and used the word *fairly* when explaining to the jury the weight of the evidence which must be considered to find Coyle insane.

"As the law presumes sanity to be the normal condition of the prisoner, and insanity an abnormal condition, the burden rests upon him to prove his insanity as an excuse from an act which would otherwise be criminal. The evidence, therefore, which is intended to establish this defence, must be satisfactory to the jury, and the conclusion such as fairly results from the evidence. And, gentlemen, let me say here in this connection, that in a trial of this kind, for murder, the jury need not be satisfied beyond reasonable doubt that the prisoner was insane at the time the act was committed; but that insanity may be established, as I charged you this morning, by satisfactory and fairly preponderating evidence."[5]

McClean reminded the jury that the penalty for first degree murder was death, but also told them that Coyle, even if acquitted due to their finding him insane at the time the act was committed, would be "kept in strict custody, in such place and in such manner as the said Court shall seem fit, at the expense of the county in which the trial is had, so long as such person shall continue to be of unsound mind."[6]

After almost five hours, Judge McClean closed his charge to the jury. "Now gentleman, there is this solemn issue for your determination. On one side, the lives of the women of the Commonwealth must be protected and preserved from murderous assaults upon them. The felon guilty of murder of the first degree must satisfy with his life the violated law, and as a most solemn warning to others not to conceive or attempt the perpetration of a like offence. Then, on the other hand, you have before you the prisoner, with evidence of numerous witnesses that he was insane at the time of the commission of this act – that he was acting under an irresistible impulse, not able to control his will. If that is the fact, it would be a crime to convict, and a disgrace upon the administration of justice."[7]

Newspaper reports felt that McClean's charge to the jury was thorough, giving a "full and elaborate review of the evidence, and cited at length English, American and German authorities on moral insanity." However, they agreed it was somewhat slanted in favor of the defense. "The universal judgment of those who heard the charge was that it was in favor of the prisoner."[8] Predictably, Coyle's lawyer Henry Fisher was happy with tone of the judge's charge and "stated at its conclusion that it was entirely satisfactory."[9]

At 2:30 p.m., the case was given to the jury and the jurors were led from the courtroom to begin their deliberations. Coyle showed no emotion as he was led from the courtroom to await the verdict. The boisterous spectators retired to local hotels and taverns, and anxiously awaited the verdict.

Court reconvened promptly at 6 o'clock. At five minutes past the hour, the jurors slowly filed in, and everyone could predict what the verdict would be by their solemn expressions. Clerk Timmons asked if they had reached a verdict on the charge of murder in the first degree. Jury foreman Captain Samuel H. Eichholtz rose, and in a clear voice said "Guilty in manner and form as he stands indicted."[10]

A spontaneous outburst of approval erupted and the judge had to rap his gavel in order to quiet the courtroom. Fisher did not ask for the jury to be individually polled, and Coyle himself "received the verdict indifferently and calmly, not manifesting the least feeling."[11] His mother however, broke down and burst into tears, exclaiming "Oh! Gentlemen, how could you take away my only boy from me? May God forgive you for it!"[12] John tried to console her, but she continued to cry piteously, and Mr. Coyle helped her from the courtroom.

The jurors deliberated less than four hours, and voted three times before reaching a decision. On the first poll, they stood at ten guilty, one for acquittal, and one abstaining. After discussion, another vote was taken and the count was eleven guilty, one not guilty. On the third and final vote, the jurors unanimously agreed Coyle was guilty of first-degree murder as charged.

District Attorney Swope asked for a judgment on the verdict at once, but Fisher indicated he was planning to file a motion for an Arrest of Judgment. Judge McClean set the date to hear arguments for the following Monday and excused the jurors, thanking them for their service. Coyle talked freely of the trial and the verdict, and before being led back to the Adams County prison said that if the worst was to come, he wanted Sheriff Plank to hang him and not Sheriff Altland from York County.

On Monday morning, May 7, Henry Fisher filed the defense motion in Arrest of Judgment, listing nine reasons why Coyle should be given another new trial. The defense requested a continuance, and the court granted his request, "being influenced largely in granting the continuance by the fact of Mr. Fisher's hoarseness, which would have made it uncomfortable for him to proceed with the argument at that time."[13] Fisher suggested Friday, May 11, which Judge McClean accepted, and Court was quickly adjourned.

However, the following day, the judge received a letter from Henry Fisher, indicating that his co-counsel, William Chapman, was also sick. In addition, Chapman had a case to plead before the Supreme Court, and they both had to prepare for appearances in Common Pleas Court on May 21. He concluded "all things considered, it seems impossible for us to be present and argue the motion before say the 30th inst. I exceedingly regret this, but see no help for it."[14]

After speaking with District Attorney Swope, Judge McClean replied to Fisher, informing him that the court would not agree to another delay. He wrote "all other professional engagements of himself and Mr. Chapman I must deem subordinate to what remains to be done in this case."[15] The judge received another letter from Fisher the next day, stating "If the commonwealth's officer will persist in his refusal, we shall of course be compelled to let the matter go by default and take our writ of error."[16]

Apparently Fisher was willing to let the Court rule on the motion for a new trial without either defense lawyer present, and would simply appeal the case to the Supreme Court. Although Judge McClean was initially sympathetic to Fisher's illness, he refused to grant him leeway for matters of convenience. He wrote, "I considered it the duty of Mr. Fisher to be in court today and argue his motion, if he had any good cause to show for a new trial, and the sickness of Mr. Chapman was no sufficient reason for Mr. Fisher's failing to appear."[17]

Court convened as scheduled on Friday, May 11, without Coyle's lawyers present in the courtroom. Of the nine arguments cited, only two had been used in his motion for a new trial in York. Fisher had previously stated to the court that his principal reasons were the last four, so McClean quickly over-ruled the first five.

1st, "It is respectfully submitted that the learned Court erred in refusing to allow the prisoner to withdraw the plea of Not Guilty, so as to enable him to plead to the jurisdiction of the Court before being called upon to plead to the indictment."*

Ruling: "The first is not sufficient in law. The prisoner had been arraigned in York; the plea of not guilty was there entered and there he was tried. The record was accordingly made and sent with the prisoner to this county upon a change of venue."

2nd, "The jurors impaneled and sworn in the case, and having the prisoner in charge, were allowed to separate repeatedly between the time they were sworn and impaneled, and the rendition of the verdict."

3rd, "Oliver F. Neely, who was sworn and impaneled as one of the said jurors, was not a competent juror, his name having been unlawfully in the jury wheel at the time he was drawn; all of which was unknown to the prisoner, or his counsel, or either of them, until after the rendition of the verdict."

Ruling: "The second and third reasons are of an inquisitive character, containing no specifications in support of them, nor are they accompanied with any other evidence to sustain them. The records show that the name of Oliver F. Neely was not in the jury wheel for the year 1882, and that he had not served previously in 1883 as a juror."

4th, "It is respectfully submitted that the learned Court erred in over-ruling the prisoner's objections to the opinions of Michael Beckel, and

---

* Prior to jury selection, Fisher had entered the same motion questioning whether or not Adams County was a legal jurisdiction and had asked for Coyle's plea of Not Guilty to be withdrawn. Both had been previously overruled.

other witnesses against the prisoner, on the question of his soundness or unsoundness of mind."

<u>Ruling</u>: "The witness, although an illiterate man, testifies to the actions and words of John Coyle, Jr., which indicate soundness, and having testified to facts within his knowledge, during a long acquaintance and whilst living near the party, he could be permitted to express the opinion which he did, that the party was of sound mind."

<u>5th</u>, "In allowing the District Attorney to separate in to many small, and apparently immaterial parts, the entire chain of strong, affirmative evidence given of the prisoner's unsoundness of mind, and asking the medical witnesses for the Commonwealth, (in rebuttal,) on each isolated part of the prisoner's defence, the question "Would *that* show insanity?" instead of fairly embracing all the material facts, or a group of them, in one question."

<u>Ruling</u>: "I can see no error in the District Attorney asking the medical witnesses as to the separate causes of insanity, as alleged in behalf of the prisoner, and then subsequently grouping them together in one question, as he did."

<u>6th</u>, "The verdict is against the law and the evidence."

<u>Ruling</u>: "The verdict was not against the law and the evidence."

<u>7th</u>, "The verdict is against the *weight* of the evidence. The *affirmative* evidence adduced on behalf of the prisoner's insanity alone "fairly preponderated" over the mere *negative* evidence by which it was attempted to rebut it, and taken in connection with that of several witnesses called *by* the Commonwealth, to wit: Mary Ann Coyle, Dr. J.W.C. O'Neal, and others, it proved the prisoner's insanity at the time of the homicide beyond reasonable doubt."

<u>Ruling</u>: "Nor was the verdict against the weight of the evidence. The evidence of the prisoner's sanity was overpowering."

<u>8th</u>, "Mr. Swope, District Attorney of Adams County, during the summing up to the jury evidence in case, persisted, in the face of

objections made by the prisoner by his counsel, in reading to the jury as "good law" in the case lengthy portions of scriptures from the XX and XXI chapters of Exodus, &c., such as: "He that smiteth a man so that he die shall surely be put to death;" "eye for eye, tooth for tooth, hand for hand, foot for foot, burning for burning, wound for wound, stripe for stripe." "He that sheddeth man's blood, by man shall his blood be shed," and much more of the same sort. The verdict is against the law and the evidence."

Ruling: "Contrary to better practice, the prisoner's counsel were allowed the largest license in reading scientific and legal books to the jury as a part of their argument, and there can certainly be no valid objection to the reading by the District Attorney in his summing up to the jury from portions of the Pentateuch. Murder is expressly forbidden by the divine and demonstrably by the natural law; and from these prohibitions arise the true unlawfulness of this crime. Upon these two foundations, the laws of nature and the law of revelation, depend all human laws; that is to say, no human law should be suffered to contradict these. – 1 Blackstone's Commentaries, 42. The time will never come when the Book of Books shall be excluded from our courts."

9th, "It is a constitutional right, of which the accused cannot be lawfully deprived, and which cannot be waived, to be met by his accusers face to face. Of this right John Coyle, Jr., the accused in this case, was deprived by the Commonwealth, in that its prosecuting officer neglected or refused to bring Miss Annie Goodyear, *nee* Myers, who, by the records in the cause, appears to be the prosecutrix and accuser of the prisoner in this case, face to face with him, by calling her to the witness stand, and allowing her to be interrogated on oath or affirmation touching the matter of the said accusation."

Ruling: "The reason is framed in a misapprehension of the facts. Mrs. Annie Goodyear, *nee* Myers, does not by the records in the cause appear to be the prosecutrix and accuser of the prisoner. Her name does not appear at all in the list of witnesses endorsed upon the indictment, neither did she make the original of any information."

"No reason has been presented, or exists, in my opinion, for the arrest of judgment or for a new trial. Therefore, May 11, 1883, motion overruled"[18]

Immediately after overruling the motion, Judge McClean proceeded to pass sentence, and interjected his own opinions of the verdict. The judge ordered the prisoner to stand, and Coyle walked indifferently to the Clerk's desk. When asked if he had anything to say why the sentence of death should not be pronounced, he replied in a low voice "It's not for me to say anything now."[19] Coyle stood alone to receive sentencing, as neither of his lawyers felt it important enough to be in court with him.

"You have enjoyed the advantage of the services of counsel of eminent ability, who exercised their highest skill in the examination and cross-examination of witnesses, in the presentation of testimony and the argument of the case to the jury. You have had a fair trial. The full weight of evidence in support of your defence was exhibited to the jury in the charge. You had a jury of intelligent, judicious and fair-minded men, who calmly considered your case and determined your guilt. I do not know of any other twelve persons in this county who would acquit you under the evidence. My opinion is that no jury anywhere would acquit you under the same evidence."[20]

Coyle interrupted the judge, exclaiming "I'd sooner be dead than live; everybody looks cruel at me; the papers wouldn't leave me alone; I couldn't help it; I didn't know what I was doing."[21]

When the courtroom quieted down, McClean continued. "You have led a wicked and degraded life. You have violated, by act and deed, almost all of the commandments of the moral law. It does not appear that you ever manifested any love or reverence for God and the Savior. You have repeatedly taken his name in vain. You have pursued your evil courses on his holy day, being found in a house of prostitution on Sunday. You have repeatedly and shockingly violated the commandment: 'Honor thy father and thy mother, that thy days may be long upon the land which the Lord thy God giveth thee,' – the first commandment with promise."[22]

Upon hearing this, Coyle interrupted once again, stating that his father was to blame for all his troubles. He claimed he was not brought up properly, nor was he treated right. Judge McClean replied that even though those things may have been true, it did not absolve him from doing his rightful duty.

"You must suffer the extreme penalty of the violated law. You have hurried into eternity Emily Myers, without any just cause or provocation; and for this you must die. In a certain sense this punishment may also be said to be vicarious. It is that others may take the terrible warning to heart, and not commit the crime that you have been guilty of. In this way you may at last do good.

It is said by many that Christianity is intended to raise us universal, unbound love; but it is possible to possess a sincere regard for the happiness of another being, sympathize strongly with his sufferings, and yet subject him to severe suffering and even death. How often does the Judge pass sentence on a criminal for who he feels deeply? We are to love the bad man, but we are also to love society, to love our families, our friends, our country; and if the bad man tries to ruin them, we are bound to prevent him, and his punishment is prevention.

To punish the wicked is to save the good, and to defend the community is the truest charity. While we punish the crime, we can feel the deepest grief for the criminal. Punishment, then, is not unconnected with Christian love. We should want this love were we to look quietly and unresistingly on the crime of a bad man who strikes at the order and well-being of society.

The punishment of death for enormous crimes is a mere modification of the right of self-defence, which may as justly be exercised in deterring from attack as in resisting it. Society has a right to demand punishment for its own security. And for the greatest crime known to the law, the testimony of experience, as well as the voice of God, proclaims that death is the only adequate punishment."[23]

Coyle interrupted one last time, expressing his feelings towards his faith, his parents, and the witnesses who had appeared against him. For the first time, he expressed remorse, saying "I'm sorry for it all; all I care about is my aged mother. Father is able to bear it, but it will nearly kill my mother."[24] He said was satisfied and ready to die, and remarked that he had long ago made peace with his maker.

Thanking Judge McClean for the kindness shown him during the trial, he said he was treated kindly in Adams County, but treated badly in York. He intimated that not all was known about the murder, but it was not worth saying any more about it. Bitterly, Coyle told the judge that "his mother and father told the truth, that the witnesses for the Commonwealth swore to lies. That he knew what kind of people they were."[25]

After a few seconds pause, Judge McClean told Coyle he was "glad to learn from the prisoner's words that he had put his trust in Jesus, the friend of sinners,"[26] and proceeded to pass judgment. At 11:40 a.m., May 11, 1883, the Honorable William McClean, pronounced the sentence of death on the prisoner. "That you, John Coyle, Jr., be taken from hence to the Jail of the county of Adams from whence you came. And from thence to the place of execution, and to be hanged by the neck until you are dead. And may God have mercy on your soul."[27]

After Judge McClean finished passing the sentence of death, Coyle calmly and quietly spoke so that only those sitting very close to him heard him. "Thank you, sir."[28]

Although the local consensus regarding the verdict and sentence of death was unanimously in favor of the outcome, those further away from the trial took a different view of the execution. The day after sentencing, the *New Holland Clarion* wrote an editorial questioning the wisdom of the hanging taking place in Gettysburg. "Gettysburg must be anxious to have a hanging as the *Compiler* claims that if Coyle the convicted murderer of York county is to be hanged at all it must be in Adams county where he was convicted. One should suppose Gettysburg saw enough of human slaughter twenty years ago, not to desire to see another human being die in any other manner that by a natural death."[29]

A week after the verdict, a complete copy of the Coyle trial record was sent to Governor Robert Emory Pattison, as required by law in capital cases. Pattison had recently succeeded Henry Hoyt as governor and inherited the responsibility of dealing with the Coyle case. If the guilty verdict was upheld upon appeal to the Pennsylvania Supreme Court, his office would ultimately decide whether Coyle should live or die.

If Coyle's death sentence was not overturned by the Supreme Court, and a pardon was not granted by Governor Pattison, Sheriff Plank would be responsible for carrying out the execution. The Act of March 13, 1860, required the hanging to take place "within the walls or yard of the jail of the county in which he shall have been convicted."[30] Although of little consolation to Coyle, he had previously stated that if he was to be executed, he preferred Sheriff Plank to be the one to do it instead of Sheriff Altland from York.

As expected, Henry Fisher aggressively pursued his appeal, and the Supreme Court agreed to hear the Coyle case for the second time. The Writ of Error requesting the records from the Adams County trial was returned from the higher court on May 29, just within the twenty days allowed by law, and a certified copy of the proceedings was transmitted to the Middle District of the Pennsylvania Supreme Court on June 30, 1883.

For the next six months, Coyle remained in custody at the Adams County Prison, uncertain of his fate. He occupied his time in prison knitting mats, nets and hammocks, and drawing. He offered what he made for sale to his occasional visitors, using the money to buy food, smoking materials, pens, and paper. His cell was "a variety show of funny pictures, cheap chromos, advertisement cards and valentines: but chief among these are his own original attempts at depicting certain comic events of his life and trials."[31]

His drawings included a picture of a boatman piloting a leaky flatboat on the river with the caption "John Coyle's last row to hell," a depiction of a black bass that once jumped into his boat, and a self-portrait with the inscription underneath "John Coyle, the murderer of the molasses bread." Coyle also spent his time reading the many newspaper accounts of his trial, at one point bragging "with all these publications he guessed he is the biggest man in the state."[32]

Coyle described the days he spent waiting for his execution beginning with "I get up in the morning, open my window and whistle, then take a smoke, after which I sing some psalms and say my prayers." Taking pains to emphasize to his visitors that he spent most of his time reading the Bible and getting comfort and consolation from it, he said his days ended "in saying my prayers and going to bed."[33]

Chapter 25

Pennsylvania Supreme Court
January, 1884

"I feel like the fellow in jail who is watching his scaffold being built"
... Dwight D. Eisenhower

Coyle's lawyers spent the remainder of 1883 preparing for their Supreme Court appearance the following January. The Arguments for the Plaintiff in Error[*] contained nine points, only two of which were presented in the motion for Arrest of Judgment immediately after the trial.

Fisher decided to drop his arguments related to the jury, the use of Bible scriptures, and the fact that Coyle did not have the opportunity to face his accused. Instead, he focused on the admissibility of evidence from various rebuttal witnesses, the legality of the Adams County Court, and the manner in which certain medical witnesses were questioned.

The Supreme Court, in reviewing the brief submitted by the defense, objected to the manner in which Fisher presented his arguments. His abstract consisted of a detailed review of the case, and the Supreme Court noted "their graphic history of the case is not in accordance with the facts, is an imposition on this Court, and must receive our earnest protest."[1]

Specifically, the rules of the appellate court required that the submitted argument "must contain a closely condensed statement of all the facts." The lengthy version submitted by Fisher was "a flagrant violation of the requirements of this rule." In addition, Fisher

---

[*] *The plaintiff in a Supreme Court appeal is the defendant from the original trial, and the Arguments for the Plaintiff in Error summarize the issues being presented to the Supreme Court for consideration.*

"introduced contradictory testimony, as if they were facts, ... which were proven on the trial to be wholly unfounded by a number of witnesses for the Commonwealth."[2]

Furthermore, the defense was chastised for their attempt to sway the Justices with irrelevant facts. "Their history should have concluded with a statement of the circumstances immediately surrounding this sad homicide and not been encumbered with a history of the prisoner's life, in which it was attempted to impress this Court with the fact that he was subject to fits of melancholy, great depression of spirits, was crazy, utterly unfit, mentally, to be entrusted with any business requiring judgment or discrimination, etc., when the reverse of all this was established on the trial of the case by overpowering evidence, and with the clearness of the noonday sun."[3]

1st Assignment of Error

Judge McClean should have allowed Coyle to withdraw his plea which was entered into the record during the first trial because he would not answer guilty or not guilty when asked.

Fisher: "He had a legal right to file a special one [plea] for himself [in Adams County], but the record was in the way."

Swope: "The act [regulating change of venue] is mandatory, however, in requiring the case to be tried in the county to which the venue is changed, it is upon the record as made up in the county from which the venue is changed."[4]

2nd Assignment of Error

This allegation claimed that the Act of Assembly making Adams County a separate judicial district was unconstitutional. At the time it was passed, and when Coyle's trial was held in Gettysburg, the county had fewer than 40,000 inhabitants. Therefore, the second trial was null and void. This claim had also been raised in the motion for a new trial before Judge McClean and had been overruled.

Fisher: "'Whenever a county shall contain forty thousand inhabitants, it shall constitute a separate judicial district' carries the plainest implication that UNTIL it contains so many, it shall NOT constitute such a district. And this implication is fairly expressed also in the sentence which immediately follows: 'Counties containing less than IS SUFFICIENT to constitute separate districts, shall be formed into convenient single districts.' We apprehend that the word Single in this clause can by no means be construed that a county containing less than forty thousand inhabitants may constitute a separate district."

"If the Constitution forbids a county, containing less than forty thousand inhabitants, to constitute a separate district, then the county of Adams could not be a lawful district, and could have no jurisdiction to try the prisoner. Its sentence of death pronounced on John Coyle, Jr., is simply void."

"We say, we present this point in all good faith, and that we had nothing to do with the selection of the place of trial. If we could have, we would have sent the case farther away from York county; The general public sentiment there is not to try whether John Coyle, Jr., was sane on insane when he committed the act, but, whether he was or not, to hang him any how. And by the time the jury reached the consideration of the case, the public feeling of York county had spread into Adams just about the same. The District Attorney of York County, apparently representing its public sentiment, appeared also in Adams County, and energetically participated in the trial and prosecution of the prisoner."

Swope: "The venue was changed by Judge Wickes, President Judge of York County, on motion of the prisoner's counsel, to the adjoining County of Adams. If there was merit in any objection to Adams County, the place to which the venue was changed, the prisoner's counsel should have presented it before his honor Judge Wickes, when he indicated the change, who could have and would have, if there was some merit in it, altered his choice. They should have done it then, or forever held their peace. It is certainly contrary to all law for the prisoner to tacitly agree to a change of venue, I mean not offer his objections when the choice is made, but only complain when the verdict is against him."

[Concerning public sentiment] "Is this not 'too utterly utter,' and insulting to the good people of both York and Adams? The prisoner was tried before a jury of his own choice; before twelve 'good men and true,' who knew nothing of the case; and who, after a protracted trial, with unwilling steps, with trembling lips, with tearful eyes, yet with one voice, returned the verdict they did, simply because, under the evidence and the law, they could not help it."

[Concerning the participation of Edward Ziegler] "Counsel for the prisoner on the trial, before the jury, indulged in similar untruthful and unkind remarks about the District Attorney of York County, saying that he was the leader of the mob spirit of York County ... The man, or men, who could make so untruthful and unkind statements, and do it 'without blushing, and apparently without and emotions of shame, had reached the acme of all impudence,' and deserved no further notice."[5]

3rd, 4th, 5th, 6th, 7th, and 9th Assignments of Error

These six points dealt with alleged errors in allowing the testimony of rebuttal witnesses called by the Commonwealth. Fisher claimed the prosecution could not contradict defense witnesses and the questions asked did not refute evidence previously entered. He also questioned the specific wording of many of the questions asked by the prosecution.

Fisher: "As to the alleged conversation with Imsweiler, it was wholly immaterial, and the Commonwealth was bound by the answers of John Coyle, Sr., and had no right to contradict them."

"Whether their denial was true or false, the evidence of Warfield was in no sense rebutting, or contradictory of the parents, nor was it even offered for that purpose."

"No evidence whatever had been offered on behalf of the prisoner to prove that he had ever been affected by concussion of the brain ... the Commonwealth called medical experts, in rebuttal, to prove that in their opinion, concussion of the brain would not be occasioned by such discharge of the gun. The admission of this evidence was plainly error."

Swope: Swope countered by asserting that Fisher had not submitted a full account of the testimony related to each issue, as required by Rule 24 of the Supreme Court. "When the error assigned is to the admission or rejection of evidence, the specification must quote the full substance ... These specifications, together others that follow, are in direct disregard of this rule ... We consider, therefore, that this court would treat these specifications as if they were not made."[6]

8th Assignment of Error

The last argument concerned the testimony of medical witnesses called by the prosecution during rebuttal. Fisher claimed that hypothetical questions were asked about individual symptoms of insanity, and argued that they should have been framed as a single question.

Fisher: "The manner set forth in the 8th assignment of error was, we think, greatly prejudicial to the prisoner. It was expert testimony of a very damaging kind. The Commonwealth had called Drs. Gable, McKinnon, and O'Neil as experts, though neither of them pretended to a very accurate knowledge of insanity or much experience in treating insane patients."

"But we complain of the manner in putting the questions to the witnesses – would such and such a fact, 'show insanity?' But we submit that a hypothetical case, to put to a witness, should contain a full and fair statement of all the facts and circumstances; not in detail, one at a time, as was done in this case. There were many facts proved, going to show mental unsoundness when taken all together and as a whole"

"Each separate symptom may be entirely inconclusive. All of them together may point to inevitable conclusion. To take each isolated fact proved, and ask as a medical expert, 'does that show insanity' was treating the prisoner unfairly. The whole force of his defence was frittered away piecemeal. The mode of putting the question and of course the answer of the witness to the question so put, strongly impressed the jury against the prisoner; and it did not remove the impression, when the whole facts were put together in one question, on the cross-examination. We submit that this was in error."

Swope: Swope argued that since the original evidence of the defense was entered in pieces, he was justified in rebutting the evidence in the same manner.

"All the evidence of the defence tending to show prisoner's insanity was small, isolated and fragmentary, not connected in any way, but covering a period of ten years, from the accident with the gun in 1871 to the day of the homicide on May 30, 1881. The hypothetical questions of the Commonwealth put to its expert witnesses, in order to agree with the evidence for the defence, necessarily had to be small, isolated and fragmentary. The questions, all of them, were put to the witnesses according to the facts as proved."[7]

The Supreme Court delivered its opinion on January 7, 1884. All of the arguments were overruled, and the guilty verdict from Adams County was upheld. The Remittitur of the Supreme Court was returned to Judge McClean on February 1, and stated "And now, January 7th, 1884, Judgment affirmed and it is ordered that the record be remitted to the Court of Oyer and Terminer of Adams County for the purpose of execution." John Coyle would have to die.

Three weeks later, the death warrant from Governor Pattison authorizing John Coyle's execution was issued to Sheriff Plank. The execution was scheduled for Tuesday, April 25, 1884, between 10:00 a.m. and 3:00 p.m. However, when Plank went to read the warrant to Coyle, he realized April 25 was a Friday. The warrant was returned to Governor Pattison and was changed to read "Tuesday, April 22."

"Whereas, at a court of Oyer and Terminer and General Jail Delivery held at the Borough of Gettysburg in and for the County of Adams at April Sessions, A.D. 1883, a certain John Coyle, Jr. was tried upon an indictment, certified by the Court of Oyer and Terminer in and for the County of York into the Court of Oyer and Terminer of the County of Adams by change of venue on the 12th day of December A.D. 1882, for the crime of Murder, and on the 5th day of May A.D. 1883, was found guilty of Murder in the First Degree and was thereupon to wit, on the 11th day of May A.D. 1883 sentenced by the said court, that he be taken from hence to the Jail of the County of Adams from whence he came and thence to the place of execution and to be there hanged by the neck until he be dead.

Now therefore, this is to authorize and require you the said Jacob H. Plank Esquire, High Sheriff as aforesaid or your successor in Office to cause the sentence of the said Court of Oyer and Terminer and General Jail Delivery to be executed upon the said John Coyle, Jr. on Tuesday the Twenty Second day of April A.D. 1884, between the hours of Ten A.M. and Three P.M. in the manner directed by the 76th section of the Act of the General Assembly of this Commonwealth, approved the 31st day of March A.D. 1860, entitled 'An Act to Consolidate reverse and amend the laws of the Commonwealth relating to penal proceedings and pleadings' and for so doing this shall be your sufficient warrant.

Given under my Hand and the Great Seal of the State at Harrisburg, this twenty-first day of February, in the year of our Lord one thousand eight hundred and eighty-four, and of the Commonwealth the one hundred and eighth."[8]

Upon receiving the revised Death Warrant, Sheriff Plank read it to Coyle on February 26. John appeared to tire of listening and when Plank was through, remarked "it was about as long as the Declaration of Independence."[9] He seemed resigned to his fate and continually professed his religious conversion. Of his execution he stated "I experience no horror at the thought of hanging; but I don't think of it or worry myself about it, it's no use" and added "I wish it were over."[10]

Interest in the Coyle case spread far beyond central Pennsylvania, and notice of the impending execution appeared in papers as far away as New York City. The *New York Times* published a notice the following day with the headline "John Coyle to be Hanged. The Date of His Death Fixed for the Second Time."[11] The Coyle case was considered big news, and speculation surrounding an appeal directly to the governor was widely reported.

Coyle's parents did not give up hope of sparing their son from execution. They retained the services of David McConaughy, a Gettysburg native and prominent lawyer, to handle the application to the Board of Pardon for a commutation of Coyle's sentence and broker communications with Governor Pattison if necessary.

McConaughy served as a Pennsylvania State Senator for Adams County from 1865-1868 and was the uncle of Judge William McClean, the presiding judge in the Coyle murder case. He was most likely chosen to champion Coyle's last efforts at avoiding execution due to his political connections within the state government. As an ex-senator, he may have known Governor Pattison personally and certainly knew the inner workings of the Board of Pardon.

McConaughy suggested to Coyle that he write a letter pleading his case. In the event the application to the Board of Pardon failed, McConaughy would have to apply directly to the governor and wanted a personal appeal from the prisoner on file. On March 29, Coyle drafted a short letter to Governor Pattison pleading for mercy and life imprisonment instead of death.

"Gettysburg March 29, 1884

To the Governor of the State of Pennsylvania,

Your Sorrowfull death warent came to hand and was read to me by Sheriff Plank now   Mr. Pattison for the Sake of my poor old mother and my Selfe not being right In my mind at the time of the Sorrowfull crime and a large number of witteness Swore falcely against me a weak minded man I pray to God to have mercy upon me a weak mined man and to please Sir Reverse the Sentence of Death to Imprisonment for life   that it is hard enough but more honorable on account of my poor old mother   I hope you will please Sir have mercy upon your Afflicted fellow man   at the time of the act I was out of my mind and out of my mind to this present day and never will be right In my mind for I have suffered mutch through Sickness and further Mr Pattison I am a poor cripple with only one hand and my poor mother will tell you the truth I am not right in my mind

Yours Resptfully,
John Coyle Jr." [12]

McConaughy felt it important to have an additional medical expert offer a view of Coyle's condition, and sought the assistance of Dr. T.T. Tate for an unbiased opinion. On Friday, April 11, Dr. Tate visited with John in prison for about thirty minutes. Tate returned the next day to examine John's skull and discovered that Coyle's temporal bones[†] were deformed, and he surmised that this abnormality was the cause of Coyle's mental instability. After a third visit, Dr. Tate wrote his statement and had it notarized the following day.

[†] *The temporal bones start above the temples and extend around the skull behind the ears.*

"Gettysburg April 13th, 1884

On the 31st of May, 1883, I first saw John Coyle, Jr. I visited him in company with a gentleman from Chambersburg who engaged him in conversation for at least one half hour. I heard the conversation but never spoke to him myself at that time. I met him again in the jail later in the season. I think it was in August. He was engaged in knitting a fly net. I talked with him then about ten minutes and from that time I never saw him until last Friday, April 11th when I visited him by request, and conversed with him continuously for about one half hour. On the next day, Saturday, April 12th, I again visited him and talked with him quite awhile. I then made an examination of his head and found an abnormal condition of the temporal bones; which in my judgment is always indicative of some mental derangement. Today, Sunday April 13th I visited again to see him, and spent an hour in his cell, during this time he was being shaved, and took this opportunity in hearing his incoherent and disconnected remarks to the barber. And I felt convinced that the impression formed on my first visit were now strengthened, and that Jno. Coyle, Jr. is not a sane man. His reasoning faculties are [dett.....d]. There is no regular chain of thought manifested in his communication; his sunken temples, his stiffened and wet hair, his general wild and empty expression, and his indifference to his fate and surroundings in general, convince me beyond a doubt, that Jno. Coyle Jr. to day is not a responsible man.

I am a practicing physician, graduate of the Penn. Medical College in Philadelphia in 1855.

Adams County,
T.T. Tate" [13]

Tate's impression of Coyle was contradicted by the reporters who had been granted interviews with Coyle over the previous months. According to their reports, "Whatever may have been Coyle's condition at the time of the murder, those who have had access to him during his imprisonment, were impressed with the intelligence and rationality of his conversation. With alternations of hopefulness and despondency, under the varying prospects of escape from the death penalty, he manifested levity or seriousness, as was natural with a person of his training, but throughout there has been no indication of insanity. He has clung tenaciously, however, to the theory of his counsel on both trials, that at the time of the murder he was laboring under such a degree of mental excitement as to amount to dementia and that, therefore, he should not be held responsible."[14]

McConaughy continued to press aggressively forward with the application to the Board of Pardon, and provided the local newspapers with a notice of his intent to file the application as required by law. He followed up with a letter to the Board of Pardon, certifying he had given directions to have the notice published and that he had informed District Attorney Swope and Judge McClean of the application.

Informing the court was a legal requirement of the application. After receiving the notice from McConaughy, Judge McClean sent a letter to the Board of Pardon confirming receipt of the notice "simply to say that I understand application will be made for the pardon or commutation of sentence of John Coyle awaiting execution for the murder of Emily Myers on May 30, 1881 for which he was last convicted before me."[15] As the letter was sent late on Monday night, April 14, McClean hurriedly sent a telegram to his uncle David McConaughy assuring him that the letter had been mailed but would not go out until morning.

The following morning, Tuesday, April 15, with only a week remaining before the execution was to take place, McConaughy filed Coyle's application with the Board of Pardon containing a summary of the case:

"To the honorable The Board of Pardons of the Commonwealth of Pennsylvania...

The prisoner hereby prays your honorable Board to recommend his pardon or a commutation of his death sentence, and he submits herewith through his counsel, the grounds upon which this, his application is based. And he will file with the same a statement of the facts to sustain the grounds in the form of a history of the case together with the proofs of all the motions required to be given by the rules established by your Board, and a communication from the Hon Wm. McClean the President Judge of the Court who presided at the trial of the case, as also a certified copy of the whole record thereof, and the Judge's charge and notes of testimony. The District Attorney of Adams County and the President Judge of the said Court having been informed of the intention to file this application, and there not being time sufficient to make or procure proof of said notice prior to this the precautionary filing and presenting of said application at the meeting of your Board preceding the day fixed for the executing of the sentence of death, the 22nd day of April.

Grounds of Application

First. The testimony in the trial on the question of the sanity of the prisoner at the time of the committing of the fatal act was so conflicting that it should have produced a verdict of not guilty on the ground of insanity. And although a motion for new trial and in arrest of Judgment was promptly made and filed yet on account of illness of both of his counsel and their consequent inability to attend at the time fixed for argument of the motion and Rule therein with the reasons assigned including the ground above specified.

The motion and Rule therein were within four days from motion filed and Rule granted, and at insistence of the attorney for Commonwealth and without argument discharged by the court, in the absence of the defendants counsel such action only he under the omnipotent pressure of popular passion penetrating the [hallowed] sanctuary of justice as it [   ] had the jury done.

<u>Second</u>. Notwithstanding that the evidence of the principal witnesses and other witnesses of the Commonwealth clearly disclosed the fact of the unsoundness of mind and insanity of the prisoner before and at the time of committing the fatal act, and that this was supported by strongly corroborating evidence of witnesses called in the part of the defendant, and the verdict against the weight of the evidence and the refusal of motion for new trial and in Arrest of Judgment without argument or opportunity for it, and the consequent sentence all upon the theory of the sanity of the defendant. Yet it is submitted and on the part of the defendant it is proposed and the defense is prepared to show by convincing testimony the fact not only of the existence of the insanity of the defendant before and at the time of the trial, but such insanity of the Defendant to have continued and to be now existing at the time of making and filing this application, and this by testimony both of competent medical experts and of other witnesses who have been near the prisoner and had full opportunity of knowing before and also since the trial that John Coyle Jr. has been and now is not sane or sound of mind and not a proper subject of criminal conviction, sentence and execution." [16]

Realizing time was quickly running out, McConaughy sent a letter to Governor Pattison the same day the application was filed, requesting a "respite of the death warrant pending his application this day filed in and to the Board of Pardon." [17] The letter was signed by Fisher, Chapman and McConaughy.

For the next two days, Coyle and his parents anxiously awaited news from Harrisburg. The Board of Pardon agreed to review his case, but not until their next regular meeting in May. However, that fell after the date of Coyle's execution, so their acceptance was contingent upon a stay of execution. It was most likely the first time that Governor Pattison, in office only a few months, was dealing with the question of whether a condemned man should live or die.

Marietta newspapers were confident that Coyle would be granted a reprieve. "The fact of the application being made to the Pardon Board does not of itself compel the Governor to prevent the execution of the sentence at the appointed time, but inasmuch as the board has showed its willingness to make the question of Coyle's sanity the subject of further investigation it is not improbable that the murderer will be given the benefit of the delay necessary for such inquest."[18]

After reviewing the application, the personal letter from the prisoner, Dr. Tate's evaluation, and the Adams County trial record, Pattison made his decision. Late Friday evening he requested William Stenger, the Secretary of the Commonwealth, to send a telegram to Gettysburg indicating his refusal to intercede and ordering the execution to proceed as scheduled the following Tuesday.

The sheriff immediately informed Coyle of the governor's decision, and upon hearing the news, Coyle broke down. He pleaded with Plank to save him and asked the sheriff to visit the governor on his behalf. When told there was no hope, he "fell upon his knees and cried to the Sheriff like a child, begging him for mercy at his hands and says he (the Sheriff) was now his only friend."[19] Although awake until after 4 o'clock in the morning, Coyle seemed more composed, and "displayed a great amount of cheerfulness"[20] on Saturday.

After receiving the governor's late night refusal to grant a stay of execution, McConaughy knew he had to act quickly. With only four days remaining until the execution, he would have only one more chance to save Coyle's life.

———— ≈≈≈ ————

Adams County Prison
Saturday, April 19, 1884

Professor Philip Bikle from Pennsylvania College[‡] and the Reverend John Demarest from the Presbyterian Church visited Coyle Saturday morning, bringing him some religious tracts and praying with

---

[‡] *Pennsylvania College was a sister institution of the Lutheran Theological Seminary. In 1921 it officially became known as Gettysburg College.*

him. Since the end of February, when the Death Warrant had come down from Harrisburg, the two spiritual advisors had been the only visitors allowed to see Coyle, other than the jailers, his parents, and his lawyers. Following his professed religious conversion while in prison in York, Coyle had memorized portions of the New Testament and the Psalms and "became quite apt in quoting Scripture, and while his answers to questions on the plan of salvation had not the exactness and clearness of language of the catechism, they were generally correct, at least on the essentials."[21]

When asked if there was anything he needed to discuss, Coyle explained that he was still having a hard time forgiving his enemies. Although he was less bitter, he still felt "his death was in answer to the demands of the 'prejudiced and hard-hearted' community in which he lived."[22] Coyle frequently read the Imprecatory Psalms[§], and his lingering resentment was evidenced in the well worn pages of that section of his Bible.

Coyle called the Sheriff to his cell and asked for a cup of wine, saying, "I've never been any trouble to you and I'll stand this bravely to the end. I only ask for wine for fear that I may break down."[23] After consulting with the clergyman and the prison physician, Sheriff Plank "in the goodness of his heart, allowed him a gill[**], which seemed to brace him up."[24]

Mrs. Coyle arrived mid-morning on Saturday and stayed with her son most of the day. While they talked, their conversation was frequently interrupted by the loud sounds of the gallows being moved into place and assembled in the rear yard of the prison. John's cheerfulness was quickly replaced with dread and fear, and the ministers tried to console him as best they could.

[§] *The Imprecatory Psalms are the passages in the Bible which contain curses or prayers of punishments for one's enemies.*

[**] *One half cup or 4 ounces.*

The hammering continued most of the afternoon, each stroke pounding into John's subconscious as if counting off the remaining seconds of his life. The new scaffold, a "substantial structure and fitted with the latest improvements,"[25] had been designed and built in Gettysburg specifically for the Coyle execution by Charles Comfort at a cost of $125. Made of six-inch-square oak beams, the six-by-six-foot platform stood seven feet off the ground, reached by a flight of nine steps on the east side. The crossbeam holding the noose was fourteen feet from the ground and the rope was designed to allow the condemned to fall three-and-a-half feet before breaking his neck.

A rail enclosed the platform and the entire structure was painted a dull, dark lead color. A space on the ground surrounding the scaffold was roped off for the Coroner's jury and the physicians who would be attending the execution. After it was assembled on the south end of the prison yard, the hanging rope was strung and tested. The trap on which Coyle would stand to die consisted of two doors, supported by two bolts running into the frame of the scaffold. A lever, when pulled by an attached rope, acted on both bolts by removing them simultaneously from the frame, allowing the doors and the condemned to fall.

As the construction of the gallows continued, Coyle became more and more distraught. Mrs. Coyle stayed with him the rest of the day, leaving briefly at supper time to take a rest in her hotel room. Bikle and Demarest left with her, promising to return the following day. When she returned, she had sharp words with the Sheriff, berating him for allowing her son to hear the sounds of the gallows construction all afternoon. She left late in the evening, and John slept soundly from 10 o'clock until early the next morning.

John's mother returned on Sunday morning, as did Professor Bikle and Reverend Demarast, who arrived after their morning church services. McConaughy stopped to visit in the early afternoon to inform them that he had arranged for another medical examination to take place the following day by two eminent physicians from Philadelphia. Temporarily hopeful, John soon sank back into a resigned acceptance of his fate, realizing this would be his last chance.

As a last desperate effort to save Coyle from execution, McConaughy contacted two prominent alienists[††] from Philadelphia. He persuaded them to travel to Gettysburg to examine Coyle and corroborate Dr. Tate's opinion from earlier in the week. Tate was adamant that Coyle's skull abnormality was an overlooked symptom of his insanity, and at his insistence, McConaughy telegrammed Dr. Charles Mills and Dr. Eruest Goodman.

They agreed to come as soon as possible, promising to arrive on Monday morning, the day before Coyle's scheduled execution. If they were convinced, after examining Coyle, that he was insane due to a physical deformity, they would accompany McConaughy to Harrisburg for a final chance to convince Governor Pattison to grant a last minute reprieve.

Coyle was unable to sleep after his visitors left late in the evening and lay awake until 4 o'clock in the morning contemplating his last full day to live. All night he "paced his cell and talked to himself, saying he never had any education and that his training did not enable him to distinguish right from wrong."[26] He was up again at daybreak on Monday and anxiously awaited the arrival of the morning train from Philadelphia at 10 o'clock.

Dr. Mills had a reputation as a skilled alienist and was a firm believer in phrenology, the study of the shape of the human skull as it related to character traits and mental capacity. This philosophy was common in the 1880s and was used to analyze Charles Guiteau after his trial in 1882 for the assassination of President Garfield.

According to phrenological philosophy, the area of the skull behind the temporal bone, the same bone that Dr. Tate indentified as being abnormal in John Coyle's skull, was responsible for "destructiveness." McConaughy was encouraged, and was hopeful that the expertise and opinions of Drs. Mills and Goodman would add credibility to his eleventh hour plea to Governor Pattison.

[††] *An alienist was a specialist in studying and treating mental disorders, as the insane were thought to be alienated from normal mental processes.*

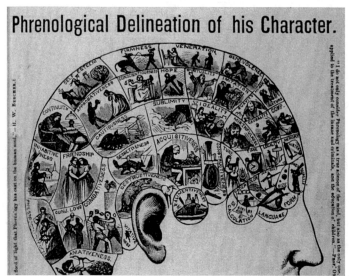

"Symbolical Head, Illustrating the Natural Language of the Faculties"[27]

Dr. Mills was a vocal advocate against capital punishment for the mentally disturbed and felt that criminals should be studied, not executed. He lobbied for changes in lunacy laws and the creation of special asylums for the criminally insane. His felt that knowledge of right and wrong, or the presence or absence of delusions, were not always valid tests of insanity. In Mill's opinion, there were other equally valid tests for mental disorders, such as the skull abnormality Dr. Tate had identified during his examination of John Coyle.

Upon arriving in Gettysburg on Monday morning, Dr. Mills and Dr. Goodman, along with Dr. Tate, made a careful exam of Coyle lasting an hour and a half. They concluded, as Tate had done, that Coyle's temporal bone was misshapen. It was exerting abnormal pressure on his brain and probably the cause of his persistent migraine headaches, but was not absolutely conclusive evidence of insanity. However, their consensus was that Coyle was definitely unfit to hang.

Coyle, grasping at any reason to be hopeful, was confident that he would be granted a reprieve, exclaiming he "would jump high if pardoned."[28] McConaughy immediately sent a telegram to Harrisburg requesting an audience with Governor Pattison at 8 o'clock that evening. McConaughy and Drs. Mills and Goodman left on the 4:25 p.m. train from Gettysburg, optimistic they would be bringing good news back to John and his mother. Coyle went to bed with renewed hope that the results of the medical exam would be successful in granting him a reprieve.

However, by 11 o'clock that night, no word from Harrisburg had been received. It was generally regarded as bad news since a positive outcome would have been sent immediately. The newspaper offices which had stayed open in anticipation of hearing the decision, eventually closed. They sent their reporters home for the night, thinking that all chances of receiving any communication from Harrisburg were gone.

Shortly before midnight, with twelve hours remaining until the scheduled execution, a telegram was received in Gettysburg with the message "The Governor would not interfere, and Coyle must hang – sane or insane."[29] It was sent at once to the prison, and Sheriff Plank was awakened and informed of the decision. He had expected such an answer, but decided not to interrupt Coyle's sleep to tell him. He would let Mrs. Coyle know when she arrived in the morning and allow her to deliver the news to her son.

<u>Chapter 26</u>

Adams County Prison, Gettysburg, Pa
Tuesday, April 22, 1884

"Do it up right"

... *John Coyle Jr.*

Coyle awoke at 6 o'clock on Tuesday morning after a surprisingly sound eight hours of sleep. For the first time in several days he had an appetite, and informed the guard he was hungry and wanted the meal he had requested the night before. About an hour later, Mrs. Plank brought him a hearty breakfast of Susquehanna shad, beefsteak, coffee, bread and butter. As a surprise, the Sheriff had convinced his wife to bring along a small pitcher of molasses, as he knew it was John's favorite. Coyle ate quietly, and alone, until his mother arrived at 7:30 a.m., shortly after he had finished eating.

Since arriving in Gettysburg on Saturday morning, Mrs. Coyle spent almost all her time with her son, leaving only to rest at the insistence of Sheriff Plank. In a fit of anger Saturday evening, she told Plank that rather than her son suffering death on the gallows, she would furnish him with poison so he could kill himself. "This, and other circumstances prompted the strictest vigilance on the part of the Sheriff and the jail officers, and every precaution to guard the prisoner against such attempts was taken. During Mrs. Coyle's visit on Saturday night she wanted to give John an apple. The privilege was promptly denied and the apple taken in charge."[1]

When she arrived on Tuesday, Mrs. Coyle complained loudly of her belongings being searched before entering the cell, but the Sheriff was taking no chances. After making sure that she was not bringing anything in with her, he told her of the governor's decision and she was allowed to join her son. Mr. Coyle had not yet arrived, as the first train from Hellam was not due in until shortly after ten.

Mrs. Coyle was clearly upset, and John could tell his mother was bringing him bad news. She hesitated, not quite sure how to tell him, and sat down on the bed for several minutes before speaking. She finally informed him the governor had refused to intervene on his behalf overnight, despite all the efforts of the past few days. Expecting that to be the case, he took the news calmly.

At 9 o'clock Professor Bikle and Reverend Demarest arrived at the jail. Over the past few weeks, John's self-appointed spiritual advisors had made frequent visits to see John and had been with him almost constantly the last several days. They spoke to him about his belief in the Savior, assuring him that Christ would take care of him, and hoped that he fully comprehended the importance of making his peace with God and forgiving all his perceived enemies.

His father soon arrived and joined them. They all sat quietly for some time, listening to the boisterous crowd gathering outside. To distract himself from the sounds of the hundreds of people inside the jail yard, and the many more who stood outside the prison grounds, John picked up his Bible and read aloud the parable of the Prodigal Son from the Gospel of Luke. They all kneeled in "earnest and fervent prayer, John praying aloud and long."[2]

At 10:30 a.m., "the aged parents took their final leave of their son. The scene was a sad and affecting one, the old gray heads bowed over his shoulders, embracing him as only parents can embrace a child, the hot tears of grief and distress rolling fast and thick down over their wrinkled cheeks."[3] John called for the Sheriff and made a last minute request that "he do not let so many people in to see the hanging."[4] Plank said nothing, leading his parents from the cell to one of the rooms in the Sheriff's quarters at the front of the prison.

A small boy, eager and determined to see the excitement going on within the high jail wall, took a ladder from inside the barn and propped it up the best he could manage. Climbing slowly and carefully up and onto the roof, he was disappointed when it proved to be too low for him to see down into the prison yard. However, a score of perhaps twenty or more had managed to scale the top of the twenty-foot-high wall surrounding the rear of the jail, despite the vociferous orders from a nearby trio of constables to "git down, there."[5]

Ticketholders began arriving as early as 9 o'clock, but only a privileged few were allowed to enter the rear yard that far in advance of the execution. The sheriff had issued tickets to nearly 400 "deputies" appointed just for the event, and over the next few hours they were admitted in small groups. 200 tickets were allocated for spectators from York who arrived on a special train at 10 o'clock, and many others had been given to physicians and reporters. The roads leading into town were jammed with wagons and horses, and the trains brought even more people from points farther away.

By 11 o'clock, several thousand had gathered outside the jail. The neighboring streets were crowded with people who could not see into the yard, but wanted to be present nevertheless. Tickets to the hanging were being scalped outside the wall, with some buyers offering as much as $5 for a chance to get inside. One enterprising man managed to cut off a small piece of the hanging rope when it was being tested on Saturday, and was milling through the crowd proudly displaying his souvenir. Judge McClean wanted to attend the execution, and adjourned court early to give anyone with tickets the opportunity to be there.

Public executions were a rarity in Adams County, and the Coyle hanging was the first in Gettysburg in over thirty years. Since the formation of the county in 1800, only four men were executed by hanging, all having been convicted of first-degree murder. The first was James Hunter in 1818, followed by James Green in 1853, and John Coyle in 1884. Henry Heist was the last to be hanged in Adams County in 1894.[*]

---

[*] *Pennsylvania changed the laws regarding execution in 1913, making the electric chair the state's official method of capital punishment.*

———⌇———

Plank, along with Sheriff Eyster of Carlisle and Constable John Shield of Gettysburg, performed a final examination of the scaffold and declared it ready. Plank returned to Coyle's cell with the two deputies, handcuffed the prisoner, and read him the death warrant. The procession to the gallows, led by the twelve members of the Coroner's Jury of Inquest[†], walked down the corridor to the rear of the prison. They exited through the thick black curtain hung over the entrance, and moved into the prison yard to the designated roped-off area under the scaffold. Dr. Diehl of Gettysburg, Dr. Buchen from Hanover, Dr. Schwartz from Emittsburg, Maryland, and Dr. Brinkley of York joined the jury beneath the gallows.

After the doctors entered the yard, the last group slowly made their way down the long hallway. District Attorney Samuel Swope was at the front of the procession, followed by Sheriff Plank, Professor Bikle, John Coyle, and Reverend Demarest. When they reached the end of the corridor, they paused for a few moments, allowing the jury and physicians time to take their places. John stared at the rope which was fed from a lever on the scaffold, through the curtain, and into a small room immediately to his left.

The rope would be pulled by a hidden executioner, so John would never know who sent him to his death. Ironically, one of the ropes for the execution had been obtained in York, the town which Coyle felt had been so prejudiced and unfair towards him during his first trial. However, this rope was not the one designated for the execution, and would only have been brought into service if the first had failed during testing. The hanging rope, five-sixteenth of an inch thick, had been sent pre-made with a noose from Philadelphia and tested with a 200 pound sand bag.

[†] *Following the execution, a Coroner's inquest would be held to document the circumstances of the execution and the cause of death.*

At 11:18 a.m., Coyle stood bravely at the end of the corridor, and at the end of his life, waiting for the heavy black curtain to be pulled aside. He thought of his grieving mother and father and the futile efforts they, along with so many others, had made during the past few weeks in an attempt to save his life. It had been an emotional month for his parents and his lawyers, and soon everyone would move on with their lives. All except John.

At 11:20, the undertaker Jeremiah Culp took his place with the attending physicians and the Coroner's jury in the roped off area under the platform. Sensing that the time was near, the crowd quieted, waiting for Coyle to enter the yard. A moment later, the black curtain was pulled aside and District Attorney Swope came into view, followed by Sheriff Plank, Professor Bikle, John Coyle and Reverend Demarest. Crossing the yard and climbing the steps to the gallows with a firm and steady step, Coyle took his place under the center of the crossbeam, facing east.

Reverend Demarest offered a prayer and Professor Bikle read several of the John's favorite scripture verses. Following the benediction, Sheriff Plank asked the prisoner if he had anything he wanted to say. Coyle turned to District Attorney Swope and spoke a few words in an inaudible tone, not wanting to acknowledge or address the crowd directly. Observers noted "During these services and remarks, the prisoner kept his eyes fixed on the ground, and, save the look of distress on his countenance and a tremor of his lips, maintained a firm composure."[6]

Swope repeated Coyle's words to the crowd, saying that he forgave all his enemies and held no ill will against any of them. Coyle thanked the sheriff and all who befriended him for their kindness, and gave love to his friends. As Coyle stood solid as a post, not moving a muscle, Sheriff Plank "with a trembling hand, pinioned the legs together and placed the rope around his neck, after which the black cap was placed over his head and daylight was forever shut out from his view."[7] As the noose was placed around his neck and adjusted, Coyle whispered his last words "Do it up right."[8]

After the spiritual advisors left the platform, District Attorney Swope, in a clear distinct voice, proclaimed, "In the name of the Commonwealth, and in observance to the Death Warrant issued to the Sheriff by the Governor of this State, the Sheriff will now proceed to execute John Coyle, Jr. for the murder of Emily Myers, committed on the 30th day of May, 1881."[9]

District Attorney Swope and Sheriff Plank descended the steps, leaving Coyle alone on the platform. Upon reaching the last step, the rope was pulled from within the prison, and "The platform dropped with a dull and heavy thud and the soul of John Coyle, Jr. was sent to meet its God."[10] Coyle fell about three-and-a-half feet and nearly touched the ground, and with the exception of a few slight muscle contractions, he did not struggle.

The effect of the execution on the crowd varied. Some turned away before the trap doors were opened, not wanting to see Coyle fall, and several others who watched fainted. However, after it was over, everyone in the jail yard pressed forward to see his body swaying at the end of the rope.

The physicians waited a few moments before measuring Coyle's pulse. The short drop would have broken his neck, causing instant paralysis and immediate unconsciousness. However, death from strangulation typically does not occur for up to twenty minutes, so the doctors periodically checked the body for a heartbeat.

Three minutes after falling, Coyle's pulse was measured at 150 beats per minute. At seven minutes it was 65 beats and after ten minutes had fallen to 35 beats per minute. A few minutes later, Mr. Coyle came out from behind the curtain, with his ubiquitous cigar in his mouth, to view the body of his son hanging from the rope. At 11:48, sixteen minutes after the rope had been pulled, Coyle's heart ceased to beat and he was declared dead.

Coyle was left hanging for an additional five minutes. His corpse was then taken into the corridor of the prison and examined by the doctors and the Coroner's Jury. Once they confirmed the death, he was turned over to the undertaker, Jeremiah Culp, who placed Coyle in a plain walnut coffin that had been chosen by his parents. The coffin was then put into a plain pine box for shipping and loaded onto the back of a wagon. His parents accompanied the body to the office of the Adams Express Company, where it was placed on a train to Hellam, the closest station to the ferry.

The train left Gettysburg, passing through Hanover on its way to Hanover Junction, near present day Seven Valleys. All along the route, people lined the tracks watching for the train, and whenever it stopped they ran to the express car to catch a glimpse of the murderer's outer coffin. As the train entered Hanover, a man caused a scene by displaying a piece of the hanging rope, which had been cut up by the crowd and distributed as soon as Coyle had been taken down. Mrs. Coyle soundly berated him, by saying, among other things, that the stranger "might yet see one of his children hanged."[11]

When the train reached Hanover Junction, the express car was switched to a train heading towards Hellam by way of the York and Wrightsville Railroad. Almost nineteen years earlier to the day, on April 21, 1865, the body of President Abraham Lincoln had passed through Hanover Junction en route to Harrisburg. The train carrying John Coyle's body left the station mid-afternoon, and arrived at the Hellam Station at 5 o'clock.

John's coffin was removed from the train, but the wagon to take it to the ferry had not yet arrived. The large crowd that gathered at the station to meet the train wanted the coffin opened so they could see John's body, but Mr. and Mrs. Coyle adamantly refused. Bitter words were exchanged with several of the bystanders, and Mr. Coyle declared that they had lied on the witness stand during the trials and told them "none of you false witnesses shall see Johnny."[12] When pressed for details about the funeral, Mrs. Coyle told them it would take place on Thursday, two days hence, and added "John was now in heaven, if there is such a place."[13]

While they waited for the wagon, the Coyles went across the street to a hotel, where Mr. Coyle got a drink and filled a bottle to take home with him. In about an hour, Samuel Fried, a neighbor of the

Coyles, arrived with the wagon and the coffin was loaded for the three-mile journey back to the ferry.

Two days later, on Thursday, April 24, John Coyle's body was laid to rest. His parents originally planned for him to be buried in the Marietta Cemetery but the board of the Marietta Cemetery Association refused. They did not want to anger the family or community, and felt it inappropriate for the murderer to be interred so close to his victim. Instead, the Coyles dug a grave on the hillside under an apple tree on their farm, about fifty yards east of the house. Approximately 250 people attended the funeral, most likely out of curiosity rather than any feelings of sympathy for the deceased or his parents.

For the first time in almost four years, John Coyle finally returned home.

Afterward

Chapter 27

Accomac

Shortly after John was buried, a simple headstone was erected at the head of his grave with the inscription:

MY SON
JOHN D. COYLE
BORN
March 15, 1855
DIED
April 22, 1884
*Aged 29 yrs 1 mo
& 7 Days*

-----

*Mother, weep not for me. I
am not dead, but sleeping here*

Collection of Author

Unfortunately, Coyle's body was not allowed to rest in peace very long. Less than a week after the burial, an attempt was made to steal the body. It was thought the grave robbers were local doctors who wanted to study John's brain for signs of insanity, but they escaped without being caught. The *Hanover Herald*, on May 3, reported:

"Attempted Grave Robbery – The body of John Coyle, Jr., the executed murderer of Emily Myers, had been placed in its resting place on the banks of the Susquehanna River a short time only before an attempt was made to steal it. The burial place looked down upon the home of Coyle's boyhood and, fearing that the grave would be an objective point for the body snatchers[*], John Coyle, Sr., the father of the hanged man, kept watch over his remains. On Friday night, several men were seen moving about the Coyle homestead in a suspicious manner. They finally turned in the direction of the grave and when in the act of robbing it the father fired at the ghouls with a shotgun and they beat a hasty retreat. It is not known who the persons are, but it is suspected that they are doctors who do not live a hundred miles away from Coyle's Ferry."[1]

However, the *Marietta Register* discounted the story of the grave robbing as exaggerated sensationalist reporting, claiming "it evidently arose from the over-excited fears of the father, who imagined previous to the report that there would be an effort made to steal his son's body. We do not think that there are any persons so low in this section of the country as to steal dead bodies, and the parties seen may have been curious to see where the body was buried, or were in that vicinity for other purposes, and not body-snatching. We have not heard that the persons alleged to have been fired at, were seen to have any implements with which to effect a disinterment of the remains."[2] In New York City, the account of the attempted grave robbing was reprinted a few days later in the *New York Times* under the headline "Trying to Steal a Murderer's Body."[3]

News of Coyle's execution spread quickly, and was reported across the country the same day he was hanged. In Reno, Nevada, where hangings were more common than in Pennsylvania, the evening paper printed a short notice entitled "Necktie Party," stating that "John Coyle was hanged at 11:25 this morning for the murder of Emily Myers, May 30th, 1881."[4] Most likely, no one in Reno had ever heard of John Coyle or Emily Myers, but a hanging was always news.

The *Marietta Register* felt it inappropriate to print details of the Coyle's private lives, but instead chose to send a message to parents: "The publishing of every small happening of days gone by, will

---

[*] *In the 1800s, body snatchers, or "resurrection men," stole corpses from recently interred graves for anatomical studies.*

not do any good to the community. His ending was the just result of a bringing-up amid associations that were none of his seeking, except by his birthright, and is a warning to all parents that example has much to do with the shaping of the course of their children ... the deed has been committed; the crime has been expiated – let the dead rest."[5]

News continued to be reported two weeks after the hanging. The *Gettysburg Compiler* informed its readers that "Mrs. Mack, of Harrisburg, and aunt of Emily Myers, made application to the Court for the heart (preserved in alcohol) and dress of the murdered woman, used in the trial, and she was given them. A cousin of John Coyle got the pistol with which the brutal murder was committed."[6]

The story of John Coyle did not die easily. References to the murder and ensuing trials continued to be mentioned in newspaper accounts as late as 1983. The murder weapon resurfaced in the news in 1910 with a brief mention in the *Adams County News* more than twenty-five years after Coyle had been executed: "An old style, rusty revolver exhibited in the windows of R.S. Magee's hardware store at Wrightsville, recalls the murder of Miss Emma Myers by John Coyle in the barn that now stands at the Accomac pleasure resort, on the York County side of the river opposite Marietta. The crime was committed with this revolver thirty years ago."[7] However, with the passing of time, some details of the murder began to be distorted. The article stated "he shot her three times,"[8] and indicated a change of venue was granted immediately and the trial was removed to Gettysburg without being first held in York County.

After the execution, the scaffold was stored for the next ten years before being used to hang Henry Heist on January 17, 1894. It remained in the basement of the Gettysburg courthouse until early 1916, when Sheriff James Stoner from Westminster, Maryland, visited Gettysburg to inspect it for possible use in an upcoming execution in Carroll County, Maryland. By that time, the electric chair had taken the place of hanging as the legal method of execution in Pennsylvania, and the scaffold would never again be needed in Adams County.

The platform was moved to Westminster and used to hang Solomon Sudler, an eighteen-year-old black man convicted of killing his white employer, on April 14, 1916. It was the last hanging in Carroll County, and most likely the last time the Coyle scaffold was ever used for an execution.

Stories related to John Coyle and the murder of Emily Myers periodically appeared in the *Gettysburg Times* well into the twentieth century. The attempted robbery of John Coyle's body was mentioned on May 8, 1934 in a regularly published section called "Out of the Past – Fifty Years Ago."[9] In 1962, more than eighty years after the murder, summaries of the Coyle trials were published in a fourteen-part series written by B.F.M. MacPherson. The installments ran from October 8, 1962 to December 22, 1962 in a local history column entitled "A Bit of History about Early Settlers."

In 1969, an article by John J. Laity appeared in *The Sunday News* in York. It summarized the murder and described the tombstone of John Coyle, by then fallen over and overgrown. Even a century after the Coyle execution, the event was remembered in the *Gettysburg Times* as recently as 1983. A short article entitled "100 Years Ago," recalled the trial which was "now in progress here in Adams County."[10]

Mr. and Mrs. Coyle remained at the ferry for several years following the murder of Emily Myers and the execution of their son. Their health continued to decline, and although it is unknown exactly when Mrs. Coyle died, Mr. Coyle continued to live in at the inn for five years after burying John in the orchard.

In March of 1889, Coyle's financial troubles mounted, and by June the ferry property had been seized by the sheriff and sold at public auction to satisfy lingering debts. John Coyle, Sr. had borrowed five hundred dollars from James Duffy in April 1881, a month before the murder, and the money had not yet been repaid. The enormous legal fees from the trials and appeals, coupled with declining revenue due to the bad publicity, made it difficult for the Coyles to survive, let alone repay the money they had borrowed from Duffy.

James Duffy passed away in the fall of 1888, and his widow Martha sought to recover the money Coyle owed her husband's estate. By 1889, the eight-year-old debt amounted to over $600 and Duffy won a judgment for the amount plus damages. A writ of *Fieri Facias*[†] was issued on March 19 to Sheriff Grenewald of York County, ordering him to have the money before a judge in York County Court on April 1.

The sheriff seized Coyle's thirty-nine-acre ferry property, which "remained in his hands unsold for want of buyers,"[11] and Grenewald was unable to produce the money to satisfy the debt on the date due. A writ of *Venditioni Exporas*, an order to sell seized property at public auction, was issued April 23 and scheduled for June 1.

A few days before the sale, nearly a foot of rain fell over Pennsylvania in a twenty-four hour period. On the afternoon of May 31, the South Fork Dam fourteen miles upstream of Johnstown failed and the Conemaugh River flooded the town, killing over 2,000 people. On the Susquehanna, flooding occurred over the next several days and exceeded the great flood of 1865 by eighteen inches at Columbia.

The river at Coyle's Ferry was swollen with debris, including logs from the Williamsport log booms. In fact, "so thick did this mess of drift run that one could have stepped from piece to piece from one shore to the other."[12] During the weekend, the river continued to rise, and on the day Coyle's Ferry went on the auction block, "a large barn floated down whole passed Marietta until it reached the rocks near the point, when it was broken into pieces. Barns, stables, outhouses, chicken coops, furniture of all kinds, large trees with their foliage of bright green, torn up by the roots all rushed by at the rate of six miles an hour on the muddy water."[13]

[†] *A court order requiring the Sheriff to satisfy an unpaid judgment by selling all, or part, of the possessions of the person against whom the judgment was rendered.*

Although more severe flooding occurred at Marietta in 1894, 1936 and 1972, the opinion at the time of the 1889 flood was that "few people who saw the flood of 1865 were expected again to see its equal, and especially as the result of a rain storm, and from this time forth the greatest flood in this Susquehanna will be recorded from June 1st to 2nd 1889."[14] Even though Coyle's Ferry was most likely flooded on Saturday, June 1, it was auctioned off in York as scheduled.

The highest bidder was none other than Martha Duffy, who paid the sum of five hundred dollars. Exactly twenty five years after buying the property from Israel Goodman and re-selling it to John Coyle, Sr. in 1864, the Duffy family once again owned the ferry.

Presumably, Martha Duffy allowed John Coyle to remain on the property. However, a month later, in July of 1889, "John Coyle, residing opposite Marietta, was taken seriously ill and few hopes are entertained for his recovery. An affection of the kidneys is the cause of illness."[15] Coyle apparently did not live long after his property was seized and sold at auction to Martha Duffy. In September, it was noted "The Coyle property, in York County, has been purchased by Amos Grove. It is his intention to make it a summer resort."[16]

Amos Grove, a former house painter and confectionary store owner, came from a well-connected family in Marietta. For many years, Grove had been in charge of the boarding house at the ten-day Landisville Camp Meeting held each summer. The revivals featured music and religious speakers, and people traveled for many miles to stay at the encampment. Grove provided boarding at $1.00 per day, $7.00 for the week, charging "50 cents for dinner, 40 cents for breakfast or supper, children under twelve years of age, half price."[17]

Grove, fifty-three when he purchased the ferry from Martha Duffy in 1889, used his talents to turn the property into a prosperous summer destination. He spent the next several months making improvements, including the conversion of the barn where Emily had been murdered into a dance pavilion.

While Grove emphasized the lodging, food, and entertainment aspects of the property, he continued to use the ferry as a means of bringing people to the resort. Grove also began the tradition of serving chicken and waffles at Accomac, which became the house specialty for the next sixty years.

Amos Grove, ca. 1880
photo courtesy of LancasterHistory.org

One of the first changes made by Amos Grove was the name of his property. For the previous twenty-five years, it had been known as Coyle's Ferry, but with the notoriety following the murder of Emily Myers, Grove wanted a fresh start. "Accomac" was a new and unusual name to many people, and in Marietta, it was misunderstood by some. The *Marietta Register* noted "A man in town, who had failed to grasp the name of the new resort over the river, remarked the other evening that a certain party was 'over the river at Apple Jack'. When asked if he meant the new resort, Accomac, he said, 'Yes, that's the name; I had forgotten, but knew it sounded like apple-jack'."[18]

Prior to opening Accomac for the first season in 1890, Grove worked hard to fix up the property. Hoping to attract a large number of people from Marietta, he made arrangements for transporting patrons from the train station across the river. Almost every weekend, rain or shine, dance parties or camping groups enjoyed the facilities at Accomac. The *Marietta Register* kept the public informed on the many parties and picnics held during the first summer of operation in the "Local Jottings" section of the weekly paper.

April 19, 1890 - "'Accomac' is what Mr. Amos Grove calls the property over the river purchased by him. It has been known as Coyle's Ferry for a quarter century. When the alterations to the grounds and buildings are completed it will be a fine place. The opening will take place June 1st."[19]

May 31, 1890 – "The new summer resort, "Accomac," opposite this place, will be opened for the season on Monday. Every facility for ferrying over the river will be there, including a large flat that will carry a trainload of passengers at a trip. The buildings have all been overhauled, painted and put in first class condition, and a large dancing pavilion will shortly be erected."[20]

June 7, 1890 – "The family of Mr. Amos Grove removed to Accomac, opposite this place, last week, and the resort is now open for the reception of guests. The pavilion being built will be completed next week. It is eighty feet in length, with a promenade outside around three sides and will be a very attractive structure when completed, beneath which hundreds can gather with comfort. "Accomac" would hardly be recognized this year as the same place known as "Coyle's" for twenty years past, the improvements having been so many."[21]

July 5, 1890 – "Persons visiting Accomac can get dinner for 40¢, breakfast and supper for 30¢, and night lodging for 25¢. Soft drinks always on hand, also cakes, pretzels, ice cream and cigars."[22]

July 5, 1890 – "During the past few weeks a large number of persons have been at Accomac, opposite this place, either guests for the day or part of a day ... On the 4th a dancing picnic was held at the pavilion by young folks from Marietta and Columbia, music being furnished by an excellent orchestra."[23]

July 12, 1890 – "A camping club of a dozen young men from York, Pa., arrived here on Wednesday morning's passenger train, at 10:16, and were taken across the river on a flat. They have pitched their tents on ground belonging to Accomac, and intend to remain for ten days."[24]

July 12, 1890 – "A very pleasant dancing party was held at Accomac during the day and part of the evening, at which ladies and gentlemen from this place and Columbia were present, music being furnished by Erisman's orchestra. There were about 60 present at this party."[25]

August 2, 1890 - "Accomac is becoming noted for the fine chicken and waffle suppers which are furnished."[26]

August 16, 1890 - "A very pleasant affair was the dancing party held at Accomac on last Friday evening, at which forty ladies and gentlemen were present, the majority of whom were from this place. The rain, just previous to the arrival of many from this side in boats somewhat dampened the spirits of those who were out on the water, but clear weather followed, and the song of the dance soon smoothed over the difficulties preceding it. The party adjourned about 1 o'clock."[27]

Following a successful inaugural season at Accomac, Grove and his wife Sarah returned home to Marietta for the off-season, leaving the ferry and hotel in charge of their twenty-five year old son Harvey, who would "remain in charge of the premises in York County and keep bachelor's hall until spring."[28] They returned the next summer and continued making improvements to Accomac, including a new side-wheel steam boat, and hosted over a thousand overnight guests. A circular in June of 1892 announced the beginning of the Grove's third year at the resort.

ACCOMAC.

OPENING OF THE THIRD SEASON OF THE

Popular Summer Resort, ACCOMAC,

THE POPULARITY OF WHICH IS ATTESTED BY THE REGISTRA-
TION OF NEARLY 1200 GUESTS THE SECOND SEASON.

WILL OPEN TO GUESTS

On Monday, June 6th, 1892.

One of the attractions will be a Steam Ferry Boat,
which will be used for excursions to Chickies and Chestnut Falls. A Flat Boat will be used to convey teams
across the river, towed by the steamboat.

If you want to spend a day, week or month, you will find this the place
to which to go.

Accommodations good; charges $1.00 per day; children under 12 years,
half price.

Picnic and dancing parties will find the charges reasonable. Ample
shelter in case of rain. There is a dancing pavilion on the grounds 80 feet
long.

Persons visiting the resort will be kindly treated and every attention
given.

Ample stabling for horses.

Chicken and waffle suppers a specialty.

For further information, address the proprietor,

AMOS GROVE,

P. O. Box 18,   MARIETTA, PA.

Accomac advertising flier
courtesy of LancasterHistory.org

The enclosed side-wheel paddle steamer called the "Accomac" was a much larger version of the broken-down boat that the Coyles had attempted to put into service the summer of Emily's murder. Grove began using it just in time for the Fourth of July in 1892 as announced in *The New Holland Clarion*. "A steamer which will ply between Accomac, York county, and Marietta has been placed on the Susquehanna. It is 40 feet long and will accommodate 75 people. It will make excursion trips from Chickies and Chestnut Falls and meet all trains at Marietta."[29]

Steamboat Accomac, Collection of Author

Unfortunately, 1892 was the last summer season at Accomac for Amos Grove. He died the following year on April 2, 1893, and Sarah was left to run the expanding business. On opening day the following year in May of 1894, Michael Engler was serving as the proprietor. Two years later in 1895, Leonard Waller and his family moved to the Accomac and operated the ferry, hotel, and steam service for the widow Grove for the next four years. By 1899, Sarah was sixty years old and ready to return to Marietta to live with her daughter Alfaretta, so she began looking for a buyer.

The unrecorded deed from Martha Duffy to Amos and Sarah Grove ten years earlier may have indicated whether Duffy still had a lien on the property when Sarah wanted to sell it in 1899. On April 20,

Grove sold the property back to Martha Duffy "for and in consideration of the sum of one dollar (also other good and valuable consideration) lawful money."[30]

The wording "one dollar lawful money" was used in the deed solely in order to make the agreement a legally binding document and did not necessarily mean that Grove sold the property for only that amount. Contract law required that both Grove and Duffy exchange something of value, referred to as "consideration," even if it was an insignificant amount. The deed contained no detailed information on the value of the other "good and valuable consideration," so the actual amount paid is unknown. Chances are it was transferred back to Martha to satisfy an unpaid mortgage or lien.

In any case, the property now belonged to the Duffy family for third time in thirty-five years. Much like the two other times the Duffy's previously owned Accomac, it would not remain in their ownership long. Within three months, Martha was ready to sell it again, this time for good.

On July 22, 1899, Martha Duffy sold the thirty-nine acres to Leonard Waller for the sum of $2,800. Waller, born in Marietta in 1840, was a river pilot between Lock Haven and Peach Bottom for thirty years. After retiring, Waller sold liquor in Marietta for five years, eventually deciding to try his hand at the hotel business. Beginning in 1889, he and his son John operated the Indian Queen Hotel at 130 West Front Street[‡] in Marietta for four years. Waller had just begun running the Indian Queen the year the Susquehanna flooded, the same year Amos Grove bought the Accomac from Martha Duffy.

Waller came out of a two-year retirement in 1895 at age sixty to operate the ferry following Amos Grove's death. His wife Mary, son John, and daughter-in-law Matilda lived at Accomac, along with four of John's children, ranging from two months to eight years old. John was

[‡] *By 1889, the Indian Queen Hotel was known as Eckman's Hotel. Today It is still a restaurant and tavern called McCleary's Public House.*

put in charge of the steamboat service and together the family worked hard to continue the prosperity of Accomac as a resort destination.

After purchasing Accomac from Martha Grove in 1899, Waller held the property for fourteen years. He "built up an enviable reputation as the genial landlord of a comfortable house."[31] Among Waller's other interests were operating a large shad fishery on the property and raising poultry.

Waller's poultry operation at Accomac was significant. In July of 1909 he wrote a testimonial for an advertisement for the Cyphers Incubator Company in Buffalo, NY: "Last February, I bought from your agents, Messrs. Sprecher & Gans, one of your No. 1 Standard Incubators. I set the machine running and hatched 98 as fine little chicks as ever came through an eggs shell. I set, all told, 498 eggs, and hatched 427 chicks, which is not so bad for my first attempt. Then I got 100 Peking duck eggs, and hatched 78 of them. I will say that Cyphers Incubators will hatch every good egg entrusted to them."[32]

In addition to their son John, the Wallers had a daughter Emma, who lived with her husband Robert Gitt in Harrisburg. On July 8, 1914, Waller sold Accomac to his son-in-law for the sum of one dollar. Robert Gitt operated a jewelry store and presumably was not interested in living along the river, owning a hotel, or running a ferry. Within a year, Gitt sold the property to Norman Pickle on March 8, 1915, with the stipulation that Pickle assume the $2,200 outstanding mortgage from Allison Hill Trust Company of Harrisburg.

Little is known of Accomac during the time it was owned by Gitt. By the time it was purchased by Norman Pickle, the property was showing its age and in desperate need of repair. Although each of the previous deeds, including the one from Gitt to Pickle, contained the "right use and Franchise of a certain Ferry Known as Coyles Ferry,"[33] chances are by 1915 it was no longer being used as such. Subsequent deeds do not mention the ferry right as a part of the property sale.

"Accomac," PA." ca. 1906, during Waller ownership
Collection of Author

"The Accomac and Wild Cat Boats on the Susquehanna at Marietta, Pa."
ca. 1909, during Waller's ownership.
In the distance, the barn where Emily was murdered is on the right.
Collection of Author

"*Hotel Accomac and Pavilion, Marietta, Pa.*"
ca. 1919 shortly after Norman Pickle assumed ownership.
Collection of Author

"'*The Idle Hour' (Cottage). Part of the Ac-co-mac Resort, for Rent by Week,
Furnished. Norman Pickle, Prop., Marietta, Pa.*"
Site of the old saw mill, Collection of Author

Although Pickle continued to provide lodging, the need for overnight accommodations diminished as patrons became more mobile and could easily travel home rather than staying overnight. Accomac was only a short automobile ride from York and Lancaster, and soon became a popular dining destination. Over the next thirty-six years, the easygoing and affable Pickle developed and marketed the property as Ye Old Accomac Inn, providing restaurant and banquet services in a relaxing country setting.

In addition to serving food, Pickle catered the now famous chicken and waffle dinners to parties of picnickers at Wild Cat Falls two miles upriver. He modernized Accomac by adding electrical and telephone service, and turned the former sawmill pavilion into a rental cottage. He also landscaped the grounds and made other cosmetic improvements to the property.

Shortly after 11 o'clock the night of May 16, 1935, a couple parked near Accomac noticed flames shooting up from the end of the front porch roof. After an unsuccessful attempt to arouse the occupants, they drove to the nearby cottage of Reverend Earney, who immediately ran to the Hotel. Being familiar with the layout, he was able to wake up one of the employees, Lester Goodling. Goodling woke up Norman Pickle, Theodore Caracher, and Norman Smith, and then escaped by climbing out a second-story window, crawling across the porch roof and jumping to the ground.

The three other occupants were able to reach the first floor by one of the interior stairways and exited through the front doors. Led by Norman Pickle, the scantily dressed group tried to extinguish the blaze with blankets and a bucket brigade. The fire was burning an area of about ten square feet, but spread quickly through the dried-out window frames and entered the second floor.

Meanwhile, Caracher went back inside to call the Wrightsville Fire Company. He was able to make the request for help just before the fire burned through the telephone line and he was disconnected. Hoping the call had been understood, he rejoined the bucket brigade.

Pickle entered the burning building in an attempt to retrieve some old deeds to the property that were stored in a safe. One of these was the original 1759 agreement between James Anderson, Sr. and Philip Syng, Jr., and Pickle did not want it lost in the fire. Fumbling with the combination, he was finally able to open the safe and put the deeds in a nearby wastebasket to carry them outside, but was overcome with the dense smoke and had to leave. Lester Goodling then tried to get the papers, but was likewise driven back by the smoke and had to be revived in a nearby bungalow.

Fire companies from both Wrightsville and Hellam soon arrived and made a heroic effort to put out the blaze, pumping water through three hoses from the nearby creek. Firefighters stayed most of the night and the fire was eventually extinguished, but the structure was a total loss. Accomac was completely gutted, with only the exterior stone walls left standing. The fire was attributed to a short circuit in the electrical line leading to a light on the front porch, and damages estimated at $15,000 were only partially covered by insurance.

In addition to the lost deeds, the inn was full of antique furniture, including a secretary and table claimed to be over 150 years old, clocks, tapestries, and rare linens from England and Germany. "The losses sustained when the flames consumed the antiques are irreparable,"[34] according to Pickle.

Plans were immediately made to rebuild, and only four months later Accomac reopened for business. Stone from the original building, along with stone from an old bridge in Lancaster County was used to reconstruct the hotel according to its original dimensions, and the new Accomac closely resembled the old structure.

A brochure published shortly afterwards described the "new three story stone inn risen from the ashes of Ye Old Accomac Inn, destroyed by fire May 16, 1935. Modern in every respect, the new inn is constructed from stone taken from the ruins of the old one. It is open throughout the entire year. A large porch and 'sunset' terrace prove added attractions for guests to enjoy the colorful sunsets along with the beauties and cool breezes of this natural cove. Attractive, comfortable, modern lodgings and fresh, wholesome home-cooked Southern Pennsylvania food efficiently served, offer a lure to all those, both urban and rural, who seek recreation amid the beauties of Pennsylvania's mountains and streams. The Inn is equipped to render service for dinner parties and banquets, as well as service to home groups and individuals desiring separate meals or refreshments. Reservations can be made by phoning Wrightsville, Penn. 9012R4, or by addressing the proprietor Norman T. Pickle, Hellam R.D. 1, York Co, Penn."[35]

Norman Pickle continued to operate Accomac until his death at age seventy-nine in June of 1950. He kept the property for a total of thirty-six years, the longest period of ownership since James Anderson, Jr. The resort was a favorite destination for newlyweds, and a popular venue for graduation picnics and business conferences. Pickle was known as a genuine, friendly host and was an accomplished organist who played for his church in Marietta, as well as for many of the weddings held at Accomac.

Shortly after Norman Pickle's death at Accomac, the executor of his estate, James Caracher of Marietta, inherited two tracts of property totaling about eighteen acres of the original thirty-nine acres, including the Accomac Inn. Two years later, on June 9, 1952, Caracher sold both tracts to Morton and Francis Nauss for $29,500. Formerly employed at a hotel in Fort Lauderdale, Florida, the Nauss family expanded the Accomac menu to include more sophisticated choices, but retained the well-known chicken and waffles.

Morton Nauss passed away in 1967, and four years later on May 4, 1971, his widow Francis sold the property to the current owners, Accomac Inn Inc. (H. Douglas Campbell and former partner E. Wickey Helmick). The menu has been updated to upscale cuisine featuring locally grown produce and a variety of gourmet entrees. The award-winning Accomac Inn offers a relaxed atmosphere for private parties and special occasions, both inside the dining room and on the long screened-in porch overlooking the Susquehanna River.

Sitting on the front porch, one can imagine the surveyors of William Penn exploring the river hills, flatboats bringing pioneers across the river into the wilderness, and Lafayette sitting in the tavern penning a letter to the Continental Congress. Others who sat on the porch heard the cheers of the crowd as the steamboat Codorus was launched in front of the inn, or saw the reflected glow of the Wrightsville Bridge burning during the Civil War. The view remains much the same as the early morning in May when Emily Myers walked out the front door of the inn, watched the geese wing upriver, and listened to the train whistle across the river in Marietta.

Accomac Inn, ca. 2011
Collection of Author

Notes ......

Chapter 1

[1] "Mr. Vennor's Almanac for 1882." <u>The New York Times</u> August 21, 1881.
[2] "The Weather for May." <u>York Dispatch</u> April 29, 1881.
[3] "The Murder Trial, Third Day." <u>York Daily</u> October 22, 1881.

Chapter 2

[1] Stranahan, S.Q., *Susquehanna, River of Dreams*. 1993, Baltimore: Johns Hopkins University Press.
[2] American Antiquarian, S., *Transactions and collections of the American Antiquarian Society.* Transactions and collections of the American Antiquarian Society., 1820.
[3] Browne, W.H., Dielman, L.H., and Maryland Historical, S., *Maryland historical magazine.* Maryland historical magazine., 1906.
[4] Abdel Ross Wentz, *The Beginnings of the German Element in York County Pennsylvania.* The Pennsylvania German Scociety Proceedings and Addresses, 1916. XXIII.
[5] Janney, S.M., *The life of William Penn : with selections from his correspondence and autobiography.* 1882, Philadelphia: Friends' book association.
[6] Pennsylvania Department of Internal Affairs, *Part I - Land Office Boundary Lines.* Annual report of the Secretary of Internal Affairs of the Commonwealth of Pennsylvania. Pt. III, Industrial statistics., 1906.
[7] Ibid.
[8] Ibid.
[9] Pennsylvania Dept. of Internal Affairs, *Report of the Secretary of Internal Affairs of the Commonwealth of Pennsylvania : containing reports of the surveys and re-surveys of the boundary lines of the commonwealth, accompanied with maps of the same.* . 1887, Harrisburg: E.K. Meyers.
[10] Pennsylvania Department of Internal Affairs, *Part I - Land Office Boundary Lines.* Annual report of the Secretary of Internal Affairs of the Commonwealth of Pennsylvania. Pt. III, Industrial statistics., 1906.
[11] Abdel Ross Wentz, *The Beginnings of the German Element in York County Pennsylvania.* The Pennsylvania German Scociety Proceedings and Addresses, 1916. XXIII.
[12] Pennsylvania Department of Internal Affairs, *Part I - Land Office Boundary Lines.* Annual report of the Secretary of Internal Affairs of the Commonwealth of Pennsylvania. Pt. III, Industrial statistics., 1906.
[13] Ibid.

[14] Abdel Ross Wentz, *The Beginnings of the German Element in York County Pennsylvania*. The Pennsylvania German Scociety Proceedings and Addresses, 1916. XXIII.

[15] Dorsey, J., Patented Certificate 3707, Partners Adventure, Phillip Syng and Thomas Brown, 200 Acres, Patent Record FF 7, p. 347, MSA S1190-3839, p. 3, <http://www.msa.md.gov/megafile/msa/stagser/s1100/s1190/003800/003839/tif/dsl03839-3.jpg> Baltimore County Circuit Court Land Survey, Subdivison, and Condominium Plats MSA S1190, Baltimore, MD.1732

Chapter 3

[1] Abdel Ross Wentz, *The Beginnings of the German Element in York County Pennsylvania*. The Pennsylvania German Scociety Proceedings and Addresses, 1916. XXIII.
[2] Pennsylvania. Provincial, C., *Minutes of the Provincial Council of Pennsylvania from the organization to the termination of the proprietary government : ... containing the proceedings of the council*. [Colonial records of Pennsylvania], v. 1-3. 1838, Philadelphia: printed by J. Severns.
[3] Ibid.
[4] Ibid.
[5] Pennsylvania Department of Internal Affairs, *Part I - Land Office Boundary Lines*. Annual report of the Secretary of Internal Affairs of the Commonwealth of Pennsylvania. Pt. III, Industrial statistics., 1906.
[6] Ibid.
[7] Ibid.
[8] Ibid.
[9] Ibid.
[10] Ibid.
[11] Pennsylvania. Provincial, C., *Minutes of the Provincial Council of Pennsylvania from the organization to the termination of the proprietary government : ... containing the proceedings of the council*. [Colonial records of Pennsylvania], v. 1-3. 1838, Philadelphia: printed by J. Severns.
[12] Ibid.
[13] Ibid.
[14] Abdel Ross Wentz, *The Beginnings of the German Element in York County Pennsylvania*. The Pennsylvania German Scociety Proceedings and Addresses, 1916. XXIII.

Chapter 4

[1] "Pic Nics." Columbia Spy July 21, 1883.
[2] "Encampment at Wild Cat." Columbia Spy August 20, 1870.

[3] Atlantic Publishing Engraving Company, *Encyclopædia of contemporary biography of Pennsylvania.* 1889, New York: Atlantic Pub. & Engraving Co.

Chapter 5

[1] Pennsylvania Department of Internal Affairs, *Part I - Land Office Boundary Lines.* Annual report of the Secretary of Internal Affairs of the Commonwealth of Pennsylvania. Pt. III, Industrial statistics., 1906.
[2] Ibid.
[3] Browne, W.H., Dielman, L.H., and Maryland Historical, S., *Maryland historical magazine.* Maryland historical magazine., 1906.
[4] Brugger, R.J., *Maryland, a Middle Temperament, 1634-1980.* 1996, Baltimore: Johns Hopkins Univ Press.
[5] Browne, W.H., Dielman, L.H., and Maryland Historical, S., *Maryland historical magazine.* Maryland historical magazine., 1906.
[6] Brugger, R.J., *Maryland, a Middle Temperament, 1634-1980.* 1996, Baltimore: Johns Hopkins Univ Press.
[7] Jordan, J.W., *A history of the Juniata Valley and its people.* 1913, New York: Lewis Historical Pub. Co.
[8] Scharf, J.T., *History of Maryland, from the earliest period to the present day.* 1879, Baltimore: J.B. Piet.
[9] Ibid.
[10] Ibid.
[11] Ibid.
[12] Ibid.
[13] Hively, N.O., *The manor of Springettsbury, York County, Pennsylvania : "it's history and early settlers".* York County original land records, v. 6. 1993, [U.S.A.]: N.O. Hively.
[14] Hively, N.O., *The Chanceford Townships : Chanceford and Lower Chanceford Townships, York County, Pennsylvania.* York County original land records, v. 8. 1997, [U.S.A.]: N.O. Hively.
[15] Hanna, C.A., *The wilderness trail; or, The ventures and adventures of the Pennsylvania traders on the Allegheny path.* 1911, New York; London: G.P. Putnam's Sons.
[16] Norcross, G. and Chambers, T.W., *The centennial memorial of the Presbytery of Carlisle.* 1889, Harrisburg: Meyers Print. and Pub. House.
[17] Ibid.
[18] Briggs, C.A., *American Presbyterianism : its Origin and Early History.* 1885, New York: Charles Scribner.
[19] Presbyterian Church in the U. S. A., *Records of the Presbyterian Church in the United States of America* 1841, Philadelphia: Presbyterian Board of Publication.

[20] Ibid.

[21] Swain, W.T., *James Anderson, Star Member of the Donegal Presbytery*. 1996, Harrisburg: The Presbyterian Church.

[22] Gibson (ed.), J., *History of York County, Pennsylvania*. 1886, Chicago: F.A. Battery Publishing.

[23] Egle (ed.), W.H., *Notes and queries. Historical, biographical, and genealogical, relating chiefly to Interior Pennsylvania*. Vol. II. 1893, Harrisburg, Pa.: Harrisburg publishing company.

[24] Hensel, W.U., *Historic Marietta*. Marietta's Centennial 1812-1912 Historical Address and Programmes of the Centennial. 1912, Lancaster: New Era Printing Company.

[25] Ibid.

[26] Stewart, R., *Colonel George Steuart and his wife Margaret Harris; their ancestors and descendants with appendixes of related families, a genealogical history*. 1907, Lahore, India: Printed at the "Civil and military gazette" press.

[27] Norcross, G. and Chambers, T.W., *The centennial memorial of the Presbytery of Carlisle*. 1889, Harrisburg: Meyers Print. and Pub. House.

[28] Fowler, D.G., *A City Church : the First Presbyterian Church in the City of New York, 1716-1976*. 1981, New York: The Presbyterian Church.

[29] Klein, H.M.J. and Williams, E.M., *Lancaster County, Pennsylvania : a history*. 1973, New York: Lewis Historical Pub. Co.

[30] Stewart, R., *Colonel George Steuart and his wife Margaret Harris; their ancestors and descendants with appendixes of related families, a genealogical history*. 1907, Lahore, India: Printed at the "Civil and military gazette" press.

[31] Ellis, F. and Evans, S., *History of Lancaster County, Pennsylvania, with biographical sketches of many of its prominent men*. 1974, Evansville, Ind.: Unigraphic.

[32] Ziegler, J.L., *An authentic history of Donegal Presbyterian Church : located in East Donegal Township, Lancaster Co., Pa*. 1902, Mount Joy, Pa.: [s.n.].

[33] Davison, E.M., McKee, E.B., and Group for Historical Research, W.P., *Annals of Old Wilkinsburg and vicinity : the village, 1788-1888*. 1940, Wilkinsburg, Pa.: The Group.

[34] Ziegler, J.L., *An authentic history of Donegal Presbyterian Church : located in East Donegal Township, Lancaster Co., Pa*. 1902, Mount Joy, Pa.: [s.n.].

[35] Kessler, C.H., *Lancaster in the Revolution*. 1975, Lititz: Sutter House.

[36] Gibson (ed.), J., *History of York County, Pennsylvania From the Earliest Period to the Present Time, Divided into General, Special, Township and Borough Histories, with a Biographical Department Appended*. 1886, Chicago: F.A. Battery Publishing.

Chapter 6

[1] Ziegler, J.L., *An authentic history of Donegal Presbyterian Church : located in East Donegal Township, Lancaster Co., Pa.* 1902, Mount Joy, Pa.: [s.n.].

[2] James Anderson Sr. and Ruth Anderson to James Anderson Jr. Deed Book N-255, Located at: Lancaster County Archive, Lancaster, Pa.1772

[3] Strain, R.W., *Review of Facile Princeps by Alexander Mackie.* The Journal of Insurance, 1958. 24 (4): p. 96-100.

[4] Van Rensselaer, C., *The Presbyterian magazine.* The Presbyterian magazine., 18517. VII.

[5] James Anderson Jr. to The Corporation for the relief of poor and distressed Presbyterian Ministers and the Widows and Children of poor and distressed Presbyterian Ministers. Deed Book P-272, Located at: Lancaster County Archive, Lancaster, Pa.1772

[6] Klein, H.M.J. and Williams, E.M., *Lancaster County, Pennsylvania : a history.* 1973, New York: Lewis Historical Pub. Co.

[7] Adams, J., *The relation of Christianity to civil government in the United States : a sermon, preached in St. Michael's Church, Charleston, February 13th, 1833, before the convention of the Protestant Episcopal Church of the Diocese of South-Carolina.* 1833, Charleston: A.E. Miller.

[8] *Anderson's Ferry.* Historical papers and addresses of the Lancaster County Historical Society., 1907. XI (1906-1907): p. 252-257.

[9] Gibson (ed.), J., *History of York County, Pennsylvania.* 1886, Chicago: F.A. Battery Publishing.

[10] Marquis DeLafayette, *Letter to Henry Laurens, Feb 3, 1778.* The South Carolina Historical and Genealogical magazine, 1906. VII.

[11] Gottschalk, L.R., *Lafayette joins the American Army.* 1937, Chicago, Ill.: University of Chicago Press.

[12] Prowell, G.R., *Rival Ferries over the Susquehanna in 1787 - Wright's and Anderson's.* Historical papers and addresses of the Lancaster County Historical Society., 1921. 25 (1): p. 143-144.

[13] Ibid

[14] Mereness, N.D. and National Society of the Colonial Dames of America, *Travels in the American colonies.* 1916, New York: Macmillan Co.

[15] Faris, J.T., *Seeing Pennsylvania.* 1919, Philadelphia; London: J.B. Lippincott company.

[16] John Davis Batchelder, C., *The Cabinet of President Washington.* The Atlantic monthly., 1857.

[17] York Centennial Committee of Arrangements, Stuck, E., Lochman, A.H., J, G., Gunnison, E.N., and McElroy, G.W., *The historical sketch, and account of the centennial celebration at York, Pa., July 4, 1876.* . 1876, York, Penna.: Democratic Press Print.

[18] McMaster, J.B., *History of the people of the United States from the revolution to the civil war*. 1924, New York: Appleton.

[19] Faris, J.T., *Seeing Pennsylvania*. 1919, Philadelphia; London: J.B. Lippincott company.

[20] Egle, W.H., *Pennsylvania genealogies; Scotch-Irish and German*. 1886, Harrisburg: Lane S. Hart, printer.

[21] Ibid.

Chapter 7

[1] Taylor, W.B., *Memorial addresses on the life and character of John Alexander Logan, (a senator from Illinois), delivered in the Senate and House of representatives, February 9, to 16, 1887, with the funeral services at Washington, D.C., Friday, December 31, 1886*. 1887, Washington: Govt. Print. Off.

[2] "Colonel Frank J. Magee." The Columbia Spy October 22, 1887.

[3] "Drs. J.N & J.B. Hobensack." The Columbia Spy April 2, 1881.

[4] "Manhood! How Lost! How Restored!" The Columbia Spy April 2, 1881.

[5] Mclean, Charge of the Court,Pennsylvania Dept of Pardons,#15-21 Death Warrants File, Harrisburg, Pa.,1884

[6] Ibid.

[7] Ibid.

[8] Hunter, W.J., *Manhood wrecked and rescued; how strength, or vigor, is lost, and how it may be restored by self-treatment*. 1900, New York: Physical Culture Pub. Co.

Chapter 8

[1] Court of General Quarter Sessions, Road and Bridge Dockets Clerk of Courts,York, Pa.June, 1800

[2] Ibid.

[3] Richard Gerstell, *American shad in the Susquehanna River Basin : a three-hundred-year history*. 1998, University Park, Pa.: Pennsylvania State Univ. Press.

[4] Ibid.

[5] River Fisheries of the Atlantic States, Shad fishing at night on the Susquehanna River; laying out the gill-net. [Online Image]. Available: http://content.lib.washington.edu/u?/fishimages,35820 May 11, 2011.

[6] Ellis, F. and Evans, S., *History of Lancaster County, Pennsylvania, with biographical sketches of many of its prominent men*. 1974, Evansville, Ind.: Unigraphic.

[7] Ibid.

[8] *The Borough of Marietta*, in *Atlas, Lancaster County Penna.* 1875, Everts & Whitman: Philadelphia.

[9] Klein, H.M.J. and Williams, E.M., *Lancaster County, Pennsylvania : a history*. 1973, New York: Lewis Historical Pub. Co.

[10] Pennsylvania Supreme Court, Sergeant, T., and Rawle, W., *Reports of cases adjudged in the Supreme Court of Pennsylvania*. Vol. VII. 1823, Philadelphia: Abraham Small.

[11] York County Deed Index 1749-1912 S Given Name A-J, Articles of Agreement between Henry Share, James Mehaffey, John Pedan, Mathias Rank, James Duffy, John Hane and James Anderson, York, PA.1813

[12] Pennsylvania Supreme Court, Sergeant, T., and Rawle, W., *Reports of cases adjudged in the Supreme Court of Pennsylvania*. Vol. VII. 1823, Philadelphia: Abraham Small.

[13] Ibid.

[14] Ibid.

[15] York County Deed Index 1749-1912 S Given Name A-J, Articles of Agreement between Henry Share, James Mehaffey, John Pedan, Mathias Rank, James Duffy, John Hane and James Anderson, York, PA.1813

[16] Ibid.

[17] Ibid.

[18] Pennsylvania Supreme Court, Sergeant, T., and Rawle, W., *Reports of cases adjudged in the Supreme Court of Pennsylvania*. Vol. VII. 1823, Philadelphia: Abraham Small.

[19] Diffenderffer, F.R., *A History of the Farmers bank of Lancaster, the Farmers national bank and the Farmers trust company of Lancaster, 1810-1910*. 1910, Lancaster, Pa.: Farmers trust Co. of Lancaster.

[20] Klein, H.M.J. and Williams, E.M., *Lancaster County, Pennsylvania : a history*. 1973, New York: Lewis Historical Pub. Co.

[21] James Anderson IV, Last WIll and Testament of James Anderson, York County Archives,York, Pa.1815

[22] Inventory of Bonds of the Estate of James Anderson IV. Located at: York County Archive, York, Pa.1815

[23] Pennsylvania Supreme Court, Sergeant, T., and Rawle, W., *Reports of cases adjudged in the Supreme Court of Pennsylvania*. Vol. VII. 1823, Philadelphia: Abraham Small.

[24] Ibid.

[25] Sheriff Deed Pedan to Glatz,Common Pleas Court Docket, August Term 1828,Q-27, York, Pa.

[26] Sheriff Deed Marietta and Susquehanna Trading Company to Glatz,Common Pleas Court Docket, April Term 1824,L-289, York, Pa.

[27] Sheriff Deed Runk to Glatz,Common Pleas Court Docket, August Term 1825,N-107, York, Pa.

[28] Klein, H.M.J. and Williams, E.M., *Lancaster County, Pennsylvania : a history*. 1973, New York: Lewis Historical Pub. Co.
[29]

[30] Blackson, R.M., *Pennsylvania Banks and the Panic of 1819: A Reinterpretation*. Journal of the Early Republic, 1989. 9 (3): p. 335-358.
[31] "Bank Notes at Par in Philadelphia." Lancaster Journal Various, 1818-1819.
[32] Windolph, F.L., *A Mysterious Bank Robbery*
Vol. 94. 1970, Philadelphia: Historical Society of Pennsylvania.
[33] Ibid.
[34] Ibid.
[35] Ibid.
[36] "Marietta and Susquehanna Trading Company." Lancaster Journal Agust 3, 1821.
[37] "$1000 Reward." Lancaster Journal September 12, 1823.
[38] Windolph, F.L., *A Mysterious Bank Robbery*
Vol. 94. 1970, Philadelphia: Historical Society of Pennsylvania.
[39] Ibid.
[40] Ibid.
[41] "Sheriff's Sale." Lancaster Journal August 1, 1834.
[42] Windolph, F.L., *A Mysterious Bank Robbery*
Vol. 94. 1970, Philadelphia: Historical Society of Pennsylvania.
[43] Ibid.
[44] Hensel, W.U., *Historic Marietta*. Marietta's Centennial 1812-1912 Historical Address and Programmes of the Centennial. 1912, Lancaster: New Era Printing Company.
[45] Blackson, R.M., *Pennsylvania Banks and the Panic of 1819: A Reinterpretation*. Journal of the Early Republic, 1989. 9 (3): p. 335-358.
[46] *The Borough of Marietta*, in *Atlas, Lancaster County Penna.* 1875, Everts & Whitman: Philadelphia.
[47] "Our Borough." The Advocate September 19, 1833.

Chapter 9

[1] Jordan, J.C., *An Historical Citizen*. Proceedings and COllections of the Historical Society of York, 1904. II (1): p. 55-69.
[2] Brown, A.C., *Autobiographical Sketch of the Formative Years of John Elgar, 1784-1858, Builder of America's First Iron Ship*. The William and Mary Quarterly, 1956. 13 (1): p. 87-93.
[3] Johnson (ed.), F.C., *The Old Steamer Codorus*. Historical Record ... the early history of Wyoming valley and contiguous territory ... 1893. IV: p. 23-25.

[4] Taub, L.S., *Greater York in Action*. 1968, York, Pa.: York Area Chamber of Commerce.

[5] Dept, U.S.W., *Report of the Chief of Engineers, United States Army*. Annual Report of the Secretary of War for the Year 1881, 1882. Vol. II, Part 1.

[6] Johnson (ed.), F.C., *The Old Steamer Codorus*. Historical Record ... the early history of Wyoming valley and contiguous territory ... 1893. IV: p. 23-25.

[7] Dept, U.S.W., *Report of the Chief of Engineers, United States Army*. Annual Report of the Secretary of War for the Year 1881, 1882. Vol. II, Part 1.

[8] "To Capitalists." The Pioneer October 17, 1827.

[9] Lancaster County Court April Quarter Session, Commonwealth vs Jacob Glatz, Fornication & Bastardy,Lancaster County Historical Society,Case #7, APR 1828 F007, Lancaster, Pa.,1828

[10] Lancaster County Court January Quarter Session, Commonwealth vs Jacob Glatz,Indictment Assault & Battery with intent to ravish,Lancaster County Historical Society,Case #8, Jan 1842 F008, Lancaster, Pa.,1842

[11] Lemuel P. Jenks, *Machine for Drilling Stone*, in *Specifications of Letters Patent No. 9, 379, dated November 2, 1852*, United States Patent Office, Editor. 1852: United States.

[12] Lemuel P. Jenks, *Arrangement of the Conductors in Centrifugal Gold-Washers*, in *Specifications of Letters Patent No. 6,783, dated October 2, 1849*, United States Patent Office, Editor. 1849: United States.

[13] Articles of Agreement between Jacob and John Glatz and Lemuel P. Jenks, 3T 321, February 23, 1846,York County Archives,York, Pa.1845

[14] Ibid.

[15] Ibid.

[16] Ibid.

[17] Ibid.

[18] Last Will and Testament of Jacob Glatz,Lancaster County Historical Society,Inv 1845 F007 G, Lancaster, Pa.,1845

[19] Inventory and Appraisment of the Goods and Chattel rights and credits of Dr. Jacob Glatz. Located at: Lancaster County Historical Society, Lancaster Pa.,1845

[20] "The Old Keesey Ferry." The Mariettian October 8, 1859.

[21] "Quite a large ..." The Weekly Mariettian July 28, 1860.

[22] "Noel, "mine host" of the Glatz Ferry House ..." The Weekly Mariettian December 22, 1862.

[23] "We learn that the old Keesey Ferry ..." The Mariettian January 10, 1863.

[24] Ibid.

[25] "Old Keey-Glatz Ferry has ..." The Weekly Mariettian May 16, 1863.

Chapter 10

[1] Rhodes, J.F., *History of the Civil War, 1861-1865*. 1917, New York: Macmillan Co.

[2] "War News." <u>Lancaster Intelligencer</u> June 30, 1863.

[3] Antietam Battlefield Memorial, C., *Pennsylvania at Antietam : report of the Antietam Battlefield Memorial Commission of Pennsylvania and ceremonies at the dedication of the monuments erected by the Commonwealth of Pennsylvania to mark the position of Thirteen of the Pennsylvania Commands engaged in the battle*. 1906, Harrisburg, Pa.: The Commission.

[4] "The Invasion of Pennsylvania, Preparations for Defence." <u>Columbia Spy</u> June 20, 1863.

[5] Ibid.

[6] Ibid.

[7] Ibid.

[8] Ibid.

[9] Ibid.

[10] "Men of Lancaster County Arouse!" <u>Lancaster Intelligencer</u> June 30, 1863.

[11] Mingus, S.L., *Flames Beyond Gettysburg: The Gordon Expedition, June 1863*. 2009, Columbus, OH: Ironclad Publishing.

[12] "The Invasion of Pennsylvania, Preparations for Defence." <u>Columbia Spy</u> June 20, 1863.

[13] "General Ewell." <u>Lancaster Intelligencer</u> June 30, 1863.

[14] McClure, J., *East of Gettysburg, A Gray Shadow Crosses York County, Pa.* 2003, York, Pa.: York Daily Record, York County Heritage Trust.

[15] Ibid.

[16] Rhodes, J.F., *History of the Civil War, 1861-1865*. 1917, New York: Macmillan Co.

[17] Gordon, J.B., *Reminiscences of the civil war*. 1904, New York: Charles Scribner's Sons.

[18] Spangler, B., *History*. Marietta's Centennial 1812-1912 Historical Address and Programmes of the Centennial. 1912, Lancaster: New Era Printing Company.

[19] Gordon, J.B., *Reminiscences of the civil war*. 1904, New York: Charles Scribner's Sons.

[20] Mottelay, P.F. and Campbell-Copeland, T., *The Soldier in our Civil War; a Pictorial History of the Conflict, 1861-1865, Illustrating the Valor of the Soldier as Displayed on the Battle Field*. Vol. II. 1893, New York: S. Bradley Pub. Co.

[21] Gordon, J.B. <u>Report of Brig. Gen. J. B. Gordon, C.S Army, commanding brigade. June 3-August 1, 1863 - The Gettysburg Campaign. O.R Series I -</u>

Volume XXVII/2 [S# 44]. 1863. Available:
http://www.civilwarhome.com/gordongettysburg.htm, 7/1/10.
[22] "Further from Harrisburg." Philadelphia Press June 29, 1863.
[23] McClure, J., *East of Gettysburg, A Gray Shadow Crosses York County, Pa.*
2003, York, Pa.: York Daily Record, York County Heritage Trust.
[24] Spangler, B., *History*. Marietta's Centennial 1812-1912 Historical Address
and Programmes of the Centennial. 1912, Lancaster: New Era Printing
Company.
[25] Lancaster, P.D.o., *Hospital scenes after the battle of Gettysburg, July,
1863.* 1864, Lancaster, Pa.: Daily Inquirer Steam Job Print.
[26] "Mr. Eckert having leased ..." The Weekly Mariettian July 18, 1863.
[27] "Mr. Eckert, of the Glatz Ferry ..." The Weekly Mariettian August 8, 1863.
[28] "We understand the Mr. James Duffy." The Mariettian May 28, 1864.
[29] James Duffy to John Coyle. Deed Book 5G-212, Located at: York County
Archive, York, Pa.1870
[30] Leonard H. Greenewald (Sheriff) to Martha Duffy. Deed Book 11F-218,
Located at: York County Archive, York, Pa.1889
[31] Early, J.A., *A memoir of the last year of the war for independence, in the
Confederate States of America, containing an account of the operations of
his commands in the years 1864 and 1865.* 1867, Lynchburg: C.W. Button.
[32] "This vicinity is in great tribulation ..." The Mariettian July 9, 1864.
[33] "A Week of Excitement." Columbia Spy July 16, 1864.
[34] "Untitled." The Weekly Mariettian March 23, 1867.
[35] "Untitled." The Weekly Mariettian June 9, 1866.

Chapter 11

[1] "Horrible Murder." York Dispatch May 30, 1881.
[2] Ibid.
[3] "A York County Horror." Columbia Spy June 4, 1881.
[4] "Taking Testimony." York Dispatch October 21, 1881.
[5] "The Coyle Ferry Tragedy." York Dispatch May 31, 1881.
[6] Ibid.
[7] Ibid.
[8] Ibid.
[9] Ibid.

Chapter 12

[1] Pennsylvania Prison Society, *County Prisons.* The Pennsylvania Journal of
Prison Discipline and Philanthropy, 1855. X (2).
[2] Ibid.
[3] Ibid.

[4] Pennsylvania Board of Commissioners of Public Charities, *First Annual Report of the Board of Commissioners of Public Charities.* Annual report of the Board of Commissioners of Public Charities., 1871.

[5] Ibid.

[6] Ibid.

[7] Pennsylvania Board of Commissioners of Public Charities, *Ninth Annual Report of the Board of Commissioners of Public Charities.* Annual report of the Board of Commissioners of Public Charities., 1879.

[8] Ibid.

[9] Pennsylvania Board of Commissioners of Public Charities, *Twelfth Report of the Board of Commissioners of Public Charities.* Annual report of the Board of Commissioners of Public Charities., 1882.

[10] Ibid.

[11] Negley K. Teeters, *The Pennsylvania Prison Society, A Century and a Half of Penal Reform.* Journal of Criminal Law and Criminology, 1937. 28 (3).

[12] "Coroner's Inquest." York Gazette June 1, 1881.

[13] "Coyle's Tragedy." Lancaster New Era May 31, 1881.

[14] Ibid.

[15] Ibid.

[16] "A Rejected Suitor's Crime." The Sun May 31, 1881.

Chapter 13

[1] ""The Harrisburg Independent has learned ...". " York Daily June 4, 1881.

[2] James Duffy vs. John Coyle, Judgement entered July 30, 1881, York, Pa.1881

[3] "Taking Testimony." York Dispatch October 21, 1881.

[4] "Post Mortem Examination." York Gazette June 14, 1881.

[5] "Court." York Daily June 10, 1881.

[6] Gibson (ed.), J., *History of York County, Pennsylvania From the Earliest Period to the Present Time, Divided into General, Special, Township and Borough Histories, with a Biographical Department Appended.* 1886, Chicago: F.A. Battery Publishing.

[7] Ibid.

[8] "Court." York Daily June 10, 1881.

[9] Purdon, J., *A digest of the laws of Pennsylvania from the year 1700 to the 16. day of June 1836.* 1837, Philadelphia: M'Carty & Davis.

[10] "Court." York Daily June 10, 1881.

Chapter 14

[1] Spitzka, E.C., *Insanity, its classification, diagnosis and treatment; a manual for students and practitioners of medicine.* 1883, New York: Bermingham & co.

[2] "Jacob Gerhardt's Crime, Killing his Sister-in-Law Because She Refuses to Marry Him." York Daily June 14, 1881.

[3] "Gerhardt Awaits a Verdict." New York Times June 18, 1881.

[4] Lawson, J.D., *American State Trials; a Collection of the Important and Interesting Ciminal Trials Which Have Taken Place in the United States from the Beginning of our Government to the Present Day.* Vol. III. 1915, St. Louis: Thomas Law Books.

[5] Ibid.

[6] Ibid.

[7] Ibid.

[8] Ibid.

[9] Bousfield, R.M. and Merrett, R., *Report of the Trial of Daniel McNaughton at the Central Criminal Court, Old Bailey ... 1843, for the Wilful Murder of Edward Drummond.* 1843, London: Henrey Renshaw.

[10] Lande, R.G., *Madness, malingering, and malfeasance : the transformation of psychiatry and the law in the Civil War era.* 2003, Washington, D.C.: Brassey's, Inc.

[11] West, D.J. and Walk, A., *Daniel McNaughton :His Trial and the Aftermath.* 1977, Ashford, Kent: Headley for the "British Journal of psychiatry".

[12] Becker, W.F., *Limited Criminal Responsibility.* Alienist and neurologist : a quarterly journal of scientific, clinical and forensic psychiatry and neurology., 1880. 19.

[13] Bell, C., *The recent judicial departure in insanity cases.* The Journal of Jurisprudence, 1889. XXXIII: p. 26-34.

[14] Keneally, T., *American Scoundrel : The Life of the Notorious Civil War General Dan Sickles.* 2002, New York: Doubleday.

[15] Ibid.

[16] Ibid.

[17] Ibid.

[18] Ibid.

[19] Ibid.

[20] Lawson, J.D., *American State Trials; a Collection of the Important and Interesting Criminal Trials which have taken place in the United States from the Beginning of our Government to the Present Day.* 1914, St. Louis: Thomas Law Books.

[21] Ibid.

[22] Farquhar, M., *A Treasury of Great American Scandals : Tantalizing True Tales of Historic Msbehavior by the Founding Fathers and Others who Let Freedom Swing*. 2003, New York: Penguin Books.

[23] Ibid.

[24] Keneally, T., *American Scoundrel : The Life of the Notorious Civil War General Dan Sickles*. 2002, New York: Doubleday.

[25] Rosenberg, C.E., *TheTrial of the Assassin Guiteau : Psychiatry and the Law in the Gilded Age*. 1976, Chicago: University of Chicago Press.

[26] Ibid.

[27] Hayes, H.G., Hayes, C.J., Dunmire, A.J.D.G., and Bailey, E.A., *A Complete History of the Life and Trial of Charles Julius Guiteau, Assassin of President Garfield*. 1882, Philadelphia; Boston: Hubbard Bros.

[28] Rosenberg, C.E., *TheTrial of the Assassin Guiteau : Psychiatry and the Law in the Gilded Age*. 1976, Chicago: University of Chicago Press.

Chapter 15

[1] "The Coyle Murder Trial." York Daily October 20, 1881.

[2] Ibid.

[3] "York County Courthouse, York Pa" [map]. In *Atlas of York County Pennsylvania*. Philadelphia: Pomeroy, Whitman & Co., 1876

[4] "The Coyle Murder Trial." York Daily October 20, 1881.

[5] Purdon, J., *A Digest of the Laws of Pennsylvania from the Year 1700 to theTenth of July, 1872*. Tenth ed. Vol. I. 1873, Philadelphia: Kay & Brother.

[6] Barnes, U., Jones, H.C., and Robinson, I.E., *Barnes' Federal code, containing all Federal Statutes of General and Public Nature Now in Force*. 1919, Charleston, W. Va.; Indianapolis, Ind.: Virginia Law Book Co.; Bobbs-Merrill Co.

[7] Record of Court Docket, June 1881 - December 1882,Pennsylvania Dept of Pardons,#15-21 Death Warrants File, Harrisburg, Pa.

[8] Purdon, J., *A Digest of the Laws of Pennsylvania from the Year 1700 to theTenth of July, 1872*. Tenth ed. Vol. I. 1873, Philadelphia: Kay & Brother.

[9] "The Coyle Murder Trial." York Dispatch October 19, 1881.

[10] "The Ferry Tragedy." York Dispatch October 20, 1881.

[11] Ibid.

[12] Ibid.

[13] Ibid.

[14] Record of Court Docket, June 1881 - December 1882,Pennsylvania Dept of Pardons,#15-21 Death Warrants File, Harrisburg, Pa.

Chapter 16

[1] "The Murder Trial, Second Day." York Daily October 21, 1881.
[2] "Taking Testimony." York Dispatch October 21, 1881.
[3] "The Murder Trial, Third Day." York Daily October 22, 1881.
[4] MacPherson, B.F.M. "Contradictory Testimony." Gettysburg Times October 22, 1962.

Chapter 17

[1] "Taking Testimony." York Dispatch October 21, 1881.
[2] Ibid.
[3] Pennsylvania Supreme Court, *Pennsylvania State Reports Comprising Case Adjudged in the Supreme Court of Pennsylvania.* 1879. V.
[4] "A Plea of Insanity." York Dispatch October 22, 1881.
[5] "Taking Testimony." York Dispatch October 21, 1881.
[6] "A Plea of Insanity." York Dispatch October 22, 1881.
[7] Ibid.
[8] Ibid.
[9] "The Murder Trial, Fourth Day." York Daily October 24, 1881.
[10] Ibid.
[11] "A Plea of Insanity." York Dispatch October 22, 1881.
[12] Ibid.
[13] "The Murder Trial, Fourth Day." York Daily October 24, 1881.
[14] "A Plea of Insanity." York Dispatch October 22, 1881.
[15] Ibid.
[16] "The Murder Trial, Fourth Day." York Daily October 24, 1881.
[17] Ibid.
[18] Ibid.
[19] MacPherson, B.F.M. "Contradictory Testimony." Gettysburg Times October 22, 1962.

Chapter 18

[1] "The Murder Trial, Fifth Day." York Daily October 25, 1881.
[2] Ibid.
[3] Ibid.
[4] Ibid.
[5] Ibid.
[6] Ibid.
[7] Ibid.
[8] "The Murder Trial, Sixth Day." York Daily October 26, 1881.
[9] Ibid.

[10] Ibid.
[11] Ibid.
[12] Thornton, E.M. and Thomas, H., *A Treatise on Attorneys at Law.* 1914, Northport, Long Island, N.Y.: E. Thompson Co.
[13] Epstein, E.S., *The Attorney-Client Privilege and the Work-Product Doctrine.* 2001, Chicago, Ill.: Section of Litigation, American Bar Association.
[14] "The Murder Trial, Sixth Day." York Daily October 26, 1881.
[15] Ibid.
[16] Ibid.
[17] Ibid.

Chapter 19

[1] "The Murder Trial Ended." York Daily October 27, 1881.
[2] Ibid.
[3] Ibid.
[4] Ibid.
[5] Frey, S.C., *Com. v. John Coyle Jr.* The York Legal Record, 1882. II: p. 199-210.
[6] Ibid.
[7] Ibid.
[8] Ibid.
[9] Ibid.
[10] Ibid.
[11] Ibid.
[12] Ibid.
[13] Ibid.
[14] Ibid.
[15] Ibid.
[16] Ibid.
[17] Ibid.
[18] Ibid.
[19] Ibid.
[20] Ibid.
[21] "The Murder Trial Ended." York Daily October 27, 1881.
[22] Ibid.
[23] Record of Court Docket, June 1881 - December 1882,Pennsylvania Dept of Pardons,#15-21 Death Warrants File, Harrisburg, Pa.
[24] "The Murder Trial Ended." York Daily October 27, 1881.
[25] Ibid.
[26] Record of Court Docket, June 1881 - December 1882,Pennsylvania Dept of Pardons,#15-21 Death Warrants File, Harrisburg, Pa.

[27] Ibid.
[28] Frey, S.C., *Com. v. John Coyle Jr.* The York Legal Record, 1882. II: p. 199-210.
[29] Ibid.
[30] Ibid.
[31] Ibid.
[32] Ibid.
[33] Ibid.
[34] Ibid.
[35] Ibid.
[36] Ibid.
[37] Ibid.
[38] Ibid.
[39] "The Coyle Myers Murder Case." York Daily December 21, 1881.
[40] MacPherson, B.F.M. "Murder in the First Degree." Gettysburg Times November 9, 1962.

Chapter 20

[1] *Supreme Court of Pennsylvania. Coyle v. the Commonwealth.* The American law register, 1883. XXII (Jan 1883 - Dec 1883): p. 191-198.
[2] Outerbridge, A.A., *Coyle versus Commonwealth.* Pennsylvania State Reports containing Cases Adjudged in the Supreme Court of Pennsylvania, 1883. IV (Jan Term 1882): p. 573-580.
[3] *Coyle v. Commonwealth.* Weekly notes of cases argued and determined in the Supreme court of Pennsylvania, the County courts of Philadelphia, and the United States District and Circuit courts fo the Eastern district of Pennsylvania. By members of the bar., 1883. XII (Apr 1882 - Apr 1883): p. 277-279.
[4] Outerbridge, A.A., *Coyle versus Commonwealth.* Pennsylvania State Reports containing Cases Adjudged in the Supreme Court of Pennsylvania, 1883. IV (Jan Term 1882): p. 573-580.
[5] Ibid.
[6] Ibid.
[7] Ibid.
[8] Ibid.
[9] Ibid.
[10] Frey, S.C., *Com. v. John Coyle Jr.* The York Legal Record, 1882. III: p. 171-172.
[11] Beale, J.H., *A selection of cases on the conflict of laws.* 1907, Cambridge: Harvard University Press.
[12] Record of Court Docket, June 1881 - December 1882,Pennsylvania Dept of Pardons,#15-21 Death Warrants File, Harrisburg, Pa.

[13] MacPherson, B.F.M. "Murder in the First Degree." Gettysburg Times November 9, 1962.
[14] "The Coyle Case." York Daily November 22, 1882.
[15] "The Venue Changed." York Daily December 7, 1882.
[16] "The Coyle Case." York Daily November 22, 1882.
[17] "The Coyle Murder Case." York Daily December 5, 1882.
[18] Frey, S.C., *Com. v. John Coyle Jr.* The York Legal Record, 1882. III: p. 171-172.
[19] Ibid.
[20] Outerbridge, A.A., *Coyle versus Commonwealth.* Pennsylvania State Reports containing Cases Adjudged in the Supreme Court of Pennsylvania, 1883. IV (Jan Term 1882): p. 573-580.
[21] Ibid.
[22] Ibid.
[23] Ibid.
[24] "Letter from John Coyle." York Daily December 16.

Chapter 21

[1] *History of Cumberland and Adams counties, Pennsylvania. Containing history of the counties, their townships, towns, villages, schools, churches, industries, etc.; Portraits of early settlers and prominent men; Biographies; History of Pennsylvania, statistical and miscellaneous matter, etc., etc.* 1886, Chicago; Evansville, Ind: Warner, Beers & Co. Unigraphic, Inc.
[2] Reily, J.T., *History and directory of the boroughs of Gettysburg, Oxford, Littlestown, York Springs, Berwick, and East Berlin, Adams County, Pa. : with historical collections.* 1880, Gettysburg, Pa.: Reily, John T.
[3] Pennsylvania Board of Commissioners of Public Charities, *Fourteenth Report of the Board of Commissioners of Public Charities.* Annual report of the Board of Commissioners of Public Charities., 1884.
[4] Ibid.
[5] Record of Court Docket, February 1883 - August 4 1883,Pennsylvania Dept of Pardons,#15-21 Death Warrants File, Harrisburg, Pa.
[6] "The Coyle Case." York Daily February 3, 1883.
[7] "The Coyle Case." The Star and Sentinel April 25, 1883.
[8] MacPherson, B.F.M. "Many Witnesses." Gettysburg Times October 13, 1962.
[9] Record of Court Docket, February 1883 - August 4 1883,Pennsylvania Dept of Pardons,#15-21 Death Warrants File, Harrisburg, Pa.
[10] H.E. Wallace and D. Sanders, *The Constitution of the Commonwealth of Pennsylvania with an Introduction, Notes and References, and an Exhaustive Index.* 1874, Philadelphia: Rees Welsh.

[11] *Industrial and Commercial Resources of Pennsylvania. Historical, Descriptive and Biographical Review.* 1887, New York: Historical Publishing Co.

[12] United States. Bureau of the, C., *Census of Population: 1950 : a Report of the Seventeenth Decennial Census of the United States.* 1952, Washington: U.S. Dept. of Commerce Bureau of the Census.

[13] "The Coyle Case." The Star and Sentinel April 25, 1883.

[14] Supreme Court of Pennsylvania, Writ of Error to the Court of Oyer and Terminer and General Jail Delivery of Adams County,Pennsylvania Dept of Pardons,#15-21 Death Warrants File, Harrisburg, Pa.,1881

[15] Record of Court Docket, February 1883 - August 4 1883,Pennsylvania Dept of Pardons,#15-21 Death Warrants File, Harrisburg, Pa.

Chapter 22

[1] Defendants Evidence / Prosecution Rebuttal / Defense Surrebuttal,Pennsylvania Dept of Pardons,#15-21 Death Warrants File, Harrisburg, Pa.

[2] Ibid.
[3] Ibid.
[4] Ibid.
[5] Ibid.
[6] Ibid.
[7] Ibid.
[8] Ibid.
[9] Ibid.
[10] Ibid.
[11] Ibid.
[12] Ibid.
[13] Ibid.
[14] Ibid.
[15] Ibid.
[16] Ibid.
[17] Ibid.
[18] Ibid.

Chapter 23

[1] Ibid.
[2] Ibid.
[3] Ibid.
[4] Ibid.
[5] Ibid.

[6] Ibid.

[7] Ibid.

[8] Ibid.

[9] Ibid.

[10] Ibid.

[11] Ibid.

[12] Ibid.

[13] MacPherson, B.F.M. "Tried at Gettysburg." Gettysburg Times November 23, 1962.

[14] "The Coyle Homicide Case - Still Open." The Star and Sentinel May 2, 1883.

[15] Ibid.

[16] Ibid.

[17] MacPherson, B.F.M. "Tried at Gettysburg." Gettysburg Times November 23, 1962.

[18] Defendants Evidence / Prosecution Rebuttal / Defense Surrebuttal,Pennsylvania Dept of Pardons,#15-21 Death Warrants File, Harrisburg, Pa.

[19] Ibid.

[20] MacPherson, B.F.M. "Arriving at a Verdict." Gettysburg Times December 3, 1962.

[21] Defendants Evidence / Prosecution Rebuttal / Defense Surrebuttal,Pennsylvania Dept of Pardons,#15-21 Death Warrants File, Harrisburg, Pa.

[22] "The Coyle Homicide Case - Still Open." The Star and Sentinel May 2, 1883.

[23] "The Murder Case." Gettysburg Compiler May 9, 1883.

[24] Ibid.

[25] "The Coyle Trial Ended." The Star and Sentinel May 9, 1883.

[26] MacPherson, B.F.M. "Arriving at a Verdict." Gettysburg Times December 3, 1962.

[27] MacPherson, B.F.M. "Final Verdict." Gettysburg Times December 12, 1962.

[28] "The Coyle Homicide Case - Still Open." The Star and Sentinel May 2, 1883.

[29] MacPherson, B.F.M. "Tried at Gettysburg." Gettysburg Times November 23, 1962.

[30] MacPherson, B.F.M. "Final Verdict." Gettysburg Times December 12, 1962.

[31] "The Coyle Homicide Case - Still Open." The Star and Sentinel May 2, 1883.

[32] Ibid.

[33] "The Coyle Trial and Verdict." Gettysburg Compiler May 9, 1883.
[34] Ibid.

Chapter 24

[1] Mclean, Charge of the Court,Pennsylvania Dept of Pardons,#15-21 Death Warrants File, Harrisburg, Pa.,1884
[2] Ibid.
[3] Ibid.
[4] Ibid.
[5] Ibid.
[6] Ibid.
[7] Ibid.
[8] Ibid.
[9] Ibid.
[10] "The Murder Case." Gettysburg Compiler May 9, 1883.
[11] "The Coyle Trial Ended." The Star and Sentinel May 9, 1883.
[12] "The Murder Case." Gettysburg Compiler May 9, 1883.
[13] Frey, S.C., *Com. v. John Coyle Jr.* The York Legal Record, 1883. IV: p. 47-49.
[14] Ibid.
[15] Ibid.
[16] Ibid.
[17] Ibid.
[18] Mclean, Opinion of the Court Over-Ruling Motion for a New Trial,Pennsylvania Dept of Pardons,#15-21 Death Warrants File, Harrisburg, Pa.,1884
[19] MacPherson, B.F.M. "Final Verdict." Gettysburg Times December 12, 1962.
[20] Mclean, Sentence of the Prisoner,Pennsylvania Dept of Pardons,#15-21 Death Warrants File, Harrisburg, Pa.,1884
[21] "Coyle Sentenced." Gettysburg Compiler May 16, 1883.
[22] Mclean, Sentence of the Prisoner,Pennsylvania Dept of Pardons,#15-21 Death Warrants File, Harrisburg, Pa.,1884
[23] Ibid.
[24] "Coyle Sentenced." Gettysburg Compiler May 16, 1883.
[25] Record of Court Docket, February 1883 - August 4 1883,Pennsylvania Dept of Pardons,#15-21 Death Warrants File, Harrisburg, Pa.
[26] "Coyle Sentenced to be Hung." The Star and Sentinel May 16, 1883.
[27] Record of Court Docket, February 1883 - August 4 1883,Pennsylvania Dept of Pardons,#15-21 Death Warrants File, Harrisburg, Pa.
[28] "Coyle Sentenced." Gettysburg Compiler May 16, 1883.

29 ""Gettysburg must be anxious to have a hanging ....".." New Holland Clarion May 12, 1883.

30 "Coyle Sentenced to be Hung." The Star and Sentinel May 16, 1883.

31 "John Coyle - His Approaching Doom." Gettysburg Compiler April 8, 1884.

32 Ibid.

33 Ibid.

Chapter 25

1 Supreme Court of Pennsylvania, Writ of Error to Adams County,Pennsylvania Dept of Pardons,#15-21 Death Warrants File, Harrisburg, Pa.,1883

2 Ibid.

3 Ibid.

4 Supreme Court of Pennsylvania, Argument of Plaintiff in Error, Argument of Defendant in Error,Pennsylvania Dept of Pardons,#15-21 Death Warrants File, Harrisburg, Pa.,1883

5 Ibid.

6 Ibid.

7 Ibid.

8 Death Warrant Certificate,Executive Department, Office of the Governor,#15-21 Death Warrants File, Harrisburg, Pa.,1884

9 "John Coyle - His Approaching Doom." Gettysburg Compiler April 8, 1884.

10 Ibid.

11 "John Coyle to be Hanged." The New York Times February 23, 1884.

12 Coyle Jr., J., Letter to Governor William E. Pattison, Harrisburg, Pa.,March 29,1884

13 Tate, T.T., Medical Evaluation,Pennsylvania Dept of Pardons,#15-21 Death Warrants File, Harrisburg, Pa.1884

14 "Execution of John Coyle, Jr." The Star and Sentinel April 22, 1884.

15 McClean, W., Letter to Board of Pardons,Pennsylvania Dept of Pardons,#15-21 Death Warrants File, Harrisburg, Pa.1884

16 McConaughy, D. and Fisher, H., Application of John Coyle Jr. for Pardon or Commutation of Sentence of Death,Pennsylvania Dept of Pardons,#15-21 Death Warrants File, 1884

17 McConaughy, D., Letter to Governor for Respite,Pennsylvania Dept of Pardons,#15-21 Death Warrants File, Harrisburg, Pa.,1884

18 "John Coyle Jr., the murderer of Emily Myers ..." Marietta Register April 19, 1884.

19 "John Coyle, Jr. Hanged." York Gazette April 23, 1884.

20 Ibid.

21 "Execution of John Coyle, Jr." The Star and Sentinel April 22, 1884.

[22] Ibid.

[23] "John Coyle, Jr. Hanged." York Gazette April 23, 1884.

[24] Ibid.

[25] "John Coyle - Hung at Gettysburg Today." Gettysburg Compiler April 22, 1884.

[26] "Execution of John Coyle, Jr." The Star and Sentinel April 22, 1884.

[27] Samuel Wells, *How to Read Character*. 1870, New York, NY: Wells Publishing.

[28] "Will Coyle Hang?" York Daily April 22, 1884.

[29] "John Coyle, Jr. Hanged." York Gazette April 23, 1884.

Chapter 26

[1] "John Coyle - Hung at Gettysburg Today." Gettysburg Compiler April 22, 1884.

[2] "John Coyle, Jr. Hanged." York Gazette April 23, 1884.

[3] Ibid.

[4] Ibid.

[5] "Exit Coyle." York Daily April 23, 1884.

[6] Ibid.

[7] "John Coyle, Jr. Hanged." York Gazette April 23, 1884.

[8] "Exit Coyle." York Daily April 23, 1884.

[9] "John Coyle, Jr. Hanged." York Gazette April 23, 1884.

[10] Ibid.

[11] MacPherson, B.F.M. "Coyle Pays for his Crimes." Gettysburg Times December 22, 1962.

[12] "Exit Coyle." York Daily April 23, 1884.

[13] Ibid.

Chapter 27

[1] MacPherson, B.F.M. "Coyle Pays for his Crimes." Gettysburg Times December 22, 1962.

[2] "Attempted Grave Robbery." Marietta Register May 3, 1884.

[3] "Trying to Steal a Murderer's Body " The New York Times April 29, 1884.

[4] "A Necktie Party." Reno Evening Gazette April 22, 1884.

[5] "Coyle Hung." Marietta Register April 26, 1884.

[6] "The Last of Coyle." Gettysburg Compiler May 6, 1884.

[7] "Coyle Murder Recalled." Adams County News May 21, 1910.

[8] Ibid.

[9] "Fifty Years Ago." Gettysburg Times May 8, 1934.

[10] "100 Years Ago." Gettysburg Times April 19, 1983.

[11] Leonard H. Greenewald (Sheriff) to Martha Duffy. Deed Book 11F-218, Located at: York County Archive, York, Pa.1889

[12] "The Flood Near By." The York Dispatch June 3,, 1889.

[13] Ibid.

[14] Ibid.

[15] "Local Department." Marietta Register July 20, 1889.

[16] "Some Personal Items." The Columbia Spy September 28, 1889.

[17] "The Landisville Camp-Meeting." The Columbia Spy July 21, 1888.

[18] "A man in town ..." Marietta Register June 7, 1890.

[19] "Accomac is what Mr. Amos Grove ..." Marietta Register April 19, 1890.

[20] "The new summer resort, Accomac ..." Marietta Register May 31, 1890.

[21] "The family of Mr. Amos Grove ..." Marietta Register June 7, 1890.

[22] "Persons Visiting Accomac ..." Marietta Register July 5, 1890.

[23] "Guests at Accomac ..." Marietta Register July 5, 1890.

[24] "A camping club of a dozen young men ..." Marietta Register July 12, 1890.

[25] "A very pleasant dancing party was held at Accomac ..." Marietta Register July 12, 1890.

[26] "Accomac is becoming noted ..." Marietta Register August 2, 1890.

[27] "A very pleasant affair was the dancing party ..." Marietta Register August 16, 1890.

[28] "Amos Grove and family ..." Marietta Register October 18, 1890.

[29] "A steamer which will ply between Accomac ..." The New Holland Clarion July 2, 1892.

[30] Sarah A. Grove to Martha Duffy. Deed Book 11Q-552, Located at: York County Archive, York, Pa.1899

[31] Prowell, G.R., *History of York County, Pennsylvania*. Vol. II. 1907, Chicago: J.H. Beers.

[32] *Cyphers Incubators.* American Poultry Journal, 1910. 41 (1).

[33] Robert S. Gitt to Norman T. Pickle. Deed Book 19R-99, Located at: York County Archive, York, Pa.1915

[34] "Hotel at Accomac Destroyed by Fire." York Daily May 17, 1935.

[35] Campbell Jr, H.D. Accomac Inn History. Available: http://www.accomacinn.com/restaurant/our-history/.